Lynn Davis

D1174539

Digital Computer Technology and Design

Volume II:

Circuits and Machine Design

Digital Computer

Technology and Design

Volume II: Circuits and Machine Design

Willis H. Ware, The RAND Corporation

Santa Monica, California

John Wiley and Sons, Inc.

New York · London · Sydney

Library of Congress Catalog Card Number: 63-14071
Printed in the United States of America

TO MY WIFE

FLOY

and our children,

Deborah, Alison, and David

Each helped me in his own way.

Most importantly, all relinquished

their time with me. Except for that,

this book would never have been written.

Preface

These two volumes have grown out of my own professional career of nearly twenty years in the digital computing field, and out of ten years of teaching more than two thousand students a graduate-level course in this material. Together, Volume I and Volume II constitute an introductory treatment to digital computer technology and design. The topics reflect what I feel to be necessary for a broadly based discussion: principles of operation of the digital computer; certain background mathematical subjects such as Boolean algebra, number systems, and number codes; programming; design techniques for the major kinds of digital computer circuits; and internal machine organization. The text material covers not only the essential and traditional matter relevant to the digital computer but also explores many of the options available in the use and design of the machine. The treatment of circuits in Volume II is unique and uses an anonymous active element which can be particularized to be either a vacuum tube or a transistor.

These books are intended for teaching. I have presented basic ideas and concepts rather than a comprehensive and exhaustive treatment of details. I have chosen to present my arguments and discussion in a phenomenological and intuitive way, rather than in a rigorous, theoretical, and formal style. At the same time, I have tried to make the discussion sufficiently complete to be satisfying, and I have tried to structure it so that the transfer of information to the reader is efficient and complete. At frequent intervals and especially at strategic points, I have placed illustrative examples; in many cases, an example indicates the variety of options available for consideration of some point. With each chapter, there are collateral reading suggestions keyed to the text. At the end of each chapter are exercises (to consolidate the points which have been discussed) as well as advanced problems.

Many problems are phrased to illuminate some controversial issue or to sharpen the distinction between competing ways to achieve some desired machine behavior. The exercises and problems are not fictitious and artificial; rather, they represent important questions that can be and are asked in reality.

In large part, Volume I is self-contained, since the necessary foundation material is included. While no formal training in mathematics is necessary to read Volume I, certainly an exposure to the mathematical way of thinking is helpful. The mathematical courses in the first two years of a science or engineering college curriculum are more than enough; for many readers, achievement in the college preparatory curriculum of the high school is sufficient. The first three chapters of Volume II lean on an electronics background, especially on familiarity with non-linear circuits. The remaining chapters of Volume II require in places a familiarity with the elementary principles of physics, e.g., magnetic effects and electrical charge effects.

These books can be read by many readers and in several ways. The senior or graduate electrical engineer can certainly handle all of the material. On the other hand, if he is unconcerned with circuit details, he can omit Chapters 8 to 10. The physics or science major can read all of the material or omit Chapters 8 to 10, depending upon the strength of his background in circuits. The well-informed but scientifically untrained reader should be able to understand the bulk of Volume I, and he should expect a yield of possibly one-half to two-thirds of the material in Volume II. It is important, however, that the reader who decides to omit Chapters 8 to 10 read the opening sections of Chapters 8 and 9, in order to get an appreciation for the notion of representing information in terms of electrical signals and to get some appreciation for the function of the toggle and the gate circuit.

Volume I alone might well suffice for the reader who is interested only in having some insight into the operational principles and use of the digital machine. Likewise, Volume II alone might suffice for the reader who is already acquainted with the computing field and needs only to increase his knowledge about circuit and machine design.

To the best of my knowledge, my treatment of electronic circuits is unique and new. It struck me that in a gross behavioral sense, there is more similarity between the vacuum tube and the transistor than there is difference. I have, therefore, presented my circuit development in terms of an anonymous active element which is neither tube nor transistor but resembles both; by giving it additional detail, it can be particularized to be either. I have phrased the discussion in a way which I hope will be easily acceptable to either the tube-oriented or to the transistor-oriented individual. My goal is to demonstrate how a circuit operates as well as to show the interaction between the particular active element and the circuit. To maintain contact with reality, I have followed the generalized discussion with sections which specialize the arguments explicitly for the tube and for the transistor. I hope that the reader will find it refreshing to see that it is possible to discuss and understand circuit behavior quite apart from the particular active element involved.

The course on which this book is based has been given continuously since 1953 in the Engineering Department of the University of California at Los Angeles. It was the first engineering digital computer course to be given at UCLA, and hence it was organized to include topics of interest to the engineer and also to be introductory in level. The nature of the digital computer as a *functional device* is such that the usual undergraduate engineering curriculum does not provide the background or the context for a treatment of it. Important mathematical topics are missing, and usually there is no basis for understanding how a computer operates or how it is to be used. Volume I treats the subjects which are necessary preparation for a consideration of the computer as a *hardware device*. Section II (of Volume II) describes the behavior and design of major kinds of basic digital computer circuits for those readers whose interest is ultimately in circuit or overall machine design. Section III (of Volume II) is a discussion of internal machine organization; it treats the ways in which the basic circuits can be combined to achieve some functional behavior.

Reliability is an integral aspect of computer design at all levels. In Chapter 7, I have pointed out the guiding principles, and I have tried to weave reliability considerations throughout the discussion of circuit design and, later, the discussion of overall design. The so-called system design of a digital computer is difficult to treat, because at the present stage of technological development there is no underlying and unifying theoretical framework in which all aspects of the computer are tied together. There are issues related to system design scattered through many of the chapters. I have brought some of them together in the final chapter, and I have also demonstrated there that in one example of machine application the system design choices were sensible in the light of our prior discussion. However, my treatment of system design problems is not complete; in particular, it lacks a discussion of several typical case histories.

I happen to believe that the topics of Volume I—especially programming—collectively form an essential context for the engineer who plans to specialize in digital technology. I would, therefore, like to encourage any such reader to be familiar and competent in the material of the first volume.

I have found that my course attracts students with a variety of goals. Many, of course, are interested in practicing some engineering facet of the technology. Some are interested in only a quick glance across the field—to see what it is all about, and how such machines work or are used. Sometimes, students from other disciplines than engineering or physics attend as future users, sales personnel, and occasionally management personnel. However, if a student is interested in obtaining course credit, it is important that he have a background in non-linear electronic circuits. Otherwise, it is much too difficult to discuss the material of Chapters 8 to 10 in a reasonable time. Since my students are either college seniors or graduates, I am automatically assured of a certain level of intellectual capability. I find that this capacity plus a background in electronics are the only prerequisites that I must require.

Because of the combined length of these two books, it will probably be surprising for the reader to know that I have always covered the topics of both volumes in a one-semester three-unit course. However, I conduct the course as a lecture series supplemented by class notes. I do not normally use class time for the solution of illustrative problems, and I obviously cannot give in a classroom as much detail as I have written here. Nonetheless, I do not feel it unreasonable to insist that a student read and comprehend both volumes in one semester. I would expect him to solve a variety of exercises, but I would not expect him to penetrate very deeply into the problems. On the other hand, I believe that the total material in these two volumes is sufficient for a two-semester six-unit course, especially if the student is required to do extensive exercise and problem work as well as the collateral reading.

The exercises are intended to drill the student and to consolidate for him the ideas and concepts discussed. The problems are intended to extrapolate his comprehension well beyond the point at which text discussion stops. The problems—coupled with supplementary reading—can be used as a basis for seminar topics. Some problems are sufficiently difficult and extensive to form a basis for a group effort by several students. The problems can be used to develop additional subtlety and variations of a topic or to provide some of the details which I have purposely omitted from the text proper. The problems can also be used by the instructor as a basis for supplementing the text with additional lecture material.

Supplemental reading—like problems—plays a significant part in the learning process. Often, the same argument presented in the words of a different author or from a different viewpoint will clarify a concept for the reader. On other occasions, additional reading is necessary to obtain greater detail or breadth of a topic. I have included extensive collateral reading suggestions at the end of each chapter, and I have keyed them to the major points in the text. Except for an occasional citation, I have listed only readily available sources; and where appropriate, I have cross-referenced specific sections in other books.

Terminology in the digital field is anything but static and final. Several technical societies have prepared glossaries of terminology, but because of the youth of the digital field and its rapid and continuing development, usage changes quickly. I have attempted to use consistently what I believe to be preferred terminology. Where there are competing terms for the same meaning, I have usually cited the alternate possibilities.

A word about grammatic license. The jargon of technology often winks at traditional rules of grammar. Specifically, it is common in the digital field to make verbs from other parts of speech, or to make active verbs from passive ones. The result is sometimes picturesque, but it is usually accurate and descriptive. I have used the jargon of the field rather than more traditional grammatical structures. After all, the reader, as he practices the art and discusses it with others, will use this jargon in his speaking. He may as well read with the same phraseology as he speaks.

I have assumed that the reader will realize that a consistent set of units must be used when numerically evaluating any of the formulae stated in this book. Usually, therefore, units are not stated except where necessary to complete or to clarify the meaning.

I hope that other instructors will find, as I have, that students appreciate the expository rather than the rigorous theoretical approach. I hope that others also will find that a careful discussion of the underlying why's and wherefore's of a situation leads the student to a keener grasp of the subject. Perhaps, of all who read the book and hopefully gain an awareness in depth of the digital machine and the physical devices which constitute it, some may be stimulated to probe the boundary of our present knowledge and our present technology.

WILLIS H. WARE

Santa Monica, California
March, 1963

Acknowledgments

An author does not write a book alone. His ideas are sharpened and matured by his contact with professional colleagues; his presentation and his approach are refined through interaction with students. It would be impossible to pinpoint the contributions from innumerable sources that have collectively influenced what I have written in this book, but it is my pleasure to acknowledge here those many individuals whom I can identify as having had some part in shaping my ideas. My colleagues at John von Neuman's Computer Project at the Institute for Advanced Study were the environment in which my ideas first formed. In particular, Julian H. Bigelow, the chief engineer of the Project, showed me a way of looking at circuits that has become the phenomenological principles-of-physics style of discussion in this book. The two-thousand-plus students from the ten years of the course behind this book have played a very significant part in shaping the manner and level of presentation of my material.

My colleagues at The RAND Corporation have been the intellectual environment in which my ideas and my insights have fully matured. Paul Armer, James D. Tupac, Morton I. Bernstein, and Robert L. Patrick have discussed with me matters of programming, machine usage, applications, and machine organization. Isaac D. Nehama and Michael Warshaw have been particularly helpful to me in getting the details of the mathematical developments properly presented and in exploring with me the philosophical overtones of the computer. Keith Uncapher, Thomas O. Ellis, and Malcolm R. Davis have been my forum on circuit and hardware technology. In ways perhaps unrealized at the time, there have doubtless also been other important interactions with my colleagues. Without attempting to identify individual points, let me simply acknowledge Paul Baran, Leonard J. Craig, Richard

Stahl, and Fred Gruenberger. Although unspeaking in the usual sense, RAND's JOHNNIAC and other computers have exerted influence too.

The reviewers of a manuscript also have a profound effect on its final appearance. I know only two by name—Jack Rosenberg and Daniel D. McCracken, but there have been other anonymous individuals. Each has certainly helped shape the final product which now has become a book.

In 1953, my secretary, Mrs. Dorothy Crabb, typed the first class notes. My typist on the final manuscript has been Miss Jessie Gutteridge. I can only admire the wonderful way in which she unscrambles the tortuous trail of a sentence as it goes between lines, up the margin on one side, down the margin on the other, and disappears onto the back of the sheet. To make matters worse, she has had to struggle with handwriting that frequently had an unpredicted wiggle because an airplane hit turbulence, or a train rocked on the track, or a seatmate at the bus station accidentally bumped my arm. Without the typing skill of Miss Gutteridge, and her background in English grammar, I would not have progressed so smoothly.

I also want to acknowledge the influence on my pool of knowledge of the many other computer people with whom I have come in contact and with whom I have discussed a wide variety of ideas and subjects.

W. H. W.

volume two

Contents

volume one

Contents

Section II

Reliability

In the first part of this chapter, we considered the various sources which can contribute to the overall reliability of a digital computer system. We demonstrated that from the designer's point of view, there is a very real problem, and we now must investigate techniques which are available to him to maximize the performance of his product (1).

THE STATISTICAL VIEW

To underscore the existence of a reliability problem, we tossed large, if not huge, numbers around with abandon. As light as the discussion might have seemed, the underlying conclusion is serious. A few orders of magnitude one way or the other in the large numbers will not really matter; the numbers will stay large and never get small. As we frequently do when dealing with a large number of possibilities, we resort to a statistical point of view.

There is another reason why a statistical point of view is sensible. Even modest-sized systems consume rather large numbers of components. There is no such thing as, say, 10,000 active elements all of which are precisely alike. Any manufacturing process yields a product whose parameters are statistically distributed. Sometimes the spread of a parameter will follow a normal distribution; sometimes it will follow a skewed distribution. Whichever it is, one of the problems of the designer is to evolve a design technique which accommodates such statistical uncertainty.

Parameter Variations

Handbooks show the characteristics of a vacuum tube or a transistor as a set of curves. This cannot possibly represent reality because not all elements are alike; at best such characteristic curves represent an average behavior. Each point on such a curve represents perhaps the median behavior of a population of components. With each point there is an associated distribution curve which depends initially on the manufacturing process which produced the component, but which also will change with time as the population of components age (Figure 7.2). It is, therefore, convenient to think of each characteristic curve as flanked by a pair of curves between which a certain percentage of the population will fall. The circuit design must tolerate any component which falls within specified tolerances.

Turn the argument around; we see that once the designer determines what fluctuation of component characteristics his circuit can stand, he has effectively specified the tolerances which purchased elements must have. It is clear, however, that not all the tolerance limit can be used for the initially purchased component; otherwise, there will be nothing left to accommodate component deterioration with life. Furthermore, he has also automatically defined *end-of-life* for each element. When one or more parameters of an element have drifted to

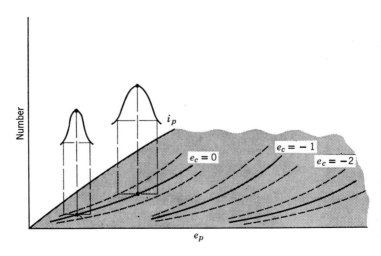

Figure 7.2. The statistical spread of vacuum tube e_p-i_p characteristics.

that tolerance which his circuit was designed to accept, the element has reached end-of-life so far as the circuit is concerned. It is to be replaced, no matter how much more life it might have in some other application.

Designer's Dilemma

There are obvious economic arguments which push the designer toward the widest possible tolerances; for example, components with closely controlled characteristics are expensive or perhaps difficult to obtain; manufacturing costs tend to rise when tolerances are small. On the other hand, if component tolerances are too wide, the designer may have to add additional components to the circuit to absorb such fluctuations. Extra components represent additional cost and perhaps even impaired performance.

As we will see later (see page 8.62), wide component tolerances tend to make a circuit (and, therefore, a machine) slower. Among other tradeoffs, the designer must consider the marginal cost of better components versus the economic value of the time which a faster machine can save on problems. Another angle is the decreased maintenance problems, and therefore lower maintenance cost which better components will almost certainly guarantee. On the other hand, it may be economically advantageous to use more but cheaper components, the extra ones being used to improve the reliability, e.g., by the use of an error-correcting code. Opposed to this is the observation that the machine should not spend a large part of its life correcting errors. If it spends half the time correcting errors, its effective speed is halved, and machine time does have a very real economic value. The factors in the tradeoff are not easy to assess and the dilemma is real.

Bear in mind that not only is the initial variation of the parameters of a particular component important, but so is the subsequent drift of those parameters through the component lifetime. The designer at the outset must have a feel for what he can expect from components. Alternatively, he can decide on a set of tolerances acceptable to him and ask his components man to find components which fit.

It may seem that the statistically oriented design philosophy is directed only toward making a digital system producible. It certainly does so, but it also makes a very significant contribution to the overall reliability of the system—because designing with this philosophy in mind leads to a system which is less sensitive to fluctuation of component parameters, and which therefore behaves better throughout its lifetime. Hence, one facet of the reliability problem is learning to design for components whose parameters have statistically distributed and uncontrollable uncertainties.

Long Live the Component

Another part of the reliability problem is extending component life, where "life" means that interval of time during which the component has parameters which fall within the limits set by the designer. Extending life generally takes the form of expecting less from a component. End-of-life does not necessarily mean a catastrophic collapse of a component.

Experience with a large variety of components has indicated that heat is a killer of components. At elevated temperatures many effects take place which tend to shorten life expectancy; also aging effects tend to proceed more rapidly at higher temperatures. One of the common techniques to extend life is to derate a component in ways which lead to a lower operating temperature.

Derating

Derating for purposes of reducing temperature takes many forms. One is to operate resistors, say, at 50% of rated dissipation. Another is to operate active elements, say, at 50% or 75% of rated dissipation. Another is to provide environmental temperature control so that envelope or container temperatures stay low. All these things are common and appear to contribute to life expectancy.

Another way of minimizing the demand on a component is to derate the voltages at which it operates, e.g., 90% of rated voltage for capacitors, 50% of rated supply voltage for tubes or transistors. Yet another one is to derate the currents handled by elements; e.g., for zero grid bias, expect only 50% of the plate current which the rating indicates; for given base current, design only for 50% of the collector current indicated by the ratings; permit a capacitor to pass only 75% of the current indicated by its rating. Such procedures are common in the design of digital machines and over the years have been shown to be effective. To some extent, components are available with ratings which presumably have been chosen to promote long life; yet there seems to be no proof like "eating the pudding," and the real test of a rating versus life is the performance of the component in the end product.

It is certainly true that components are improving with time. On the other hand, the performance expected from digital equipment is also rising so that it is not obvious that the designer's job is getting simpler. For example, a really large system might have 100,000 active elements. Even if the average life expectancy of an active element is 100,000 hours, the implication is that eventually an element will fail every hour on the average. It is conceivable that component performance may be nearing a plateau, and that future gains in reliability will have to be made by incorporating extensive redundancy, extensive error-correction schemes, or other sophisticated logical arrangements into the design.

The Designer's Creed

It is unfortunate that the feedback loop around a designer's choice of derating factors is very long. If his choice has been reasonably good, his product will be well behaved, and it may be several years before sufficient failure statistics have been collected to give even the slightest hint about the quality of his decisions. Derating procedures and ways of treating components, therefore, tend to be based on past history. We know only some things which have been successful. We have no numerical measures of worth; we cannot say that a 65% derating factor is worse than, or equally as good as, a 50% factor, much less measure the difference. A designer simply accumulates the wisdom and experience of himself and others in the field, and formulates for himself a set of rules—a creed—which plays a large part in his choice of parameter values and circuit configurations.

There will usually be two kinds of tenets in the designer's creed:

a. Those which contribute to longer life expectancies for components; e.g., resistor dissipation shall be limited to 50% of rating; junction (or plate) dissipation shall be limited to 65% of rating.

b. Those which impose component tolerances on circuit designs; e.g., resistors can be expected to vary $\pm 10\%$; for given supply voltages and base current, the output current of a transistor can be expected to vary $\pm 25\%$.

It is true, of course, that life expectancy or performance tests can be made on components. However, at best, a limited population can be measured. From the performance—statistical or otherwise—of such a sample, it is customary to draw inferences about the behavior of the whole population. For such effects as vibration, or acceleration which tend to produce catastrophic failures in components, reliability studies and subsequent component improvement programs can be effective. However, the bugaboo for the digital designer is generally the long term unpredictable and uncontrollable drifts in its characteristics as a component lives in its operating environment. Unfortunately there is always a question as to how faithfully accelerated aging tests reproduce the effects of genuine aging. There is, moreover, always a question as to what effects depend only on time and cannot be generated by an accelerated process. In the face of such uncertainties, design of a digital machine tends to be for the "worst case" situation. For all the cards stacked against him in the worst combination of ways, the designer arranges things so that the circuits are just on the edge of failure.

There is one other way in which the designer's problem is compounded. He is supposed to construct the machine so that no restrictions are levied on the programmer. He must not guarantee his reliability at the expense of such programming constraints as: "Don't consult the store more often than 10,000 times per second", or "Don't do more than three Add instructions in a row", or "Do at least one Multiply instruction in every fifteen instructions". The designer must guarantee machine performance with a routine which has any kind, number, or mix of instructions. He cannot count on the programmer to be a factor in providing reliability.

A Typical Case

A common way of derating a vacuum tube for dissipation and current is the following. On the plate characteristic curves, construct the curve:

$$e_p i_p = \tfrac{1}{2} \times \text{(handbook plate-dissipation rating)};$$

this curve defines an operating region in which the plate dissipation never exceeds 50% of the handbook rating. Also construct a curve whose ordinate is everywhere one-half of the corresponding ordinate of the zero bias curve. This defines an operating region in which the grid will not go into positive bias even though the tube emission falls to 50%. This sort of current derating assumes that aging of a tube's emission characteristic is equivalent to a simple scale factor change on the current axis of the characteristic curves.

The plate-dissipation derating curve and the current-derating curve together define an area within which the designer confines himself. The dissipation rating limits the way in which the tube can be used; it is a limitation which the component imposes on the circuit. Dissipation ratings do not drift with time. On the other hand, the current derating protects the circuit from aging and drifting of the tube emission; it represents protection for the circuit.

EXAMPLE

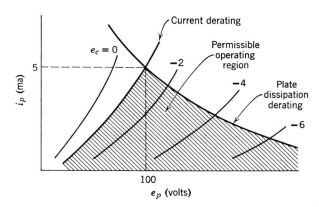

The maximum which can ever be asked of this tube is 5 ma. When the tube is new, it can supply 5 ma at 100 volts for a grid bias of about −1 volt. As emission decays with time, the grid bias will gradually decrease until at end-of-life, the tube will supply the required current just at zero bias.

For the transistor the typical situation is as follows:

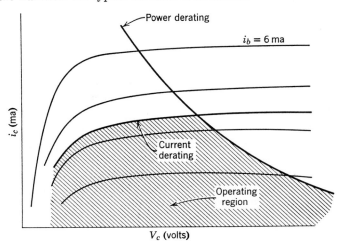

If the input in a particular circuit can be guaranteed never to fall below 3 ma, the transistor will be expected to deliver no more current than half of the 6 ma curve. The power derating curve is $V_c i_e = $ constant where the constant is some fraction of the junction dissipation handbook rating. Unlike the vacuum tube, the junction dissipation rating is a function of ambient temperature, and therefore, the ambient environment enters into the derating decision.

It is true, of course, that projected lifetimes of transistors tend to be much greater than for vacuum tubes. However, the total experience with transistors is still short enough in time that important questions about aging and long-term effects are unanswered. Various mechanisms can be identified or postulated which imply that transistors will age, and so to speak, wear out. There are reasons for believing that the current output will decline with age. Therefore, with transistors— and for that matter, for other new kinds of components—a designer is led to derate simply because his knowledge of device behavior is incomplete. He derates to be on the safe side, not because he has firm evidence that derating is mandatory. Because he is trapped in a situation in which the feedback comes slowly and over a long time, such a "do it just-in-case" attitude is likely to prevail for a long while.

COLLATERAL READING

1. Ledley, R. S., *Digital computer and control engineering;* McGraw-Hill Book Co., New York, 1960; pp. 634–642.

Heath, H. F., Jr., Reliability of an air defense computing system: Component development; *IRE Transactions on Electronic Computers,* vol. EC-5, December, 1956; pp. 224–226.

Nienburg, R. E., Reliability of an air defense computing system: Circuit design; *IRE Transactions on Electronic Computers,* vol. EC-5, December, 1956; pp. 227–233.

Astrahan, M. M. and L. R. Walters, Reliability of an air defense computing system: Marginal checking and maintenance performance; *IRE Transactions on Electronic Computers,* vol. EC-5, December, 1956; pp. 233–237.

Nussbaum, E. *et al.,* Statistical analysis of logic circuit performance in digital systems; *Proceedings of the IRE,* vol. 49, January, 1961; pp. 236–244.

Hoffmann, J., Design of experiments for evaluating reliability; *Proceedings of the 1957 Western Joint Computer Conference,* Los Angeles, 26–28 February, 1957; pp. 20–26.

Hinkelman, T. D. and M. H. Kraus, The Univac tube program; *IRE Transactions on Electronic Computers,* vol. EC-2, September, 1953; pp. 8–12.

Cohen, I. *et al.,* Accuracy control in the RCA BIZMAC system; *Proceedings of the 1957 Western Joint Computer Conference,* Los Angeles, 26–28 February, 1957; pp. 202–206.

Rosenblatt, J. R., On prediction of system performance from information on component performance; *Proceedings of the 1957 Western Joint Computer Conference,* Los Angeles, 26–28 February, 1957; pp. 85–94.

Reid, L. W. and G. A. Raymond, The ATHENA computer, a reliability report; *Proceedings of the 1958 Eastern Joint Computer Conference,* Philadelphia, 3–5 December, 1958; pp. 20–24.

Flehinger, B. J., Reliability through redundancy at various systems levels; *IBM Journal of Research and Development,* vol. 2, April, 1958; pp. 148–158.

Dickinson, W. E. and R. M. Walker, Reliability improvement by the use of multiple-element switching circuits; *IBM Journal of Research and Development,* vol. 2, April, 1958; pp. 142–147.

Lyons, R. E. and W. Vanderkulk, The use of triple-redundancy to improve computer reliability; *IBM Journal of Research and Development,* vol. 6, April, 1962; pp. 200–209.

EXERCISES

7.7. Describe how you would go about determining statistical variation in the parameters of transistors, tubes, resistors, capacitors, and inductances. In each case, identify the parameters of concern. How many components of each kind would you test? What would you do about lifetime drifts? (The goal of such testing is to produce designer's curves typified by those in Figure 7.2.)

7.8. Suggest some guidelines to assist the designer in apportioning the component tolerances acceptable to his circuit between the lifetime drift and the initial uncertainty of the parameters.

7.9. For common electronic components such as transistors, tubes, relays, resistors, capacitors, inductances, plugs, switches, etc., list the parameters which might be important to the designer and indicate how each might be derated. Suggest what seems to you to be reasonable derating factors. If you decide not to derate some parameter, defend your stand.

7.10. For the 5844 and the 2N404 (see pages 8.92 to 8.93 for characteristics), construct appropriate current derating curves.

eight

Toggle Circuits

Even though a digital computer frequently contains tens or even hundreds of thousands of components, curiously enough there are only a few basic kinds of circuits which appear. In a large system, there may typically be only a half dozen or so basic circuits, with perhaps another half dozen or so variants of these. Each of them will be repeated a large number of times. Contrast this situation with the design, say, of a television receiver; such a receiver will contain a radio-frequency stage, a first detector, a first video amplifier, a horizontal sweep circuit, and so on. It will contain just about as many different basic circuits as there are active elements (e.g., tubes) in the system.

Lo (1) gives a very concise summary of what a digital information handling network is expected to do. First of all, it must represent digital information in terms of some characteristic of an electrical signal. This might be done in terms of amplitude, frequency, or phase. Sometimes it is convenient to distinguish between amplitude and absolute level of signal. Often amplitude is associated with pulse-type signals, whereas level is associated with quasi-static signals.

EXAMPLES

1. Binary 0 might be represented by a sinusoidal signal $A \sin (\omega t)$, and binary 1, by a signal $A \sin (\omega t + \pi)$.

2. Binary 0 might be represented by a pulse signal of amplitude $+10$ volts, and binary 1 by a pulse of amplitude $+20$ volts. Because of the like signs, each kind of pulse departs in the same direction from its quiescent level.

3. Binary 0 might be represented by a voltage level of +10, and binary 1 by a voltage level of −10. Implied in this statement is the assumption that there is no third level at which the signal stays quiescently between digits.

4. Binary 1 might be represented by one pattern of currents, and binary 0 by a second pattern of currents.

As a practical matter, a digital network will almost certainly have to standardize the characteristics of the signal which one digital unit emits as a communication quantum for some other unit to read. Remember that a computer can be regarded as a switchable network whose internal sequence of configurations is governed by the routine. Since the designer cannot control the sequence of configurations, he normally plans to use a standard signal (or perhaps a set of them) to assist in the intercommunication problem. To standardize, a network must first decide what digital information is contained in a given signal, and then perhaps amplify and reshape the signal to restore it to normal proportions and characteristics. Almost certainly, the output of such a standardizing operation will not be a replica in detail of the input; the digital information contained in the output will, however, be the same as the digital information in the input.

A digital network must manipulate signals in such a way that digital output information is derived from digital input information. As we might guess at this point (and will see in Chapters 11 through 14), such manipulation generally consists of a sequence of Boolean decision-making propositions which operate on the input information. In an analog computer, manipulation generally consists of algebraic summation of voltages or currents; in the digital machine, manipulation at the most basic level is the logical combination of information states as represented by some characteristic of an electrical signal.

It is clear that there are different levels of digital manipulation. The designer implements one level of manipulation when he combines hardware in such a way that, say, an adder results. The programmer implements a grosser level of manipulation when he builds his routine. In either case, there is an underlying inference that there is direction of flow; information flows from the input of an adder to its output, or the routine is executed from the beginning toward the end.

Thus at the basic information processing level, a digital network must control the directivity of flow of information. This can be done by using unilateral elements (e.g., diodes, tubes, transistors); it can be done by having separate input and output terminals. It can also be done by time-staggering input and output information on the same terminal. At one moment of time a given terminal may act as an input and accept information, but at another moment in time it will act as an output terminal and deliver information to a destination. Alternatively, a terminal may accept information on one frequency but deliver it at a second frequency. The trick of time or frequency staggering is important for that class of active elements which basically have two rather than three terminals, e.g., the tunnel diode.

These observations will be important not only for our discussion of circuits but also for the discussion of machine organization. The constraints imposed by the observations above will partially explain why digital computers are built as they are. Furthermore, the basic notions contained in the four requirements of represent, standardize, manipulate, and direct will turn up in many places; watch for them!

This chapter and the next two will discuss detailed engineering aspects of the principal circuits used in a digital computer. Not every kind of circuit is discussed, nor is every variant of any particular circuit described. In general, the discussion is from a phenomenological point of view rather than from a rigorous mathematical point of view. It is felt that more insight into the physical behavior is obtained in this way, and that the various possible compromises and tradeoffs are more obvious and more readily understood. Some circuits which are useful in the digital art—wide-band amplifiers for instance—are adequately discussed in existing literature and are only briefly discussed here. Only those basic circuits which are peculiar to the digital computer, or those circuits which appear in the computer in some unusual way, or subject to some unusual demand, are fully discussed.

There are a great number of choices and tradeoffs that can be made in circuit design. For this reason, only principles and typical cases can be considered; the many variants of a given configuration can be easily understood as extensions of the discussion which we will give.

We are interested in understanding the behavior of circuits as circuits, and in appreciating some of their fine structure. We cannot avoid using an active element, and the question is: shall we use the vacuum tube or the transistor as the vehicle for our discussions? A case could be made for either; the vacuum tube is widely known and understood, but the transistor is widely used in many computers. The vacuum tube is optimum in some applications or environments, the transistor in others. There are differences between them. The tube is an electric field-operated device, whereas the transistor depends on diffusion phenomena for its operation. As a consequence, the input terminal to the vacuum tube is a voltage-operated high impedance point, but the input terminal of the transistor is a relatively low impedance current-operated point. On the other hand, there are many similarities between the tube and the transistor. Each exhibits capacitance between its elements; each dissipates power internally. Each has a source of current carriers, an element which controls the flow of the carriers, and an element which is a sink for carriers. Each exhibits a cutoff condition in which there is no flow of carriers from source to sink; each has a conduction condition in which there is a flow of carriers. In each, the number of carriers is controlled by one of the elements. Each has a diode at its input terminal. The input diode of the vacuum tube is between the grid and the cathode and is normally reverse biased; the input diode of the transistor is between the base and the emitter, and is reverse biased in the cutoff condition, but forward biased in the conduction condition. Under some circumstances, the input diode of the vacuum tube may be forward biased. The volt-ampere characteristics of both tube and transistor are defined by a set of curves which relate voltage between the source and sink to the current between source and sink for various conditions of the input terminal. Each exhibits a saturation effect; the voltage across the device drops to some minimum value and may be relatively constant for a range of currents. In terms of broad performance characteristics, there are perhaps more resemblances between tube and transistor than there are differences.

We want to study the fundamental behavior of circuits without becoming unnecessarily enmeshed at the outset with the characteristics or deficiencies of the active element. Because a lot of our circuit discussion is concerned solely with the volt-ampere characteristics of the active element, much of the basic discussion will be independent of the device. The arguments will apply equally well to either tube or transistor. Eventually, we will have to face the fact that any active element will not be ideal; e.g., diodes will have leakage when reverse biased, transistors will exhibit turn-on or turn-off delays, vacuum tubes will have heater-cathode leakage. The initial discussion will then have to be modified to accommodate reality; and, in fact, we may find that extra components will be required to accomodate a particular characteristic of an active element. For example, extra components can be added to, say, a transistor toggle circuit to prevent saturation in the transistor. These extra components are present for the sake of the transistor, not in order to make the toggle circuit act as it should.

To focus our attention on the circuit per se and initially away from the device, let us hypothesize a generalized active element which, in broad respects, resembles both the transistor and the tube. The device will have three terminals. One of them connects internally to a source of current carriers, a second connects internally to a sink for the current carriers, and the third controls the magnitude of the current flow between the first two. For the tube-oriented reader, these are the cathode, plate, and grid respectively; for the transistor-minded reader, the emitter, collector, and base.

For our generalized device, let us call the terminal which provides the carriers the *emitter,* the terminal which governs the flow of the carriers the *control,* and the one which gathers the carriers the *collector.** The volt-ampere characteristic between the emitter and the collector will be described by a set of curves; each member of the set will display current from emitter to collector versus voltage between them for a given condition at the control. There will be an input diode between the control and the emitter; the direction of forward current flow in this diode is from control to emitter. This diode can also be described by its own volt-ampere characteristic.

There is internal capacitance between the three elements. In particular, there is capacitance between the control and the collector. Because there is some non-zero voltage across the device for any amount of current through it, electrical power will be converted to heat. There will be a *collector dissipation* rating for the device which limits the amount of electrical power which can be absorbed.

So far as voltage and current relations are concerned, we will assume the following things:

1. The control terminal is high impedance and voltage operated.†
2. The collector terminal must be positive relative to the emitter.

* The choice of names for the three terminals is something of a problem. It seems better to select names which represent the functions which each of the terminals represents in the internal operation of the device, rather than names which describe physical construction or some geometrical characteristic. It is true that two of these three terms come from transistor technology, but it seems better to use them than to invent such a word as "cathitter" which splits the tube and transistor technology, and is familiar to no one. Hopefully, the names selected will jog the reader's mind to remember the function of each terminal. but at the same time, not confuse the reader who is solely tube-oriented.

† This appears to bias the fictitious element toward the vacuum tube. However, it seems to be true that students learn first Ohm's law, then Kirchhoff's voltage law, and finally Kirchhoff's current law. This ordering of the exposure seems to tilt one's perspective toward a voltage design of resistance circuits rather than toward a current point of view. One aspect of many circuits will be a resistance divider to shift a signal at one potential to a smaller signal at a different potential. This, plus the relative ease with which the typical engineer accepts a voltage viewpoint over a current viewpoint, makes the choice of a voltage-operated terminal appropriate. Curiously, even with the tube circuits, we will

3. The control terminal voltage is in the general vicinity of the emitter terminal voltage.

4. For a control voltage of approximately zero relative to the emitter, carriers reach the collector. For a control voltage negative relative to the emitter by some *cutoff* voltage, no carriers reach the collector. The cutoff level depends on the collector voltage.

So far as these assumptions are concerned, our device could be either a triode vacuum tube or a somewhat idealized NPN transistor, idealized in the sense that its base current is extremely small and that there are no carrier storage or turn-on delays.

Fortunately, the traditional symbols for the tube and the transistor place corresponding terminals in the same place: emitter or cathode at the bottom, base or grid at the side, collector or plate at the top. We·will preserve this convention with respect to terminals. We will use a square box to symbolize the device, and show its collector at the top, its control at the side, and its emitter at the bottom. To remind us that we do have a fictitious device, we will show no internal details in the symbol.

At some time the specific nature of the active element will require attention. When we reach that point, we hopefully will feel at home with the general behavior of the circuit, and will be ready to consider the influence of the tube or of the transistor on circuit considerations.

TOGGLES

General Toggle Considerations

The first circuit to be considered is the so-called *toggle* or *flip-flop*.*
It can be conveniently regarded as an electronic analog of the familiar two-position mechanical toggle switch. As such, it will exhibit at least these properties:

1. It has two stable positions (or *states*) into which it can be put. These two states might have such names as *off* or *on, 1* and *2, set* and *reset, 0* and *1*.

2. An external influence is necessary to change the toggle from one stable state to the other. When in one of its stable states, it has no inherent tendency to *self-flip* to the other state. The external influence

quickly progress to a design in which the input terminal is, in fact, conducting current. However, as a starter, we use a voltage terminal.

* Other names are *trigger-pair, scale-of-two,* or *bistable element*.

must be capable of doing work; e.g., for the mechanical toggle switch, the work is done against the spring of the switch.

3. Between the two stable states there is a third state which is unstable. To move the toggle from one to the other stable state, the external influence need only push the toggle to, and slightly beyond, the center unstable position. Once beyond the unstable point, the toggle will self-propel to the other stable state; if pushed not quite to the unstable point, the toggle will fall back to the original stable state.

By inference, it follows that a toggle circuit will have some input terminals on which it can receive the information to change its state, and it will have some output terminals by means of which its state can be made known to other places. The handle of a toggle switch is its input terminal; the pair of contacts is the output terminal. Observe that the input "signals" to the switch are two kinds of pushes (up or down) applied to the same input terminal.

We see that such a two-state device can store one bit's worth of information; one stable state will be defined to represent, say, 0, and thus the other stable state will automatically be defined to represent 1. Alternatively, a toggle can store the value of a Boolean variable. Furthermore, four toggles can store one decimal digit's worth of information in some binary code.

We expect that a toggle will be extremely useful in nearly every part of a digital machine. In the arithmetic unit, for instance, it will be the building block from which registers are made. In the control section, it will store the occurrence of logical decisions (i.e., changes of state of Boolean variables). In the store, it could, in principle, be the means of storing information; however, cost considerations (among others) deny this usage. In the input-output section, logical and numeric information can be stored in toggles.

How is such a device realized electronically?

The Eccles-Jordan Toggle

The canonical form, so to speak, of the toggle is the one first described by Eccles and Jordan (Figure 8.1) (2). Figure 8.1-a shows that it consists of two one-stage amplifiers connected tail-to-mouth; Figure 8.1-b shows a more conventional form of the schematic where we have introduced our generalized device.

Suppose that somehow the left-hand device has become conducting.

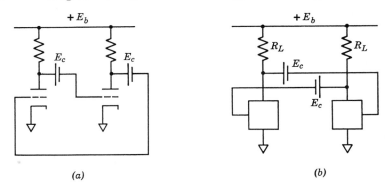

Figure 8.1. The Eccles-Jordan circuit.

If the crossover battery (E_c) is properly chosen, the control of the right hand device will be below the cutoff voltage; thus the collector of the right side will be at E_b and if E_b is properly chosen, $E_b - E_c$ will be such that the left-hand device can be in the conducting state as we originally assumed. The circuit will tend to remain in this particular configuration if not perturbed too much.

EXAMPLE

A given device can pass 5 ma of current with a collector voltage of 25 and zero-control bias; cutoff for this device is -5 volts for 50 volts on the collector. A crossover battery of 30 volts will reduce the $+25$ volt level of the conducting collector to the -5 volts required at the control. This same 30-volt battery implies that E_b must be $+30$ volts. This in turn implies that R_L is 5 volts/5 ma or 1 KΩ.

In view of our earlier discussion about drifting components and the statistical distribution of component parameters, we will rapidly decide that our design is shaky at best. If E_c has drifted or if R_L has become smaller or if the emission of the device has declined, the control of the supposedly non-conducting side may not be at its cutoff level. We would be wiser to set the lower level of the control swing at, say, -15 volts. Then the crossover battery will be 40 volts and R_L will be 3 KΩ. By "overswinging" the control, we have given the circuit some inherent protection against changes in component values or environmental conditions (e.g., changes in voltage supplies). Contrary to what may now seem to be the case, we have indeed paid the piper for the protection (see pages 8.52 and 8.62).

Suppose that the left-hand side is still conducting and that its control is forced slightly negative from its stable position. The left collector will rise slightly, carrying with it the right control. Because the right side is cutoff and its gain is low, the resulting motion of the right control might produce less than the same amount of motion in the right-hand collector. If so, the influence tending to drive the left control away from its stable position is less than the influence which is acting to support it in the perturbed position. Therefore, when the perturbation is removed, the circuit will return to its original situation.

It is clear, however, that when the externally applied perturbation is large enough, the gain around the loop (from the left control to the left collector to the right control to the right collector and back to the left control) can exceed unity, and the circuit then will tend to continue to move in the direction induced by the perturbation. If the collector swing has been properly chosen (by appropriate selection of R_L and the current change in the device), the motion of the right collector will be sufficient to drive the left control beyond cutoff, and the equal but opposite motion of the left collector will be sufficient to maintain the right side in conduction.

Thus we see that for a properly chosen set of circuit parameters, the Eccles-Jordan circuit will exhibit two stable positions. It will tend to remain locked in whichever position it finds itself, but it can be forcefully driven from one position to the other. One stable state (say, left-side conducting) will represent one value of a binary digit (say, 0), and hence the other stable state (right-side conducting) will represent the other value (1). The two stable states are in one-to-one correspondence with the two values of a binary digit; the two stable states represent the information contained in one bit. The state of the toggle (and, therefore, the value which it stores) can be determined by measuring its voltage (or current) pattern.

Notice that one of the two devices does not have to be cutoff; it is possible for the circuit to exhibit its binary nature with both sides conducting, one more so than the other. Practically, it may be unwise to design the circuit in this way because it may have less tendency to stay where it is (see page 8.22).

At this stage of our development we can identify one part of the design problem to be that which is concerned with the steady-state behavior of the toggle. This facet of the design determines what the voltage and current distribution through the circuit will be when it is in either of the quiescent or stable positions, and also determines how prone the circuit is to stay in one of the stable states. Another part of the design problem will appear later (page 8.58).

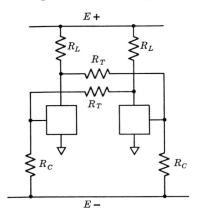

Figure 8.2. The symmetrical grounded-emitter toggle.

At this time, it is also possible to identify one aspect of the "spring" of the electronic toggle to be the current pattern which exists in the network. The external influence which attempts to perturb the toggle must combat the currents which flow in the network and, therefore, must do work against these currents.

THE SYMMETRICAL TOGGLE

The Eccles-Jordan configuration is not convenient for practical application because of the batteries in the crossover position. Neither crossover battery has a terminal common with the other one, which means that each must be an individual cell. Furthermore, a battery has large stray capacitance which makes fast acting circuits hard to design.

The modern counterpart of the Eccles-Jordan circuit is the *symmetrical grounded-emitter toggle* * of Figure 8.2 (3). This configuration will be discussed in considerable detail since it provides the basis for analyzing other forms of the toggle circuit. We see that the battery has been replaced by a resistance voltage divider whose "tail" is returned to a negative voltage. To transmit as much of the collector swing as possible to the opposite control, $R_C/(R_T + R_C)$ ought to be as nearly unity as possible. This, however, implies that R_C is

---

* The vacuum tube version is the *symmetrical grounded-cathode toggle*.

very large; therefore, to achieve the desired voltage shift from a collector down to the opposite control, $E-$ also must be very large, which leads to high dissipation in R_C. The resolution of this tradeoff is likely to be some very practical constraint; for example, limit the dissipation in R_C to one-fourth watt so that a one-half watt resistor can be used with a 50% derating on power. If the dissipation were too large, it might be necessary to use two actual resistors (in series) for R_C; this would lead to extra cost and packaging problems.

The first order of business is to select the three resistors, the two voltages, and the device.

Design through Reasoning

To gain insight into the possible tradeoffs, let us consider a design procedure which depends on an empirical iterated approach. To get started, assume that some active element has been selected, perhaps because of its long life and high reliability properties; this device will have some value of control cutoff. The first observation is that the higher the collector voltage selected, the larger must be the control swing to take the device from cutoff to conduction. This implies that the device must deliver a larger collector swing which implies a larger load resistor or voltage supply—which completes the vicious circle. Experience, if nothing else, suggests that a large load resistor implies low-frequency (i.e., slow) response; thus the fast-acting (i.e., microsecond rate or faster) circuit will tend to have smallish resistors, as well as small signal swings.

From a consideration of the desired speed of response, we will make a first guess at the load resistor and positive supply. We know that the collector swing must be equal at least to the difference between cutoff bias and zero bias. (The reason for working the control between zero bias and cutoff will appear later; see page 8.20.) Furthermore, being statistically mindful of reality, the designer recalls that a device is not a device is not a device (i.e., devices differ from each other); the cutoff bias will vary from one to the next and may also vary through its life. The designer also knows that resistors may be statistically ill behaved. Thus the initial guess at the collector swing must be revised upward to accomodate (1) the expected variation in the load (R_L), transpose (R_T), and control (R_C) resistors (see Figure 8.2); (2) the changing cutoff characteristic; (3) perhaps belatedly recognized—the changing current characteristics of the device; (4) possible fluctuation in supply voltages; and (5) the attenuation in the divider (R_T and R_C).

Three other things suddenly jolt into focus. The collector voltage of the device when cutoff is not $E+$, but is some voltage determined jointly by the three resistors—R_L, R_T, and R_C—and the two voltages, $E+$ and $E-$. Furthermore, the load of the device is not R_L but R_L in parallel with $R_T + R_C$. Finally, there is some derating schedule for collector dissipation and perhaps also for the zero-bias current of this device. Sooner or later, the current being drawn through the device, and the dissipation in its collector, will have to be verified to be consistent with the derating policy. For the moment, file these considerations for future reference.

A little later, we will discover factors having to do with speed which influence the first stab at the parameters (page 8.47 ff.), but for the moment the situation is as follows:

A device has been selected, and on the basis of some guesses (which may be guided by experience) of how various parameters of the circuit may be statistically distributed either initially or with age, initial values have been selected for R_L, $E+$, the collector swing, and the device current when in conduction.

EXAMPLE

A particular device when derated by 50% on both collector dissipation and zero-bias current can pass at most 7 ma for a collector voltage of 37.* For a collector voltage of 15 and zero bias, it passes 5 ma; for 50 volts on the collector, control cutoff is −3.5 volts. The control swing must be at least 3.5 volts; to protect against drifts, it must be larger. Initially assume that the nominal swing must be 10 volts. The collector swing must be enough bigger to offset the attenuation in the voltage divider formed by R_T and R_C. Suppose that 22 volts is the initial guess and its lower level is 15 volts; i.e., the voltage divider has an attenuation of about 0.5. The collector will, therefore,

---

* The numerical values in the illustrative examples have been chosen to coordinate with our anonymous active element. The voltages used are somewhat high for transistor technology, and somewhat low for vacuum-tube art; hopefully this will remind the reader that he is dealing with an element which can be particularized to be either a tube or a transistor. The examples can be easily scaled to either situation. By multiplying all voltages and all resistor values by a factor of 3, a typical vacuum-tube situation will obtain. By dividing all voltages and all resistors by a factor between 5 and 10, a typical transistor situation will result. In each case, the current pattern in the circuit is the same. Some rounding in the numbers has been done.

move between +15 volts and +37 volts. When conducting, the device will pass 5 ma and, therefore, R_L is

$$\frac{(37-15)\ \text{volts}}{5\ \text{ma}} = 4.3\ \text{K}\Omega.$$

The initial design choices are then $E+ = 37$ volts, $R_L = 4.3\text{K}\Omega$, conducting device current $= 5$ ma. Suppose that R_L becomes 5% too small ($= 4.1$ KΩ) and that $E+$ becomes 5% larger ($= 39$ volts). The collector swing is still 20.5 volts (about 1.5 volts smaller). The lower reach of the control will at most be 3.5 volts more positive (1.5 volts from decreased collector swing and 2 volts from increased $E+$). The control will still be at least at -7 volts (instead of -10) which is still ample.

Next, an initial design for R_T, R_C, and $E-$ must be made. The goal here is to preserve as much of the collector swing as possible for the control, but to obtain still the necessary absolute voltage shift from the collector to the control, while not consuming excessive power in R_T and R_C. These considerations are not enough to determine a unique choice for R_T, R_C, and $E-$; but then at this stage of evolution, neither is any other part of the toggle design unambiguously defined. One practical consideration should not be overlooked: it will be convenient to have each resistor value be commonly available in order to avoid paying a premium price for a special item.

EXAMPLE

Let us continue with the design started in the previous example: $i_c = 5$ ma, $R_L = 4.3$ KΩ, $E+ = 37$ volts, cutoff $= -3.5$ volts. The collector swing is 22 volts; the control swing, 10 volts. The voltage divider, therefore, should attenuate by no more than 0.46. Moreover, the +37-volt level of the collector must be shifted downward to 0 volts to provide the upper control level.

Suppose that the designer is partial to -100 volts for $E-$; the voltage divider then becomes

$$R_T \quad\quad R_C$$
$$+37\text{ volts} -\!/\!\backslash\!/\!\backslash\!-\!\!\!\!\stackrel{\downarrow}{|}\!\!\!\!-\!/\!\backslash\!/\!\backslash\!- -100\text{ volts}$$
$$0\text{ volts}$$

and for a divider current of, say, 2.5 ma, $R_T = 15$ KΩ and $R_C = 40$ KΩ. When the collector drops from +37 volts to +15 volts, the control voltage (midpoint of R_T and R_C) will drop to -17 volts—somewhat further than we really needed. We might now go back and readjust the load resistor, the current swing, etc., or some combination of these things to shorten the control excursion. As we will see later (page 8.59), the impedance level of the divider (and hence, the current through it) will strongly influence the transition speed of the toggle. For the moment, our only guidance is that $R_T + R_C$ ought to be somewhat larger than R_L while providing the necessary voltage shift. However, the larger that R_T and R_C are, the larger will be the time constant at the controls, and hence the slower will be the toggle. Thus we are led to make them not too much larger than R_L. It is clear, nonetheless, that as the current through the divider increases, the larger must be the current swing in the device to produce the same collector signal. Eventually, therefore, we will have to balance the divider current against the current capability of the device.

Suppose we accept the increased control swing for the moment. We know that $R_T + R_C$ will be in parallel with R_L so far as the collector load is concerned. Therefore, we must increase R_L to that value which in parallel with 55 KΩ ($R_T + R_C$) yields a net resistance of 4.3 KΩ; this turns out to be 4.7 KΩ.

Furthermore, the $E+$ will now have to be larger because the current flowing through $R_T + R_C$ produces a voltage drop across R_L even when device current is zero. The situation is:

$$E + \overset{4.7\ K\Omega}{-\!\!\!\bigwedge\!\!\!\bigwedge\!\!\!-}\ \underset{37\ \text{volts}}{\overset{15\ K\Omega}{\mid\!\downarrow\!\!-\!\!\!\bigwedge\!\!\!\bigwedge\!\!\!-}}\ \overset{40\ K\Omega}{-\!\!\!\bigwedge\!\!\!\bigwedge\!\!\!-}\ -100$$

Use of Kirchhoff's law leads to $E+ = 48$ volts.

So far, the design is $E+ = +48$ volts, $E- = -100$ volts, $R_L = 4.7$ KΩ, $R_T = 15$ KΩ and $R_C = 40$ KΩ.

Notice that the maximum dissipation in R_C is $(100)^2/40$ K$\Omega = 0.25$ watt so that a resistor rated at one-half watt can be used.

The designer might now try values of resistors near his selected ones to see how the situation changes; for example, 39 KΩ is a more common value than 40 KΩ and might be preferred.

Given our first guess at all parameter values, some of the uncertainties can be resolved. The actual voltages throughout the circuit can be found; the correct collector and control swings can be found. The dissipation in all elements can be computed, and the zero-bias current of the device can be checked against the derated value. Finally, all elements can be allowed to assume maximum tolerance drifts, and the voltage levels again determined. Alternatively, the circuit can be analyzed to determine what simultaneous and worst-direction set of tolerance deviations it will stand.

EXAMPLE

Suppose that the tentative design is the one from the previous example. Let us calculate the effect of resistor tolerances on the lower level of the control.

To simplify the calculation, assume that the device current remains at 5 ma even though the collector voltage varies a little. In real life, a set of device characteristics would be used.

If R_L is 10% too large (= 5.2 KΩ), the collector voltage will be smaller than usual. If R_T is 10% too large (= 16.5 KΩ) and if R_C is 10% too small (= 36 KΩ), the control will tend to be closer to −100 than usual. This set of circumstances appears to be one for which the control will get most negative. Notice that R_T and R_C influence the effective collector load; to make it as large as possible, R_C as well at R_T, ought to be 10% too large. On the other hand, so far as the voltage-divider action is concerned, it is obvious that R_T too large and R_C too small is the situation which is worst for the control and will make it most negative. Both possibilities need to be checked. Moral: not always is it possible to determine by inspection the "worst case" set of tolerance drifts.

For the circumstances noted, the situation is:

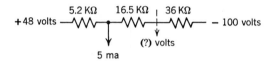

By Thévenin's theorem, the effective collector circuit is

$$+35 \text{ volts} \quad \overset{4.7\,\text{K}\Omega}{-\!\!\!\bigwedge\!\!\bigwedge\!\!-}\quad \downarrow \quad 5\text{ ma}$$

and, therefore, the collector voltage is 12 volts. It quickly follows that the control level is

$$-100 + \left[\frac{12 - (-100)}{36 \text{ K}\Omega + 16.5 \text{ K}\Omega} \cdot 36 \text{ K}\Omega \right] = -23 \text{ volts.}$$

Suddenly it is remarkably clear how important the tolerance problem is! We have not even included the tolerance on device current nor on supply voltages, and the lower reach of the control has moved 7 volts more negative.

The designer might at this point reconsider his decision to accept 5% drifts in resistor values. However, even with 5% tolerances, only part of this can be given to the purchased component (perhaps 2%); the rest (3% in this case) is retained to cover aging and other long-term drifts.

At any point along the way, including as late as the tolerance check, the design procedure may have to be iterated. The wider the tolerances which can be accommodated, the easier and cheaper it will be to obtain components. Furthermore, the wider the acceptable tolerances, the less trouble the maintenance man will have with drifting components. On the other hand, the larger the tolerances, the larger must be the swings in the circuit to guarantee that the control always goes to cutoff, and as we will see later, the slower will be the circuit. It is not obvious, therefore, that money invested in high quality stable components does not pay off. Stable components at least imply a circuit with smaller swings and, therefore, one that is very likely faster; this speed has some economic value.

As soon as the designer knows what tolerances his circuit will stand, he can, in effect, determine the end-of-life value for any component. Based on his knowledge of components, he then allocates part of this tolerance to initial procurement and production distribution, and the rest of it to aging and drifting over time.

Formalizing the Static Design

So far we have considered only that part of the design problem which has to do with the toggle in the quiescent or static condition; i.e., when in a stable state, what is the voltage and current distribution throughout the network, and how far may the components simultaneously drift in the worst directions but still preserve two stable states? We have given no thought to how fast the transition from one stable state to the other might occur (see page 8.46), nor in fact have we directed any thought to methods of effecting a transition from one stable state to the other (see page 8.32).

It is clear, however, that Thévenin's theorem, Kirchhoff's laws, and a knowledge of device behavior are the only analytical tools required to carry out the design procedure so far described. If some sort of linearizing or other simplifying assumption can be made about device parameters, the static design of the toggle can be reduced to a formal algebraic or graphical exercise. However, the insight into potential tradeoffs, into the conflicting constraints at work in the toggle circuit, and into the core of toggle behavior is better exhibited by "chasing" the design procedure around its iterative loop than by plugging numbers blindly into formulae. With the background presented above, the formalized techniques can be readily developed or learned from the literature (4). Such formalized approaches generally algebraically relate the various resistors, supply voltages, device parameters, and a specification on the expected tolerance of each parameter.

E Pluribus Unum

The toggle, as an entity, will appear repeatedly in a digital system. It must, therefore, be prepared to transmit information (i.e., electrical signals) to some communication network and be prepared to accept information from that network. It will read information out to the network through one or more *output terminals*. The information presented to the network will be represented perhaps as a voltage level or as a signal of specified kind. The toggle will accept information from the network through one or more *input terminals*. Such information will be represented as voltages or as other kinds of specified signals and will cause the toggle to enter one of its two stable states.

As we will see later, the communication network will be a switchable one, changing its detailed information routes with time as the digital system passes from one internal configuration to the next. It is the routing information in this communication network which determines how the present internal configuration of a computer shall be altered to produce the next one.

The toggle as a building block must, therefore, be designed with consideration for the other devices with which it must communicate. At least, a toggle may have to communicate directly with others of its kind. Therefore, there may well be preferred kinds of outputs from a toggle; there might also be a preferred type of input signal to which the toggle ought to respond. Another constraint might be a specification of absolute voltage level and/or amplitude of swing for an input or output terminal. In this connection, we observe that each of the controls and each of the collectors is a prospective input terminal; any outside influence transmitted to one of these points will, because of the completeness of the feedback path in the toggle, be felt throughout the toggle.

Similarly, any collector or any control is a possible output terminal in view of the tight interrelationship between all parts of the toggle. Each of these points can be at one of two voltage levels which unambiguously correspond to the two stable states.

EXAMPLES

1. A toggle is to provide an output signal which swings from 0 to -15 volts. The tolerance on the upper level is to be $-0, +\frac{1}{2}$ volt; the tolerance on the lower level, $+5, -10$ volts.

2. A toggle must respond to a properly shaped signal which is usually at −10 ± 1 volts but moves to +10 ± ½ volts when the toggle is to respond.

3. A toggle provides an output of 15, +3 or −5 volts to represent binary 1 and an output of 35 ±5 volts to represent binary 0. Because of the symmetry of the symmetrical toggle, if a given point represents a specified variable or digit, the image point represents the complement of that variable or digit.

Clearly, such specifications on the input-output terminals can be fitted into the empirical approach previously described; such restrictions might also be worked into a formalized design technique. There may be other specifications which hem in the designer—who at the moment is still concerned with the static design. For example, a toggle may be required to present a certain impedance at its input or output terminals. It may be required to furnish some specified current to either a real current or displacement current load. It may have to ignore certain kinds of input signals, e.g., reject noise. Not all of these more subtle requirements can always be easily built into a straightaway synthesis approach. Often, a synthesis followed by an analysis of the circuit for conformance to some property is the only sensible attack—all the more reason why the designer must appreciate the fine points of toggle behavior, and understand the power and capability of the intuitive, empirical iterated techniques.

How Stable is Stable?

An important facet of toggle behavior is the question of its stability when in one of the quiescent states. Does the toggle have any spontaneous tendency to indulge either small scale quasi-sinusoidal oscillations, or to flip back and forth from one state to the other? For the purposes of this discussion, assume that the toggle is in one of its stable states. For the point to be made here, it is sufficient to characterize the active element in the simplest way. Therefore, assume that for small signals, it can be represented by a voltage generator in series with an internal impedance. In magnitude the generator is the voltage of the control relative to the emitter, multiplied by a scalar constant.* With such a simple equivalent circuit for the active element, we have essentially denied any of the internal couplings which the

---

* This assumption follows vacuum tube practice, and has been used in order to avoid the somewhat more complicated equivalent circuit of the transistor.

transistor exhibits. The following argument, therefore, might have to be sharpened in some details for transistor situations.

The approach is generally that of a typical Bode-type feedback analysis (5).

Assume that a signal Δe_{CnL} * is introduced at the left control. If the left device is conducting and has a voltage amplification factor A, then the output from the left collector is

$$\Delta e_{ClL} = A \; \Delta e_{CnL} \cdot \frac{\dfrac{R_L(R_T + R_C)}{R_L + R_T + R_C}}{\dfrac{R_L(R_T + R_C)}{R_L + R_T + R_C} + r_c} \cdot \dagger$$

where r_c is the internal resistance of the device,

and

$$\frac{R_L(R_T + R_C)}{R_L + R_T + R_C}$$

is the effective load of the device. The signal at the right control is then

$$\Delta e_{CnR} = \Delta e_{ClL} \frac{R_C}{R_T + R_C}.$$

The right device is presumed to be cutoff; therefore, its equivalent internal resistance is very high. It is convenient to replace the voltage generator by an equivalent current of magnitude $\gamma \, \Delta e_{CnR}$. The right side has the same effective load as the left side and hence,

$$\Delta e_{ClR} = \gamma_0 \cdot \Delta e_{CnR} \cdot \frac{R_L(R_T + R_C)}{R_L + R_T + R_C}$$

where γ_0 is the transconductance of this device in its cutoff state. The fraction of this which appears at the left control is

$$\Delta e_{ClR} \frac{R_C}{R_T + R_C}.$$

By combining these several statements, we see that the loop voltage gain is

---

* The first subscript (Cn or Cl) refers to the element (control or collector) and the second, to position (right or left).

† At this point, the reader perhaps should jump back to the preface and re-read the comments about units and the evaluation of formulae.

$$A_{\text{Loop}} = \frac{A \left[\dfrac{R_L(R_T + R_C)}{R_L + R_T + R_C} \right]^2}{\dfrac{R_L(R_T + R_C)}{R_L + R_T + R_C} + r_c} \cdot \left(\frac{R_C}{R_T + R_C} \right)^2 \cdot \gamma_0.$$

For the circuit to be stable in one of its quiescent positions,

$$A_{\text{Loop}} < 1.$$

For a given toggle design, the loop gain can be calculated from such an expression. Alternatively, it can be used to determine the maximum value of γ_0 which will maintain stability. Since most of the resistors have been determined by other considerations and r_c is fixed by the device choice, there is very little within the control of the designer at this stage except γ_0. This is related to the degree of cutoff of the device. In practical cases, it may be found that the required values of γ_0 cannot be realized, and other ways must be found to keep the loop gain less than unity.

Notice that any external influence which raises the loop gain above unity (effectively by increasing the gain on the cutoff side) is a *trigger* which can initiate instability and, therefore, induce a transition to the other state.

We now appreciate why a toggle circuit is generally designed to operate the control to at least cutoff or beyond; it minimizes the loop gain. In fact, the constraint on loop gain can be a reason for operating the control well beyond cutoff. Otherwise, we may have to find other means for maintaining stability in the circuit, i.e., for maintaining $A_{\text{Loop}} < 1$.

We must be very careful to appreciate the proper context of the previous analytical expressions. In the actual case, the active elements in a toggle are switching between essentially the zero current state and a heavily conducting state; the behavior is wildly non-linear. The usual small signal theory is not relevant, since it depends on an assumed linearity of the device. The toggle circuit can only be treated properly by a full scale transient analysis. This is very difficult to do, and as usual with a difficult analysis, one is grateful for whatever insight and hints he can get from simplifying assumptions such as linearity.

When in a stable state, however, a toggle can be considered linear for small deviations from the stable position. Therefore, the previous expression does give the designer a reasonable quantitative feel for how close his design is to the edge of stability. Furthermore, the expression does properly relate the parameters of the toggle so that hints for bettering the stability problem can be found in it. For another thing, a clue appears which bears on the transition problem.

As we said previously—although we did not speak in terms of feedback terminology—the connections in the toggle circuit are such that if feedback ever does occur, it will be regenerative. We might guess that the more violently regenerative a toggle is, the more rapidly it will transition. Therefore, one possibility for a rapid transition is to raise the gain of the cutoff element to as large a value as possible, and as soon as possible after transition is supposed to commence. Again we are making a linear-like remark about a non-linear circuit, since gain will be a function of time during the transition interval. The practical implication, however, is that it is important to get the perturbing influence to the control of the cutoff element as fast as possible.

From this point of view, it is likely that some methods of triggering may effect a transition much more rapidly than others.

The Case for Control Current

We now have to make an additional assumption about our fictitious device. If the control voltage rises above the emitter voltage, the control will no longer be a high-impedance device, but will commence to draw current. The control will behave effectively as a secondary collector. We will assume it to be a low-impedance collector. The difference between the vacuum tube and the transistor is important here. Whatever benefit control current will turn out to have, the grid of the vacuum tube will have to be driven positive to attain it, but the transistor will provide it automatically.

A way to reduce the loop gain is to design the circuit so that the control of the conducting device draws current. This implies that the choice of R_T, R_C, and $E-$ is such that the control would tend toward some positive potential were it not for the effective clamping of the low-impedance control.* Because of the low impedance between the control and the emitter, the control is effectively clamped to the emitter (ground). Therefore, the control exhibits a rather low impedance (r) in parallel with R_C so far as the voltage divider is con-

---

* This low-impedance control point is the forward-biased diode between the base and emitter of a transistor, or the forward-biased diode implicit between a grid-in-current and the cathode of a vacuum tube.

cerned.   Because $r \ll R_C$, $rR_C/(r + R_C)$ essentially reduces to r. Thus one of the $R_C/(R_T + R_C)$ terms is replaced by $r/(R_T + r)$ which reduces to r/R_T because $r \ll R_T$.   Under this circumstance, the permissible γ_0 is much larger and probably readily attainable in practical circumstances.

EXAMPLE

Consider the particular toggle of Figure 8.3.   Take the r_c of the conducting device to be 2.3 KΩ; A of the device, 30.   For the design shown, the control will draw current.   However, for the sake of this discussion, assume that it does not.   Under this circumstance, we find that to preserve loop gain less than unity,

$$\gamma_0 \leq 18 \ \mu\text{mhos}.$$

Actually, the control conducts about $\frac{1}{2}$ ma of current and its impedance will be perhaps 100 ohms.   Now it is required only that

$$\gamma_0 \leq 1600 \ \mu\text{mhos}.$$

The first value may be a very difficult one to achieve, whereas the latter value may be a very reasonable one to expect.

There are other ways of keeping loop gain sufficiently small.   Any clamping diode (at a collector or control) provides a low impedance signal path and, therefore, reduces loop gain.   Diode clamping is one way to maintain low loop gain in a toggle designed never to cut off

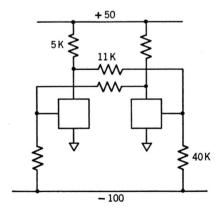

Figure 8.3.   A particular symmetrical toggle.

either side.   Entirely different circuit configurations (see page 8.75)
achieve a sufficiently small loop gain by means of degenerative feedback.

A GRAPHICAL APPROACH

Since the toggle consists of two tail-to-mouth amplifiers, the behavior
of the circuit can be studied graphically.   To do this the input-output
or transfer characteristic of the amplifier must be constructed.   While
the detailed curve can always be constructed with the aid of the device
characteristics, for the purposes here, only the general shape of the
curve is important and will be obtained by reasoning.   Assume that
we have the circuit of Figure 8.3, which has been designed for control
current.

There are two points to observe.   First, the appropriate output point
for the transfer characteristic is the one which is directly coupled to
the input of the other half of the circuit.   The transfer characteristic
that we need is from the control of one device to the midpoint of the
output voltage divider.   Secondly, since the input terminal of each
amplifier has an implicit diode connected to it, the effect of this loading on the output terminal must be considered.   The circuit to be
analyzed is therefore that of Figure 8.4.

For large negative values of control voltage, the amplifier stage is
cutoff and the collector voltage is in its upper state; therefore, the diode
is conducting.   As the control voltage becomes less negative, the col-

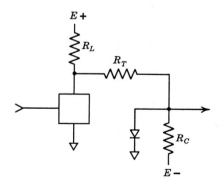

Figure 8.4. Half of the symmetrical toggle.

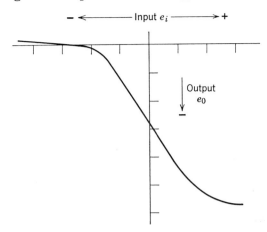

Figure 8.5. The transfer characteristic for half of the symmetrical toggle.

lector voltage begins to fall. Eventually, the diode current declines to zero, and the output terminal also begins to move negatively. By the time the control has reached zero bias, the output is quite negative. As the control is driven further into the current region, the collector current increases less rapidly than before (the device is beginning to saturate), and the collector voltage begins to move onto a plateau. By combining all these facts, we deduce the characteristic shown in Figure 8.5.

It is now necessary to superpose two copies of this characteristic in such a way that the input axis of one characteristic lies on top of the output axis of the other, and also so that the positive directions coincide. This requires two motions as shown in Figure 8.6-a; one is a rotation in the $e_i - e_0$ plane about the origin as a pivot point; and the other is a reflection of the entire plane about the e_0 axis. Furthermore, the scales on the two axis must be identical because of the superposition.

As we see in Figure 8.6-b, which has been constructed for the specific circuit of Figure 8.3, the curves intersect in three points. The two outermost ones correspond to the stable equilibrium positions of the toggle, and the center one corresponds to the middle "point of no return" for the electronic toggle—the center point of the toggle switch. If pushed beyond this center point, the toggle will spontaneously continue to its other stable position. The stable control potentials are seen to be approximately $+\frac{1}{6}$ volts and -12 volts corresponding

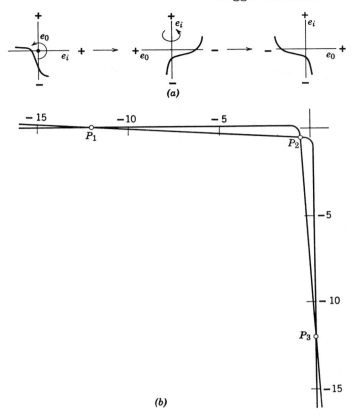

(a)

(b)

Figure 8.6. Superposition of two transfer characteristics.

to collector potentials of $+37$ volts and $+12$ volts. The point of no
return is seen to exist when each control is at about $-\frac{1}{2}$ volt.

That Middle Point

The reluctance of a toggle to depart from a stable position is best
seen from a loop transfer characteristic. Assume that the circuit
is broken at the left control, and that the implicit control-emitter
diode is replaced by an explicit one (Figure 8.7). For specific potentials applied to the left control, the transfer characteristic will
determine corresponding potentials at the right control, which reflected
in turn through the transfer characteristic determines the voltage

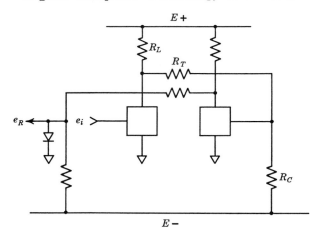

Figure 8.7. The circuit for analyzing the loop gain.

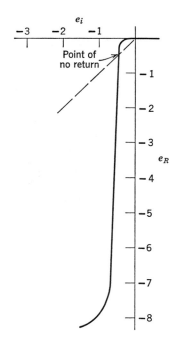

Figure 8.8. Loop transfer characteristic of the symmetrical toggle.

returned (e_R) to the left control. Figure 8.8 shows the resulting loop transfer characteristic (for the circuit of Figure 8.3). Since the scales on the two axis are equal, the 45° dotted line again marks the center point of no return, $-\frac{1}{2}$ volt. We see that so long as the left control is more negative than $-\frac{1}{2}$ volt (say -1 volt), the loop-transferred voltage prefers to have the left control be even more negative (-8 volts). Therefore, if the broken circuit were reclosed at this time, the perturbed left control will retrace its way to its negative stable position. On the other hand, if the left control is somewhat more positive than $-\frac{1}{2}$ volt, the loop insists that it shall be even more positive, and thus positive regeneration will cause the circuit to propagate to its other stable position. We again see that the center point is, in fact, a point of unstable equilibrium at which the circuit can-

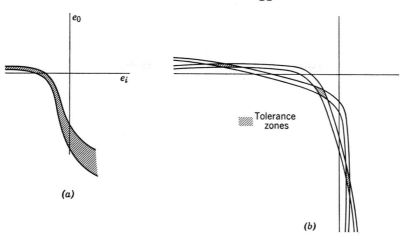

Figure 8.9. The effect of tolerances on the transfer and loop characteristics.

not remain. We also see conclusively that the outer points of a properly designed circuit are positions of stable equilibrium at which the circuit has a decided preference to remain.

If there are explicit diodes anywhere in the circuit, they must be considered in constructing the transfer or loop characteristics. The effect of circuit tolerances can be graphically displayed by constructing the characteristic curves for the worst combination of tolerances first in one direction and then in the other. The resultant pair of characteristics then defines an area within which any toggle, all of whose components are still within end-of-life, can legitimately operate (Figure 8.9). If a collector or a control is required to supply current to an external load, this can also be taken into effect in constructing the transfer characteristic.

The graphical technique conveniently displays a large number of toggle properties and possible behaviors. It is, however, a tool of analysis. Given a design, the graphical technique can provide a lot of information about the performance and quality of the design—but with respect only to the static behavior. So far as synthesis of a circuit is concerned, the graphical technique serves only to measure the deviation of the given design from the desired performance; it thus provides corrective information for the next iteration of the synthesis.

There is one very important caution to be noted. Except for broad guiding clues, do not expect the graphical analysis to hold for the transient behavior during transition. Because of time delays around the circuit, the voltage change at the midpoint of R_T and R_C on one side of the toggle is not communicated instantaneously to the control on the other side. Therefore, some of our previous reasoning must be modified during the rapidly changing events of the transition. In particular, the loop characteristic becomes a function of time and can depend upon the precise shape of the applied trigger signal. One point is clear, however; in order to transition, the toggle must be pushed to some point and held there for some minimum time which is related to the propagation delay around the loop.

A Confirmation

Does the graphical approach agree with the previous analytic attack on stability (page 8.19)? First of all, overhaul the circuit of Figure 8.3 so that the control just reaches zero volts on the upswing ($R_T = 15$ KΩ). Assuming a device which cuts off properly at approximately -5 volts, we find the transfer characteristic to be that of Figure 8.10, and the loop characteristic to be that of Figure 8.11. Assume now that the cutoff characteristic is so poor that the transfer characteristic is that of Figure 8.12; the device cuts off at -17 volts. Under these circumstances the loop characteristic is the almost straight line of Figure 8.13! The loop gain is unity all the time, and the circuit now has no predilection to stay put in a position of stability.

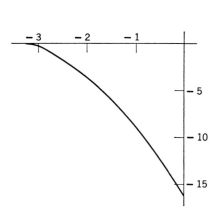

Figure 8.10. The transfer characteristic of half a symmetrical toggle without control current.

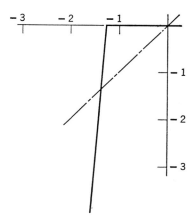

Figure 8.11. The loop transfer characteristic of a symmetrical toggle without control current.

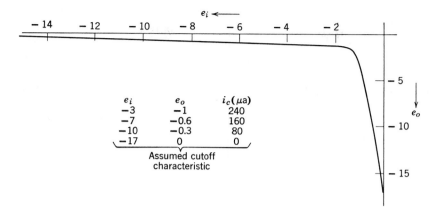

Figure 8.12. A poor cutoff device.

The assumed cutoff characteristic corresponds to the following collector currents and γ_0's.

$e_{control}$	i_c	γ_0
-17 volts	0	
-13	40 μa	120 μmhos
-10	80 μa	
-7	160 μa	240 μmhos
-3	240 μa	

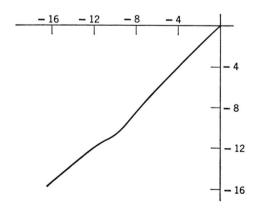

Figure 8.13. The loop transfer characteristic of a symmetrical toggle for poor cutoff devices without control current.

The analytical approach would have predicted a γ_0 of 60 μmhos for this situation; this is fairly reasonable agreement in view of the approximations and rounding in our numbers.

Those End Points

As we have seen from the previous discussion, the two outer intersections of the superposed transfer characteristics are stable ones at which the toggle prefers to remain. These points correspond to the extremities of travel in a toggle wall switch. However, unlike a mechanical toggle switch, the electronic toggle can be forcefully displaced beyond its limit point, but it will return to the natural end point when the perturbing influence is removed.

There are several things in the electronic toggle which collectively correspond to the mechanical end stops in the mechanical toggle switch. These reflect the natural tendencies for various parts of the toggle to cease motion because of the circuit configuration or because of some property of a component:

1. The upper motion of a control (and of the opposite collector) is naturally limited by the combination of R_L, γ_T, and R_C as a voltage divider and, perhaps, also by the passage of the control into current.

2. The lower motion of a control (and of the opposite collector) depends on the characteristics of the device, the effective load resistance, as well as the tendency of the collector to saturate.

These features combine to produce the characteristic shape of the transfer and loop characteristics, and to keep the loop gain less than unity at the equilibrium positions. In the particular toggle configuration in which the upper and lower swings of the both controls and both collectors are clamped, the clamping diodes are the very obvious analog of the stops in a mechanical toggle switch.

FLIPPABILITY

The inherent tenacity with which a toggle holds its loop gain less than unity increases the difficulty for an outside influence to effect a transition. Yet it is clear that a toggle must be reticent to flip, or every random noise signal would send it on its way. And there is always electrical noise in any environment! Therefore, a high degree of inherent noise rejection, which implies a high degree of steady-state stability is inconsistent with minimum difficulty of flipping. For each situation he faces, a designer must arrive at a satisfactory compromise between these two. As we will see later (page 8.37), noise rejection can also be obtained by a proper choice of triggering methods.

In any toggle circuit, one measure of the reluctance to flip (and, therefore, a measure of its ability to reject spurious signals) can be taken to be the amount of voltage (or current) perturbation which is required at any point in the toggle to raise the loop gain above unity. It is clear that not all points in the toggle will be equally sensitive to noise. The impedance of the collector may be lower than that of a control which in turn will make it more difficult to couple extraneous noise to the collector. Such spurious noise could enter either through stray capacitance coupling, through the supply voltages, on the ground bus, or through the triggering device.

In a configuration which contains clamp diodes, the amount of current in the diode measures in part the *locking strength* of the toggle. Until such diode currents are all reduced to zero, the signal paths will remain low impedance. Furthermore, the configuration may be such that the control of the cutoff device cannot move significantly until all clamps are broken; if so, the gain cannot change very much prior to clamp break.

A Bonus

Diodes—either implicit or explicit—which appear in the circuit to guarantee stability can also help the component tolerance problem. Any point in the toggle which has a diode clamp connected to it simply cannot get past the clamp voltage level. If the circuit is designed so that the point in question just reaches the clamp level when all tolerances are in the worst direction, then for any other combination of tolerances, the given point will definitely move to the clamp level. In effect, the tolerance problems created by drifting components have been absorbed by the diode clamps and the clamp voltages. Thus another economic tradeoff the designer might consider is: less stable and cheaper resistors versus the cost of the additional components (diodes) and power supplies (clamp voltages). A more difficult question to ponder is: Is a circuit with additional components more or less reliable than one with fewer?

See page 8.62 for yet another bonus feature of diode clamps.

Changing of the State

It is now time for us to investigate ways and means for changing a toggle from one of its stable states to the other. Our design has progressed to the point where a circuit exists which exhibits two stable states, and which tolerates non-trivial fluctuations in supply voltages and parameter values.

The first significant observation is that any real-life circuit has stray capacitance. Unfortunately for us, a capacitor has the property that the voltage across itself does not change unless current flows into or out of it. Therefore, the stray capacitance of the circuit can be identified as another aspect of the "spring" (see page 8.10) which tends to preserve the status quo of the toggle circuit. Not only must the current pattern in the toggle be perturbed to effect a transition, but one or more of the stray capacitances will have to be perturbed. This implies that any signal source which is capable of transitioning a toggle must exhibit an impedance sufficiently low that it can provide or accept some necessary amount of current.

Consider first a signal source attached directly to the control of the device which is conducting (point E_{CnL} of Figure 8.14). Suppose that this source moves the control negatively ever so slowly. The left collector (E_{ClL}) and the right control (E_{CnR}) move positively, and eventually the voltages at the two controls are equal. Suppose the

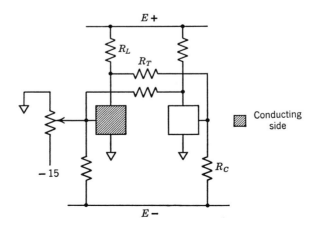

Figure 8.14. Forcing the toggle to transition.

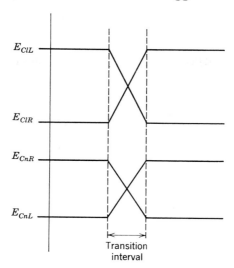

Figure 8.15.   The transition event shown schematically.

external source continues to move E_{CnL} negatively; eventually E_{CnL} will arrive at that voltage which corresponds to the lower of its static positions—E_{CnLL}.* If this process has been going on slowly enough, all other points in the toggle will be at corresponding static positions. The external source can now be uncoupled; it has successfully moved the toggle from one state to another.   Thus one way to effect a transition is for some external means to forcefully move some element of the toggle to the desired new position.   If the element is held in its new position until all other parts of the toggle have finished responding, the toggle will remain flipped.   Figure 8.15 schematically shows the situation.   The details of the transition interval are still unknown.

That Center Point Again

Suppose that the external drive which is applied to the left control (Figure 8.14) had been uncoupled when the two controls were equipotential.   If the circuit is assumed to be exactly symmetrical with respect to component parameters, chance will decide toward which

---

* This may be a strange looking notation but at least it is mnemonically easy; the third subscript is relative voltage level (upper or lower).

stable state the circuit moves. Some random noise event probably will start the circuit moving, and it will then continue in that direction. As we have seen previously, the midpoint is an unstable one at which the toggle cannot statically remain.

In real life, no toggle will ever be completely symmetrical. Therefore, the two transfer characteristics which enter into our graphical analysis (page 8.24) are unlike, and the resulting point of no return will no longer correspond to equal control voltages. The loop characteristic will also be distorted from the shape previously found. Because of asymmetry, the amplitude of trigger which is required to bring the toggle to its midpoint generally will depend upon which side of the toggle is being perturbed. To top it off, the position of this middle-point will have a long-term drift as the circuit parameters change over time.

The presence of capacitance in an actual circuit further complicates the determination of midpoint behavior. For instance, suppose that capacitance exists at each control but unsymmetrically so. The two controls will be unable to move equally easily, and therefore the circuit might show a disposition to fall one way from the center point even though previous arguments have suggested that it ought to fall either direction equally probably.

Thus, in the practical case, the precise point to which the circuit must be pushed in order to guarantee that it spontaneously continues in the same direction can be deduced only from a rather careful analysis of the transient behavior of all points in the circuit, or experimentally.

On with Changing of the State

As we have seen, any outside influence which perturbs a toggle far enough in the proper direction can flip it. Thus any one of the following is a possible way to trigger a symmetrical toggle:

1. Drive the collector of the conducting device positively
2. Drive the control of the conducting device negatively
3. Drive the collector of the non-conducting device negatively
4. Drive the control of the non-conducting device positively

Clearly, any combination of these might also be used. The injection of current can be real current (via a resistor, transistor, tube, or diode), or it can be displacement current (via a capacitor).

Direct-Coupled Triggering

Those schemes which introduce the triggering current into the toggle as real current are spoken of as *direct-coupled* triggering on the grounds that for at least part of the time, there is a conductive path between the trigger source and the toggle. Generally, unilateral devices are preferred for such coupling devices since for them, the toggle, once it begins to self-propel, can break away from the trigger source and proceed on its own. Figure 8.16 shows a representative number of direct-coupled schemes.

Consider the case (Figure 8.16-a) in which a negative signal is in-

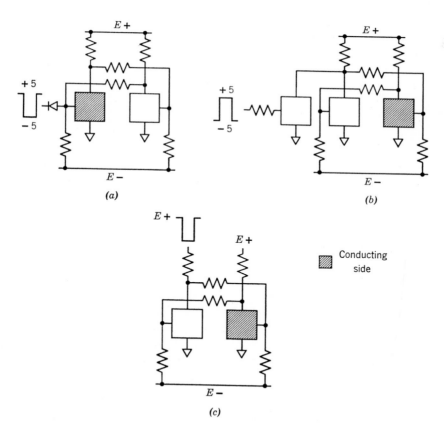

(a)

(b)

(c)

Conducting side

Figure 8.16. Direct-coupled triggering methods.

troduced onto the control of the conducting side via a diode. Suppose, for definiteness, that the levels of this toggle control can be 0 volts or -10 volts, thereby implying that the device cutoffs at perhaps -3 volts. Remember that the overswing beyond cutoff is to accommodate drifting components and perhaps also to control the γ_0.

Furthermore, suppose that the input signal goes from $+5$ volts down to -5 volts and back. Until the input signal moves from $+5$ down to 0, the diode is back-biased, and the toggle does not know that anything is happening. At 0, the signal source connects to the toggle and begins to move it. At any time that the toggle control begins to move faster than the signal source, the diode again becomes back-biased, and the toggle breaks free of the trigger.

It is apparent that schemes which operate directly on the conducting device are slightly more favorable in the sense that the gain of the conducting side assists the action of the trigger from the very outset. A collector triggering scheme (Figure 8.16-b) offers the advantage that the auxiliary trigger provides a voltage shift between the input terminal at its control and the collector entry point to the toggle.

The collector clearing scheme (Figure 8.16-c) suffers the disadvantage that the signal is somewhat removed (by R_L) from the device elements. It has the very real advantage that one signal source can be applied to a large number of toggles without additional components at each toggle.

Freedom from Waveshape

We see that the only really critical requirement on the input signal to a direct-coupled trigger circuit is that the trigger move from its quiescent level through a critical level to its activity level to initiate transition, stay beyond that critical level for a minimum interval which is related to the time required to propagate the trigger effect completely around the loop, and then return to its quiescent level at any time later (Figure 8.17). The toggle circuit does not care how the trigger gets from one level to the other; i.e., the trigger action depends only on the amplitude of the trigger, not on its particular shape. In particular, the triggering action does not depend on the rate of change of voltage at the leading and trailing edge of the trigger, nor on the detailed shape of these edges. The beginning of the transition may depend on the shape of the leading edge, and the speed with which the transition occurs may depend somewhat on the shape of the leading edge, but the certainty of the action does not. This is perhaps the best of the

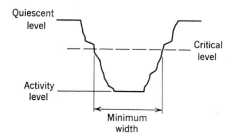

Figure 8.17. The waveshape independence of direct-coupled triggering.

advantages of direct-coupled schemes. Another is the ability of many configurations to reject spurious noise signals.

EXAMPLES

1. In Figure 8.16-a the input diode is back biased until the input signal reaches 0 volts. Therefore, any spurious signals or noise bursts of less than 5 volts in amplitude never bring the diode into conduction.
2. In Figure 8.16-b, the trigger device is cutoff until the input signal reaches the cutoff-bias level; this arrangement, therefore, rejects noise signals which are not too large.

We see that the choice of triggering method can bolster the inherent nature of the toggle to reject noise.

A disadvantage of the direct-coupled scheme is that the input signal must always be positioned correctly with respect to absolute voltage level; e.g., a 10-volt signal from $+100$ to $+90$ volts will be useless for triggering the control in Figure 8.16-a.

Capacitance-Coupled Triggering

Schemes which introduce the triggering current into the toggle as displacement current are spoken of as *capacitance-coupled* or as *A-C coupled,* on the grounds that the capacitor rejects the D-C component of the trigger signal and passes only displacement current.

An immediately obvious advantage of the A-C schemes is that the absolute voltage position of the trigger signal is no longer important since the capacitor rejects the D-C information anyway. An immediately obvious disadvantage is that a capacitance-coupled scheme will not, of itself, reject any spurious noise signals. Any voltage, either

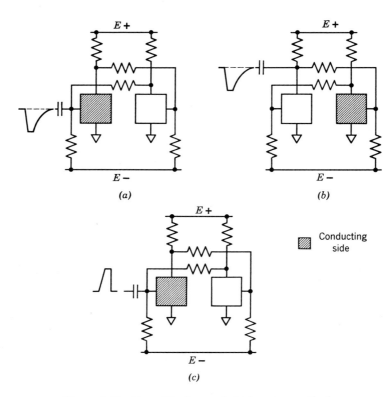

Figure 8.18. Capacitively coupled triggering methods.

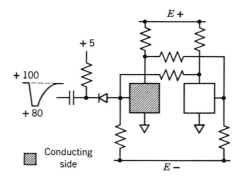

Figure 8.19. A hybrid triggering method.

noise or applied, which is developed across the capacitor will introduce some displacement current into the toggle. However, the toggle itself will reject signals which are not too large.

Some of the possible A-C coupling schemes are shown in Figure 8.18. Figure 8.19 illustrates a hybrid scheme where the diode has been introduced to reject noise.

Waveshape Dependence

Since the time rate of change of voltage across a capacitor determines the displacement current through it, it follows that the leading edge and perhaps also the trailing edge of the trigger signal suddenly become very critical. In fact, unless the leading edge rises with at least some minimum rate of change, the displacement current may be inadequate to flip the toggle. As with direct-coupled triggering, the amplitude of the trigger is still important; it must reach some critical level for a minimum time. The detailed shape of the leading edge is now also important.

If the toggle is willing to flip one way on the leading edge, why will it not flip the other way on the trailing edge? It certainly will, unless the slope of the trailing edge is such that there is enough less displacement current, in which case the toggle will not reflip. Because of its inherent locking characteristic, the toggle can override the trailing edge displacement current if it is sufficiently small.

Therefore, in passing to A-C triggering schemes, we suddenly find the complete shape of the triggering pulse to be important. This means that the designer must be concerned with every possible source which might produce a signal to flip a toggle. He must make certain that every signal arriving at a toggle entry point, no matter what route it took or from where it started, must meet the standards required by the toggle.

One way of dealing with the trailing edge problem is shown in Figure 8.19. The series diode effectively disconnects the capacitor on the trailing edge.

Large C or Small C?

The larger the coupling capacitor in an A-C triggering scheme, the smaller the rate of change of voltage across the capacitor can be and still produce sufficient displacement current for the transition of the toggle. Furthermore, since the input terminal (whatever it is) will have some capacitance to ground, the input capacitor and the unavoidable shunt component form a voltage divider which reduces the amount of trigger actually reaching the toggle. Again this argues for a large input capacitor.

In opposition, however, we have the observation that some portion of the input capacitor is seen by the toggle as a shunt capacitance to ground. For example, if the input trigger rises infinitely fast to its plateau level, the input capacitor will be effectively connected between the toggle and a lowish impedance trigger source, i.e., a virtual ground. Since the trigger does not rise infinitely fast, only a portion of the input capacitor appears as shunt capacitance, and perhaps even then, only for a part of the transition interval. Although we have not examined the transition details yet, our experience suggests that shunt capacitance will tend to slow the response speed of the toggle. This, of course, argues for a small input capacitor.

The designer is betwixt and between and must arrive at some compromise position. Can he use a large capacitor and relax the requirements on the trigger source, or must he strive for the fastest toggle and be forced to a small capacitor? The dilemma can be resolved at the expense of extra components. For example, the series-diode scheme of Figure 8.19 permits the toggle to cast itself free from the trigger source.

A Quasi–D-C Scheme

There is one form of A-C triggering which exhibits some properties of the D-C arrangement (Figure 8.18-c). A positive signal is applied through a capacitor to the control of the conducting side. Since the device on this side is already in control current, the only effect of this action is to increase the current by the amount of the displacement current through the capacitor. The toggle itself only settles more securely into the state in which it already is. The capacitor, however, changes its voltage, since one side of it is effectively held fast by the diode of the conducting control-to-emitter, while the other side is moving under the influence of the trigger. The trigger source must be of sufficiently low impedance that it can supply the capacitance current required; furthermore the precise shape of the leading edge of the trigger is unimportant so long as the trigger eventually rises high enough (just like a D-C trigger scheme!). Moreover, by controlling the leading edge, the amount of displacement current which the control must accept can be limited.

As the trigger begins to fall, the control of the conducting side begins to move negatively. This assumes that the rate of fall of the trigger is sufficiently rapid that the input capacitor does not discharge significantly and, therefore, temporarily acts like a battery. Compared to other A-C schemes, this one has greater freedom from waveform. A possible disadvantage is that the toggle responds to the trailing edge of the trigger.

The considerations on the size of the input capacitor are much the same as before. Too small a capacitor attenuates the input signal unnecessarily; too large a capacitor unduly loads the toggle. The latter point is particularly clear in this case; the interplay between toggle behavior and triggering method is painfully clear. It is very unlikely that the amplitude of the trigger will exactly match the control swing of the toggle; even if this situation did obtain initially, drifting of components will quickly change it. Therefore, the volt-

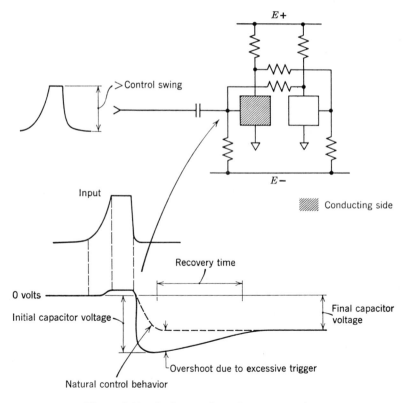

Figure 8.20. An imposed toggle recovery time.

age to which the downgoing control will be driven can be either above or below its final quiescent level. The capacitor, therefore, will have to change its voltage somewhat as the toggle slides into its new state (Figure 8.20). The current for the capacitor will have to come through the relatively high-impedance resistance network of the toggle. In other words, presence of the capacitor forces the toggle to have a post-transition recovery time. This recovery time is a direct result of the presence of the input-trigger capacitor and is separate and distinct from the time required for the toggle to settle its internal transients involved with the transition. The recovery interval implies a decrease in the rate at which the toggle can be triggered. This does not necessarily imply that a wider trigger is necessary to transition the toggle, because the width of the trigger necessary to effect a transition and the interval between successive triggers are nearly independent parameters. They are related only in that some but not necessarily all time constants of the toggle enter into the determination of both properties.

Two Different Characteristics

The point just discussed is true for most toggles in some measure. There is some minimum width of trigger which is necessary to flip a toggle; this width is closely related to the propagation time around the toggle loop. There is some other time interval, at least equal to but probably longer than the minimum trigger width, which the toggle requires to settle all internal transients which result from the transition. It is clear that the time constants of the toggle enter into both characteristic times, and that the two times are, therefore, related through common ancestral factors. However, the choice of triggering schemes may influence one of these but not the other, or it may influence both. Similarly, other aspects of the toggle circuit—such as loads—may influence one or both of these properties.

EXAMPLES

1. An A-C triggering scheme without a series diode will probably increase the trigger width because it increases loop delay, and it may also introduce additional recovery time into the toggle.

2. Clamp diodes introduced into the toggle to limit swings will certainly shorten the time that the toggle requires to settle because these diodes provide low impedance charging paths for the capacitances. However, the

only effect on minimum trigger width will be a second order one in that the clamp diodes may permit the toggle to be designed with smaller values of resistors, or with smaller signal swings.

3. A triggering scheme which simultaneously drives all four active points to their new positions obviously affects both properties of the toggle and also obviously makes the two characteristic times not only equal but dependent almost exclusively on the triggering sources.

Input Terminals

Since any one of the active terminals of the toggle (two collectors and two controls) can be manipulated by a suitable external source plus coupling circuit, any of them is a potential input terminal; either a D-C or an A-C coupling scheme can be used. We have seen that if, say, a negative signal is applied to, say, the left control of a toggle, it will (if not already there) flip to the state having the right side conducting. Further negative signals on the left side will be ignored by the toggle, unless some other event has meanwhile again changed the state.

We see that the two controls, the two collectors, and the two upper ends of the load resistors form pairs of input terminals which stand in one-to-one correspondence with the two states of the toggle.

EXAMPLE

If a negative signal on the left control makes the right side conduct, then a negative signal on the right control will make the left side conduct. The left-input terminal corresponds to the right-side conducting; and the right-input terminal, to the left-side conducting.

This is not to imply that the terminals chosen for inputs to a toggle must come from these pairs, nor that a toggle may have only two input terminals. The designer has many possibilities open to him, and he will make a choice which depends on other aspects of the machine organization, on properties of particular triggering schemes, on the characteristics of his particular toggle, etc.

EXAMPLE

A machine contains fifty toggles. On some occasions, these must all be set to a uniform state. On other occasions, they are to be independently set to either state by a multiplicity of sources. A reasonable choice of input terminals would be:

1. Individual diodes to each control of a toggle to permit setting it independently of others.

2. A collector-clearing scheme which uses one large signal source to operate on all toggles simultaneously. This signal is applied to the top end of one of the load resistors in each toggle.

The mechanical toggle switch has a different kind of input terminal. It has only one input (the handle) which accepts two kinds of signals (up push or down push).

Which Input to Trigger, and How

The choice between A-C and D-C coupling schemes represents one of the inevitable compromises of design. The cheapness of the capacitor as a passive element is weighed against the cost of a tube, diode, or transistor. The trouble of having the D-C trigger positioned correctly in absolute voltage is weighed against the noise susceptibility of the A-C scheme or against the cost of an A-C scheme bolstered by a supplementary noise rejection diode. The convenience of an A-C coupling scheme is weighed against the waveshape control problems it creates. And so it goes.

The problem of controlling the waveshape of a triggering signal should not be dismissed lightly. We now appreciate the internal behavior of a computer system well enough to recognize that a toggle may receive signals from many places via many routes. Perhaps, the number of possible internal logical configurations (and, therefore, internal routings) is large enough to prohibit control or even investigation of every case of waveshape degradation. A D-C triggering scheme is one answer to the problem. Another answer is the use of a standard, well-shaped, central trigger signal (the *clock*—see page 8.82), which is distributed throughout the machine. The clock signal is combined with the logical information which controls a toggle in such a way that a well-shaped signal is introduced directly at the toggle input.

Other things which may trouble the designer are: the impedance of the trigger source, the variation in trigger requirements with drifting of toggle component values, the possibility that toggle response time depends on trigger shape, the possibility of the trigger itself changing shape with aging of components, the dependence of trigger shape and size on the coupling scheme chosen, the variation of the input impedance of the toggle with age, and so on. When considering particular input terminals to be used, remember that the toggle reacts more slowly to some than to others; e.g., collector clearing tends to be slower than control triggering. There is also the possibility that two terminals may be operated on simultaneously with the expectation (so far as the designing logician is concerned) that the toggle will make no response.

Output Terminals

The collectors or the controls are also possible output terminals. In fact, one element of a device might be both an input and an output point. Some of the significant points to be considered in selecting an output terminal are the following.

1. The potentials at the collectors and controls of a toggle are subject to the drifts of resistor and device parameters. Sometimes, one place in the toggle is more favorably disposed in this respect. In the case of control current for the grounded-emitter symmetrical toggle, the implicit diode controls the upper control potential quite closely which makes the control a desirable output terminal. The lower control potential and the two collector potentials are more subject to parameter drift.

2. Some point of the toggle may represent a lower impedance point than others. Usually this is the collector which might, therefore, be capable of supplying some current to an external real or capacitance load. Explicit clamp diodes can always provide low impedance output points capable of providing load currents up to the amount of the clamp current. Such diodes will also absorb the fluctuation in output levels due to parameter drift.

3. Whatever else is true, toggles will have to communicate with each other via a switching network. It is sometimes helpful if the output levels of a toggle are similar to those required at the input. The choice of the control as an input and also an output terminal is very sensible in this regard. The choice of collector for output but control for input could be sensible for an A-C triggering scheme; alternatively, the control as output but the collector as input is consistent with a D-C auxiliary trigger triode arrangement (Figure 8.16-b).

To complete the analogy with the mechanical toggle switch, we notice that its output terminals are one or more pairs of contacts.

THE TRANSITION PHASE

Miller Enhancement

As we will see shortly, one of the important components of capacitance in the toggle is the internal shunt capacitances, especially the control-collector capacitance. Because both a control and its associated collector can be in motion at the same time, the capacitance may appear much larger than it truly is. This is a form of the Miller effect (6), but since the details are somewhat different than usual, a short discussion is included here.

A capacitor makes its presence known because of the current it demands when the voltage across itself tries to change. Except for this current, the presence of a capacitor would never be known. Therefore, if we were given a black box with two terminals and asked to determine what size capacitor might be in the box, a sensible approach would be to drive the terminals with a linear ramp voltage and to measure the current flowing into the terminals. If the inside of the black box were as in Figure 8.21-a, a current I would be measured and the value of the capacitor would be correctly reckoned to be $\dot{e}/I$ where $\dot{e}$ $(= de/dt)$ is the slope of the ramp voltage. On the other

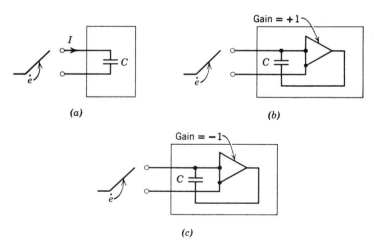

Figure 8.21. Capacitance enhancement.

hand, if the black box actually were as shown in Figure 8.21-b, no current would flow, and the apparent capacitance at the terminals would be zero although a physical capacitor would still be in the box. Again, if the box were as in Figure 8.21-c, the current flowing would be twice as large as in the first case, and the apparent capacitance would be twice the size of the physical capacitance.

In a toggle the collector and control of the same device are often in motion at the same time. Therefore, the capacitance which the control and the collector appear to have may be many times the statically measured capacitance. Furthermore, this enhanced or apparent capacitance will be a function of time, and may change radically as the collector and control swings change throughout the transition interval.

Transition Details

The points to be developed in the following sections will give considerable insight into the factors which control the speed of a toggle. Such knowledge, therefore, will suggest preferred choices to the designer even as early as the static design stage. First of all, what capacitances are there in the circuit? Beyond the enhanced control-collector capacitance in each device, there are the usual stray capacitances due to wiring, sockets, etc. For the moment, there will be no explicit capacitors.

The next observation is that some of the time constants will change markedly during transition. First, consider the control of the conducting side, which during transition will move negatively. At first, the control is in current, and although the capacitance there may be large, the time constant will be very small because r is the only significant resistive component (Figure 8.22-a). As the control moves out of current, the resistive component becomes that of R_C in parallel with $R_T + R_L$; therefore, the control time constant suddenly becomes much longer (Figure 8.22-b). All of this time, the upgoing collector is in motion so that the control-collector capacitance is enhanced in variable measure. Eventually, the whole toggle is well in motion; and as soon as the other collector begins to move downward, the r_c of that device influences the resistive component of the downgoing control's time constant (Figure 8.22-c). Depending upon how the triggering was done, the asymptote toward which the control is moving may also depend on the motion of the downgoing collector. If the triggering is being done by an auxiliary trigger triode (Figure 8.16-b), it is quite possible that this triode has pulled the toggle collector lower

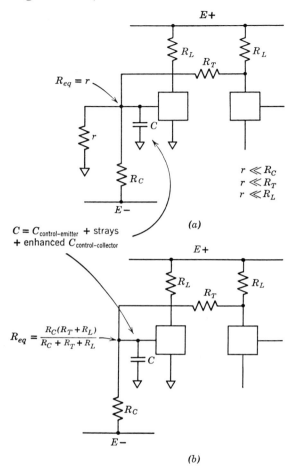

Figure 8.22. The control time constant for various parts of the transition interval.

than its quiescent position. Therefore, the asymptote toward which the downgoing control is moving will be more negative than usual. If the upgoing collector finishes moving while its control is still moving downward, the time constant of this control changes again because the capacitance component will change radically due to the cessation of enhancement (Figure 8.22-d).

The upcoming control experiences the same circumstances in reverse order except for one point. Because the toggle has been designed for control current, the upcoming control is initially heading toward an

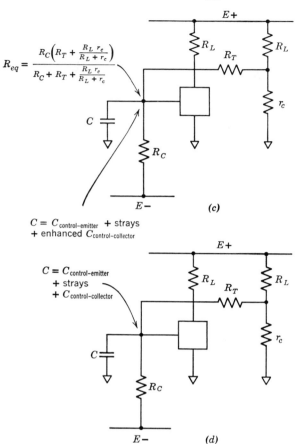

$$R_{eq} = \frac{R_C\left(R_T + \frac{R_L\, r_e}{R_L + r_e}\right)}{R_C + R_T + \frac{R_L\, r_e}{R_L + r_e}}$$

$C = C_{\text{control-emitter}}$ + strays
+ enhanced $C_{\text{control-collector}}$

$C = C_{\text{control-emitter}}$
+ strays
+ $C_{\text{control-collector}}$

Figure 8.22. (cont.)

asymptote somewhat positive. However, as it passes through 0 potential, the implicit diode begins to conduct, and the voltage motion of the upcoming control is arrested.

Depending upon the nature of the triggering, several things can occur at one or the other of the collectors. First of all, we notice that the collector load is very complex. It would consist only of R_L in parallel with $R_T + R_C$ except that the control capacitive component is at the junction of R_T and R_C. Furthermore, the collector capacitive component includes the enhanced control-collector capacitance part of the time (Figure 8.23-a). So far as the downcoming collector voltage

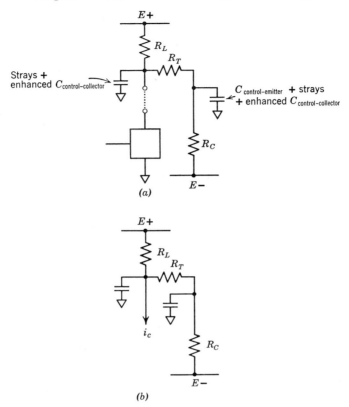

Figure 8.23.   The downcoming collector circuit.

is concerned, part of the time it is an amplified version of the upgoing control except as modified by the complex collector load.   Often the upcoming control ceases its motion before the downgoing collector is done, and for this part of the time, the collector behavior is that of a fairly complex resistance-capacitance circuit driven by the device as a source (Figure 8.23-b).   So far as the upgoing collector is concerned, part of the time it is the amplified version of the downgoing control, again as modified by the complex collector load.   As soon as its downgoing control passes through cutoff, collector current ceases, and the collector circuit is on its own as a complex resistance-capacitance network.   The downgoing control may still be moving so that part of the complexity lies in the Miller-enhanced control-collector capacitance.   Moreover, the complex resistance-capacitance network in the collector circuit experiences a discontinuity when the upcoming control (to which it is connected via R_T) bumps into its implicit diode.

Figure 8.24 shows the typical behavior of both controls and both collectors of a grounded emitter symmetrical toggle during the transition interval. The time and voltage scales are non-linear in order to show details of behavior which would otherwise be obscured. The various regions of the transition are indicated and cross-referenced to the preceding discussion.

Figure 8.25 is the same set of curves, but this time on linear time and voltage scales, and with the two control waveforms superposed and the two collector waveforms superposed. Figure 8.3 is the toggle to which these curves belong.

These curves illustrate a very important point which has not appeared before. Because of component tolerances and uncertain or variable cutoff characteristics in the devices (i.e., imperfect components) the designer has had to arrange the circuit so that during that

Figure 8.24. The detailed events during transition.

A. Change in time constant because upcoming control has stopped
B. Change in time constant due to cessation of control current
C. Change in time constant because upgoing collector has stopped
D. Current begins in upcoming control

I. Control current decreasing to 0
II. Control cutting off and the collector circuit being driven by the decreasing collector current
III. Collector current is 0 and the collector circuit is behaving as a complex resistance-capacitance network
IV. Collector voltage is stable and the control is coasting to its asymptote
V. Current building up in oncoming side
VI. Device current steady and the collector is coasting to its asymptote

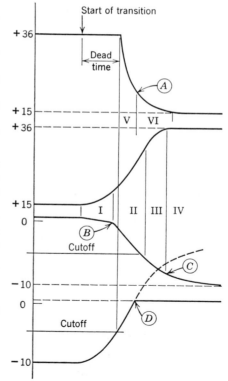

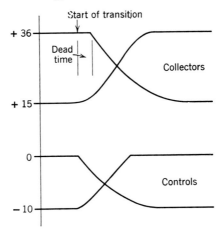

Figure 8.25. Typical transition waveforms.

part of its life before components have drifted badly, the lower control level is well below the nominal cutoff level. Therefore, the time consumed in bringing the upcoming control from its quiescent point to cutoff is completely wasted in the sense that the downgoing collector will not begin to move until the upcoming control gets to cutoff. It is quite clear, therefore, that so far as speed of transition is concerned, the designer ought not let the control go far beyond cutoff. Yet his components and their tolerances make it difficult for him to design in such a way. This is just another of the compromises that must be considered.

Calculation of the Transition Time

Knowing something of the detailed physical behavior during the transition interval, we can now consider the design problem related to the transient behavior of the toggle. As we have already seen, the static design problem can be managed very nicely, either by an algebraic method or by a graphical-empirical method. Because of the large number of different events occurring during the transition, we ought to expect that a solution of the transition interval in closed analytic form will be difficult to obtain; and even if obtained, perhaps not very useful. Because of the wild behavior of most of the time constants, not to mention the non-linearity of the devices, the only hope is a piecewise solution with whatever linearizing assumptions may be necessary. The various regions indicated in Figure 8.24 suggest an appropriate decomposition of the transition interval. For the device which is going out of conduction, these are:

1. From initiation of transition to cessation of control current
2. From cessation of control current to cutoff level on the control
3. From control cutoff to end of transition.

For the side coming into conduction, the intervals are:

1. From initiation of transition to cutoff level of the control
2. From cutoff level of the control to the beginning of control current
3. From the beginning of control current to the end of transition.

In each of these intervals, the appropriate time constants will have to be used, and probably some average value of the capacitance components and of device parameters will have to be chosen.

Each of the collectors faces the complex load shown in Figure 8.23-b; we already know that some of the capacitors and resistances change during transition. Because there are two nodes in this circuit (each with its own time constant), any Laplace or similar operational calculus attack will produce second order algebraic expressions which in turn lead to voltage-time expressions containing two exponential terms. The various resistors and capacitors of the circuit will appear in the exponent of these two terms, but some of these same resistors and capacitors will also appear in multiplicative or additive terms. It is, therefore, very difficult to use such transcendental equations for the synthesis of a toggle. The expressions simply cannot be solved to yield expressions which define the various resistors and capacitors (or perhaps time constants) in terms of specified time intervals and voltage levels. Such analytic expressions are useful, however, in analyzing a given design, since numerical techniques can be used to obtain numerical solutions.

This is one of many places in which it is extremely helpful and advantageous to have a digital computer available to assist in the design of another digital computer!

A Further Approximation

One reason for disagreement between calculated and experimental results is, of course, the various approximations which will have been made for expedience. In some circumstances, the approximations may be poor ones, and we must be alert to this possibility.

Often we can make the following additional approximation in which case the transient analysis becomes easier. In order not to interfere too much with the collector swing, the choice of R_T and R_C has been made to avoid too large a decrease in effective collector load. The effect of R_T and R_C on the steady-state voltage levels of the toggle cannot be ignored. They do decrease the collector load somewhat, and moreover they are directly concerned with determining the upper collector level. However, it might be possible to ignore R_C, R_T, and the capacitance at the control so far as dynamic collector behavior is concerned. This amounts to saying that the collector is buffered from the control by a current amplifier and does not, therefore, feel the effect of the second time constant at the control. In a given case, this might be a poor approximation because the capacitance at the control can be very large because of the enhancement feature. In making this approximation, it is necessary to consider the collector as facing the Thévenin equivalent of R_L, R_C, R_T, $E+$, and $E-$.

The analytic transient solutions will be simpler now to deal with. Only one exponential term will be involved, since the two time constants have been isolated from each other.

EXAMPLE

Consider the toggle of Figure 8.3 and assume that it is to be triggered by an auxiliary trigger triode (Figure 8.16-b). Furthermore, assume that the trigger triode can insert a step function of voltage into the toggle. Figure 8.26-a shows the circuit for the first part of the transition interval; C_1 includes the stray capacitances at the control plus the enhanced component. We probably have to guess (or estimate from experience) the amount of enhancement; the estimate can be checked later. From the equivalent circuit of Figure 8.26-a we can find the time for the control voltage to move from its slight positive value to zero.

The equivalent control circuit now becomes that of Figure 8.26-b. The initial voltage on C_1 is 0 volts, and we can readily calculate the time for the control to reach its cutoff bias; furthermore, we can sketch the exponential approach of the control to its asymptote. If we later discover that the collector which belongs with this control has stopped moving before the control itself stops, we can return to the downgoing control and refine our estimate of its last stages of motion. At the cessation of collector motion, C_1 becomes C_2 and consists only of strays plus unenhanced control-collector capacitance. We will use the same circuit of Figure 8.26-b, but we will start C_2 with an initial voltage equal to the control voltage which existed at the time the collector motion essentially ceased.

The next problem is to construct a picture of the upgoing collector behavior. Figure 8.26-c shows the equivalent circuit where E_{eq} and R_{eq} are the Thévenin

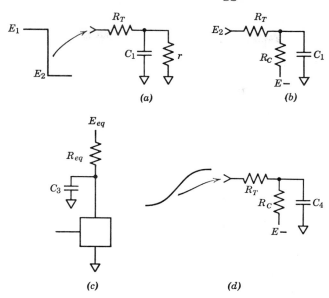

Figure 8.26. Equivalent circuits for various phases of transition.

equivalents of the complex collector circuit which consists of $E+$, R_L, R_T, R_C, and $E-$. We have assumed that the effect of the capacitance at the upcoming control is not felt by the collector. The resistor R_T limits the amount of displacement current which any such capacitance load could demand from the collector, and our assumption amounts to the observation that any such capacitance current is small compared to the demand of C_3. C_3 includes stray and enhanced components.

The most rigorous treatment of the collector would be to regard it as an exponential circuit driven by the amplified (and inverted) exponential control voltage. The first part of the collector swing is the time interval during which the control is decaying to 0 volts; the second part is the time interval during which the control moves from zero bias to cutoff bias. In each of these intervals the appropriate exponential behavior of the control will have to be used, and the piecewise solutions fitted where they meet. During the final part of the swing, the collector behaves as a simple resistance-capacitance circuit since the control has passed beyond cutoff.

It might be possible to make a further approximation. If the collector time constant ($R_{eq}C_3$) is small enough compared to the control time constant (and this is likely to be true), the collector will have no trouble following the urging of the control. We can assume that the first two parts of the collector motion are simply amplified versions of the control motion. It might be possible to go even further. Because r is so small, the time for the control to drop to 0 volts very likely is exceedingly short compared to any other times in the toggle. We might, therefore, treat the control motion (and hence the early part of the collector motion) as just one exponential.

Remember that the upcoming control started from a voltage well below cutoff level. From a Kirchhoff analysis of the resistor network, we can calculate the voltage of the upcoming collector which corresponds to cutoff level for the upcoming control. For the toggle of Figure 8.3, a cutoff level of -3.5 volts at the control corresponds to a voltage at the "other" collector of $+23$. Following our previous discussion, we can calculate the time (Δt_1) for the upcoming collector to move from its starting point to $+23$ volts; the time for the upcoming control to reach cutoff is at least this much. It could be larger because the time constant of the upcoming control might cause the control to lag behind the collector which is driving it. The time interval Δt_1 is a reasonable estimate of the *dead time* of the toggle; in this interval the previously cutoff side of the toggle has not started to respond. The dead time is a direct result of the control overswing that was provided to offset tolerance problems. Furthermore, the dead time will change during the toggle's life as the lower reach of the control fluctuates with various parameter drifts.

The next order of business is to determine the behavior of the upcoming control. Because of the assumption made in behalf of the upmoving collector, the appropriate circuit for the second control is that of Figure 8.26-d, where the driving voltage is the previously determined collector voltage. C_4 contains only strays and the control-collector capacitance. Since we assumed that the downcoming collector was triggered by a step function, this collector is not in motion and there is no enhancement. However, we will probably have to treat the circuit as a resistance-capacitance circuit driven by a pieced-together exponential voltage, because the control time constant is almost certain to be longer than the collector time constant.

We can now calculate the time interval required for the upcoming control to move from its starting point to some level which we believe will guarantee flipping of the toggle. Perhaps the center point of instability ($-\frac{1}{2}$ volt control potential for the toggle of Figure 8.3; see page 8.25) is as good a reference level as any. When the control reaches the reference level, the input trigger can be terminated. It is clear that, if necessary, the detailed behavior of the upmoving control can be determined, and that various refinements can be made in the fine structure of other voltage motions.

A Dilemma

We have seen that the toggle has an inherent tendency to remain in one of its stable positions. Furthermore, the designer may very well have taken steps to enhance this desire, e.g., control current, explicit clamp diodes, choice of particular toggle configurations. On the other hand, energy must be injected into the toggle to make it flip; work has to be done against the currents in the networks, and current has to be supplied to capacitance. The more solidly a toggle is locked into its stable position, the more difficult will it be to effect a transition. In the real case, another compromise is necessary.

Two conflicting things are being asked of a toggle: to be stable in its equilibrium state, or to be an energy source to supply the losses of transition. As usually designed, a toggle is a compromise between these two. Some stability in the equilibrium state is sacrificed in order to make the toggle readily convertible to a violently regenerative circuit capable of self-supplying much of the energy needed to complete the transition.

The implication of this latter statement is that in order to be a lowish impedance source of energy part of the time, the toggle is designed to be a lowish impedance device all of the time, and it therefore dissipates more standby power than it really ought to. This essentially represents a deficiency in the present form of some toggles.

In principle, the two requirements could be separated. The toggle could be designed with only the storage feature in mind and its equilibrium stability maximized. The energy source for the transition could be completely external to the toggle and designed so that it dissipates power only when called upon to function. This suggestion will require a trigger source connected to each of the four active elements of the toggle in view of the assumption that no transition (e.g., capacitance) demands would come from the toggle. Such an arrangement obviously produces a toggle whose transition speed is limited only by the ability of the outside sources to supply current.

Toggle configurations other than the symmetrical one do, in part, satisfy this division of function. The dynamic toggle (see page 8.80), for instance, depends completely on an external energy source for the transition demands.

An extension of this argument suggests that as a storage device only (never an energy source for transition demands), the toggle ought to dissipate no energy when residing in an equilibrium state. As we will see, the dynamic toggle meets this requirement "halfway" so to speak, and magnetic techniques, all the way. In the case of fully separated functions, the energy demand arises only during transition and is supplied by a source external to the toggle. The toggle design problems which have concerned us substantially evaporate.

THE DYNAMIC DESIGN

The dynamic design of the toggle is, therefore, more trying than the static design (7). Often the whole design procedure goes like this:

1. Obtain a static design.
2. Check it for compliance with all tolerances.
3. Estimate the capacitances which a particular construction technique and choice of components will yield.
4. Analyze the design for its transient characteristics.
5. If unsatisfactory, determine where the transient response can be altered, make the necessary changes in the static design, and return to step 1. If satisfactory, proceed.
6. Construct one or more samples of the toggle, using the previously chosen construction or packaging technique.
7. Measure the resulting static and dynamic capacitances and compare with the estimates of step 3. If there is substantial disagreement, make a new estimate of the capacitances, and return to step 3. Notice that a Branch back to step 3 may lead (at step 5) to a further Branch back to step 1! If agreement is satisfactory, proceed.
8. Measure the experimental toggle for its dynamic and static characteristics, and its susceptibility to component drifts. If unsatisfactory in any way, determine desired changes and return to step 1 or to step 3 as appropriate. If satisfactory, proceed.
9. Jump to other parts of the design problem.

Reminds one of a flow diagram and loops of computing, does it not?

An important point not to overlook is the effect of component drifts on dynamic behavior or on trigger requirements. Each of these characteristics is dependent on all parameters of the toggle and will change as the toggle ages. The effect of component drifts must be of concern to the designer for the static and dynamic behavior, as well as for the trigger requirements.

The Last Refinement

What additional tricks might the designer use to squeeze additional speed from his best design?

First, it is clear that since the toggle is two cascaded amplifiers, all the tricks of designing high-frequency amplifiers are good for designing fast toggles. Small collector loads, partly inductive loads, pentode tubes rather than triodes, high-frequency transistors—all these contribute to speed. Secondly, the intercoupling between the two stages of amplifiers must also have high-frequency response. After some experience in dealing with toggles or in analyzing them according to the previous methods, the designer discovers that, aside from the dead interval contributed by the one control being considerably below cutoff, a big—if not the biggest—contributor to loop delay is the transpose network. The long time constant at the control is the problem. There are two contributors to the long time constant: R_T and R_C have been deliberately chosen largish to avoid affecting R_L too much; and the capacitance component at the control is large because of the enhancement of control-collector capacitance.

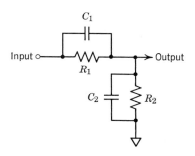

Figure 8.27. A simple resistance-capacitance attenuator.

The resistive component of the time constant can be helped by inserting current gain into the transpose branch between the collector and R_T. This will permit R_T and R_C to be chosen much smaller since they no longer affect R_L. Interestingly enough, the design calculations are now also simpler because R_L, R_T, and R_C can no longer team up as a long voltage divider.

The capacitance component can be helped in two ways, either of which can be used by itself, with or without the current amplifier. In the case of tubes, a pentode will completely avoid the capacitance enhancement problem and make the grid capacitance much smaller and constant, instead of large and violently fluctuating. The other possibility is the addition of a capacitor in shunt with R_T. This comes from the old notion of "balancing an attenuator."

If $R_1C_1 = R_2C_2$ in Figure 8.27, the attenuator in theory will have a flat frequency response, and an input step function will appear as a step at the output. The balancing trick can never be done quite perfectly in the toggle, but it can contribute significantly to faster action of the toggle. With triode elements, capacitance enhancement causes the control time constant to vary widely with the result that only some average balancing job can be done; for a pentode tube, the balancing can be more refined—so long as components do not drift too far.

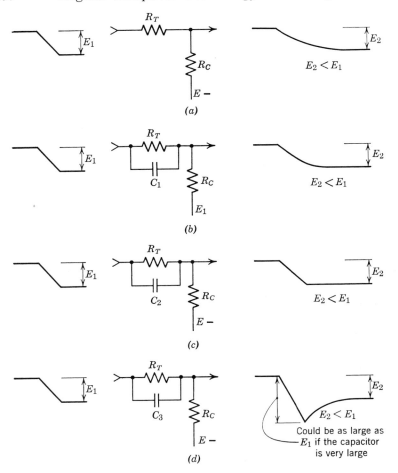

Figure 8.28. Possible kinds of behavior of a resistance-capacitance circuit.

In this last connection, it is interesting to see what effect too large or too small a balancing capacitor will have. Figure 8.28 shows a succession of four circuits driven by a ramp voltage. The first of these represents the uncompensated transpose network; the second, the under-compensated; the third, the exactly compensated; and the fourth, the overcompensated. Physical reasoning will make the various cases plausible.

The last case (Figure 8.28-d) is the most significant. The behavior can be seen to be correct by assuming that C_3 is extremely large. Under these circumstances, C_3 will not change its voltage very rapidly and will behave substantially like a battery. Therefore, the full voltage change at the input will appear initially at the output. From the nature of an attenuator, it is known that given sufficient time for the series capacitor to change its charge, the final level of the output must be such that the voltage change at the output is less than the voltage change at the input. Therefore, an overly large compensating capacitor will cause the downgoing control to overshoot its position; the control will, therefore, have to exponentially recover toward its quiescent level (Figure 8.29).

The effect of a transpose time constant $(R_T C_T)$ which is too large relative to $R_C C_C$ (Figure 8.29) because either C_T was too large initially or because some of the resistors have drifted, is to add a recovery interval to the toggle. This interval can extend beyond the normal settling-down time of the toggle. Therefore, an attempt to retrigger the toggle may fail because the normal trigger is not sufficient to overcome the abnormally large negative position of one control. The conservative designer either makes the compensation just right for the situation in which tolerances are all off the wrong way (in which case compensation does not achieve as much speed increase as it initially appeared to), or else he guarantees that the toggle as it is used in the machine does not have to be retriggered too soon. In the latter case there has been a deliberate sacrifice in the maximum operating rate of the toggle, and

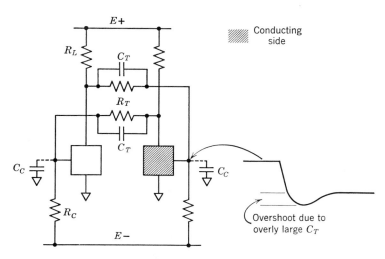

Figure 8.29. The recovery interval due to overly large transpose capacitors.

it has resulted directly from the consequences of imperfect components. There are many variants of the statement of the "fourth law of thermodynamics"; we have just seen another one.

Because of a discussion to come later (page 8.65), we note the point that the transpose capacitors have been added for a circuit reason; they assist the circuit performance. They do not alter the logical properties of the toggle nor do they interact with the characteristics of the active element.

There is another possibility for boosting circuit speed. For a specified amount of available current, the time it takes for a capacitor to move through some voltage increment is directly proportional to that increment; $\Delta t = (C/I)(\Delta e)$. Therefore, we may attempt to use the smallest possible signal swings in a circuit. Transistors are especially favorable in this respect as also are tubes with small cutoff levels and a sharp cutoff characteristic. On the other hand, tolerance problems so plague the designer that he is forced to design some overswing into the control signal. Clamp diodes, as we have previously discovered, can absorb the tolerances; we now see that as a secondary benefit, they also speed up the toggle. Such diodes will also absorb the overshoot problem which overcompensation creates.

As a final alternate for consideration, we might consider some other form of the toggle which is inherently faster because one of its feedback connections is intrinsically faster or less sensitive to capacitance (page 8.78).

The faster acting toggle is more sensitive to noise. This is not a mysterious property of the fast toggle. It is no more sensitive than the slow toggle to the amplitude of spurious signals, but because of its better high-frequency response, the faster toggle simply responds to a broader spectrum of noise signals.

THE COMPLEMENTING INPUT

One kind of mechanical switch has a "push to change" type of action. Is there a similar mode of operation for the electronic toggle? Is there an input terminal which commands the toggle: No matter in which state you are now, change to the other one? Since a toggle can store one bit, such an input changes a 0-state to the 1-state or vice versa and, therefore, *complements* the toggle (8). Since the least significant digit in the sequence of natural binary numbers alternates 0 and 1, this particular mode of the toggle is also called *counting* action; alternatively, such a toggle is sometimes referred to as a *one-stage binary counter* (page 13.47).

In contradistinction to all the terminals which we have previously considered and which have had direct access to only one side of the toggle, this new type of input must clearly have direct access to both sides of the toggle. Furthermore, on all previous input terminals only the first one of a succession of triggers at one terminal initiated activity in the toggle. The new input, so to speak, must lie on the median line of the toggle, and direct input signals first to one side of the toggle and then to the other.

As the toggle stands (Figure 8.30-a), there is only one such point, and this is the common connection between the top ends of the two load resistors (or the two ends of the control-return resistors). Other median-line terminals can, of course, be created. For instance, the two controls (or the two collectors) can be connected through suitable elements to a common point, and thereby a new terminal can be created (Figure 8.30-b). For the moment, let us attempt to achieve the new behavior by modification of the original toggle rather than by adding new external circuits or components. External equipment can be arranged to provide complementing, but this will be discussed as part of the subject of counters.

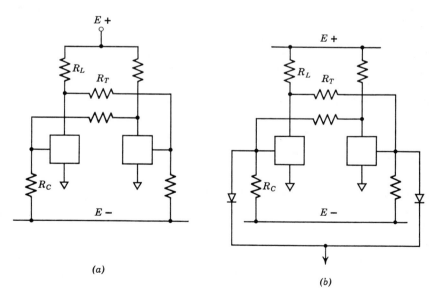

Figure 8.30. Possible complementing input terminals.

We will use the common collector-supply terminal to demonstrate the complementing input because it happens to demonstrate the principles very neatly (Figure 8.30-a). A similar argument can be constructed for other configurations. To get started, assume that a negative going signal is applied to this common point; moreover, assume that the toggle is ideal in that it contains no capacitance, not even stray capacitance. As the signal moves negatively, the previously more positive collector (say, the right one) will move negatively, in turn moving the left control negatively. Thus the left device tends to reduce its current, permitting its collector to rise. However, the top end of this same load resistor is moving downwardly in response to the driving signal. If the input signal moves through an increment of Δe volts, it will be attenuated by $R_C/(R_C + R_T + R_L)$ in getting to the left control. This same Δe will depress the left collector by at most Δe, but the left device will initially also have considerable gain—in fact, probably more gain than the attenuation which Δe has suffered in getting to the left control. Therefore, the left collector may very well move positively at first, although eventually, the collector voltage must come down as the upper end of the load resistor continues its downward motion.

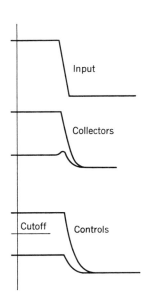

Figure 8.31. Toggle response to a negative complementing input signal.

Suppose the negatively moving input signal finally goes far enough that both controls are below cutoff (Figure 8.31).

At this time all points in the circuit are pairwise equal in potential, if all components are pairwise equal. As the driving signal returns positively toward its quiescent position, chance will determine which side comes into conduction first. There is no predisposition for the circuit to fall into the opposite state. Both devices are cutoff, and the new state will be determined by whichever of them happens to come into conduction first, or perhaps whichever of them happens to come into conduction with a larger gain. A burst of noise, or in the practical case, some dissymmetry in the circuit, will determine which side begins to conduct first and, therefore, into which stable state the circuit falls.

Obviously, none of the stray capacitances will help to resolve this ambiguous behavior. If the input signal moves rapidly compared to the natural time constants of the circuit, the stray capacitances will tend to preserve the previous state of the circuit. If the driving signal moves slowly compared to the time constants of the toggle, chance or dissymmetry controls the circuit. It is clear that the toggle must somehow develop the ability to "know" in which state it was (the stray capacitances know this) but in such a way that the toggle is guided to the proper new state.

Might the transpose capacitors (C_T) be able to fill the need? To investigate this situation, consider the specific circuit of Figure 8.32, in which the quiescent levels are shown for the left-side conducting.

Let the input signal move negatively to such a point that, say, the two collectors are each at zero volts. Furthermore, suppose that this has happened rapidly compared to the rate at which the two transpose capacitors can change their voltages. Under these circumstances, the capacitors are essentially batteries, and therefore the left control finds itself at -36 volts but the right control finds itself at only -25 volts (Figure 8.33)! Notice what has occurred; initially the left con-

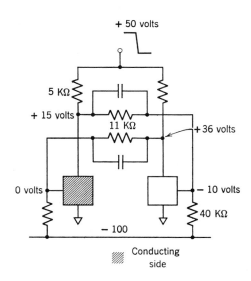

Figure 8.32. A specific toggle and complementing input signal.

trol was above the right one in a voltage sense, but now their relative positions are reversed. It is now clear that if the driving signal returns toward its quiescent position sufficiently rapidly, the right control will stay above the left one, thereby causing the toggle to change its state to that of right-side conducting. Furthermore, we see that the next such input signal will return the toggle to left-side conducting, and so on.

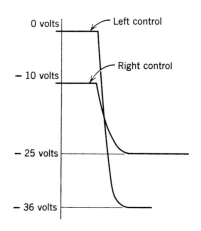

What can happen if the input signal were to come down and stay too long? Suppose the two collectors have been driven to 0 volts as before but remain there. After enough time, each transpose capacitor changes its voltage, and the circuit drifts toward a condition of symmetry. Both controls move toward asymptotes which are determined by the two resistor networks. In the case of exact component symmetry, the two drift toward the same asymptotic voltage (Figure 8.34). The circuit will now have the same indeterminacy that it had prior to the addition of the transpose capacitors. In case of dissymmetry

Figure 8.33. Control voltage crossover due to transpose capacitors.

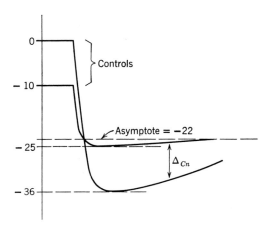

Figure 8.34. The drift of both control voltages toward a common asymptote.

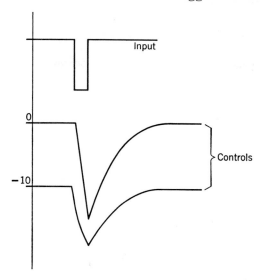

Figure 8.35.   The effect of a too-narrow input signal.

of the resistor networks, one control (say, the left one) will drift toward an asymptote which is relatively more positive.   Under this circumstance the circuit will tend to fall into the state corresponding to the left-side conducting, no matter what the previous state might have been.

The constraints on the driving signal now emerge.   The rate of change of voltage of the leading edge must be fast compared to the time constant of the transpose capacitor (essentially $R_T C_T$).   The minimum duration of the drive signal must be sufficient to allow the action which it initiates to propagate throughout the circuit.   If the input signal were too short, for instance, the two controls might not even get crossed over (Figure 8.35).   However, maximum width of the signal is determined by the following set of considerations.

1. The difference in potential between the two controls (Δe_{Cn}) decreases as the input signal becomes wider.

2. The minimum value of Δe_{Cn}, taking into account all parameter drifts and tolerances which might affect it, must be such that the uppermost control reaches its cutoff level not only first, but also by enough safety margin in voltage so that the conduction of this device is certain to build up rapidly enough (the other device might have a higher initial gain as it comes into conduction).

3. In considering the upward motion of the two controls, we must remember that they are still tending to drift toward each other during the upswing. The Δe_{Cn} which exists when one control reaches cutoff must be larger than the expected asymmetry between the cutoffs of the two devices. Otherwise, the lowermost control might reach its cutoff level first, if that particular device happened to have a more remote cutoff characteristic.

Finally, the trailing edge of the trigger must be rapid compared to the time constant of the transpose capacitor.

It is quite possible that the side which comes into conduction first has not reached a state of heavy conduction before the other one also begins. Thus, the lowermost control may go above its final quiescent level, only to be driven back down to it by the downcoming collector. It is also true, of course, that one of the upgoing collectors may be too far positive when its control comes into conduction, and have to be brought down to its quiescent level.

Figure 8.36 summarizes all of these observations about the circuit.

What about these C_T's? Should they be large or small? From the standpoint of not having to be concerned with the width of the

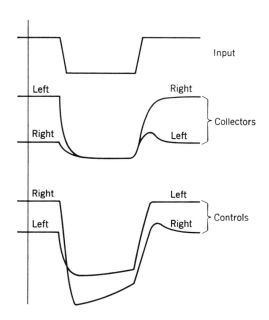

Figure 8.36. Typical waveforms during a complementing transition.

input signal, the C_T's should be large. On the other hand, the C_T which starts the transition with 36 volts across itself must finish the transition with only 25 volts, and vice versa. Time must be allowed for this—a recovery interval again—and from this standpoint, the capacitors ought to be small. Betwixt and between—the inevitable compromise.

Notice the role that the transpose capacitors now play. They are not present for a circuit purpose, but rather for the *logical* function of *storage* (or as is occasionally said, *memory*). Later it will be interesting to identify the particular part of a given counting or complementing circuit which contributes the storage property.

Vacuum-Tube Toggles

Except for renaming the inputs of our generalized active element (i.e., cathode, grid, plate), the discussion to date can be applied directly to vacuum-tube toggles (9). The grid of a vacuum tube exhibits the same characteristics which we have assumed for the control of the active element. It has a cutoff region, a region between cutoff and zero bias, and a region of grid current. There is an implicit diode between the grid and the cathode. The grid-plate capacitance can be enhanced if both grid and plate are in motion at the same time.

There are some other effects in vacuum tubes. For example, at sufficiently high frequencies, the internal leads of a tube exhibit a series inductance; also, there is a transit time of the electrons from cathode to plate. However, these effects are not likely to be important unless tubes are being used at extremely high frequencies.

The stability problem (in the Bode sense) can be troublesome in a vacuum-tube circuit because of faulty cutoff characteristics of the tube. It is possible, for example, that mechanical damage occurs to a grid or that a grid wire burns through or becomes unwelded. In any of these cases, the cutoff characteristic of the tube becomes more remote (γ_0 becomes larger), and instability may result.

In addition to triode tubes, pentodes are also available and can be used to avoid the capacitance-enhancement problem. Furthermore, it might be possible to utilize the cathode, control grid, and screen grid of a pair of pentodes for the toggle circuit, leaving the suppressor grid and the plate available for other uses, for example, gating operations (see 9.14). The screen dissipation rating, however, is substantially less than the plate dissipation rating which implies that a toggle based on the screen as the collector element is likely to be a low-current toggle.

Frequently triode tubes are packaged two to the glass envelope. Sometimes the internal structure is such that the characteristics of the two triodes are not independent but are related through common structural members. Such out of the ordinary aspects of vacuum tubes may create additional problems of tolerance and drift.

Transistor Toggles

The generalities of our previous arguments are still quite valid for the transistor toggle, but some of the details are different (10). Sometimes, it will be necessary only to reinterpret a point, rather than modify it.

The most conspicuous difference, of course, between the transistor and our assumed generalized element is in the behavior of the control. The control element of the transistor—the base—is not a voltage operated input but rather a current operated input, and consequently tends to be a low impedance terminal. This implies that the design of the divider network between the collector of one side and the base of the other side must be designed to supply a specified amount of current into the base. However, this is just like designing the vacuum-tube toggle for grid current. The divider network is chosen so that with the specified amount of base current extracted from the junction of the transpose and collector-return resistors, the potential of this junction is the same as the emitter potential.

The base differs in another respect from the grid of a tube. There are only two regions for it: the cutoff region and the current-conduction region. There is no region of base behavior which corresponds to negative, but not cutoff grid bias. The region of negative bias and current conduction for the grid is coalesced into one region of current conduction for the base. Thus our analysis of the transition interval of the toggle will need some modification. For example, the three intervals listed in page 8.53 for each control element will be but two regions for each base. Corresponding modifications will also have to be made to Figure 8.24.

There are some effects within the transistor which have no counterpart in the tube. From the time that base current is applied, there is a turn-on delay because of the finite diffusion time of carriers through the base region (11). Furthermore, there is a corresponding turn-off delay due to carrier storage in the base region. The turn-off delay depends on the depth of saturation of the transistor, and this in turn depends directly on the magnitude of the resistors in the circuit and the supply voltage. Hence parameters which drift with time can be reflected as variable time delays in transistor action. Such time delays, of course, contribute to the transition time of the toggle, and must be combined with the delays due to various capacitance charging times.

Even though cutoff, the transistor exhibits a collector leakage current which is temperature dependent. Therefore, the temperature range over which a transistor toggle must operate is of prime concern to the designer. Moreover, in the common emitter configuration, the collector leakage current is magnified for zero-base current, and we may wish to modify the circuit configuration to combat this.

The transistor, beside new effects, also exhibits new characteristics compared to the vacuum tube. Small signals can turn the transistor on and off, which implies that very fast circuits can be designed because there is very little capacitance current that need be supplied. Smaller signals also imply less power in the circuit overall. There is a very small voltage drop across a conducting transistor which implies that the transistor is a much better switch than the vacuum tube. It also suggests that there may be transistor toggle configurations which have no tube counterpart. Transistors are available in complementary pairs—the PNP and the NPN—and new circuit configurations may be possible for this reason. Transistors can be made symmetrical —the emitter and the collector can functionally interchange as the circuit changes its internal voltage and current pattern. This may suggest new kinds of triggering schemes.

The symmetrical grounded-emitter toggle is shown in Figure 8.37; the transpose capacitors are already in. Some of the components now play a somewhat different role. The divider network (R_T, R_C) must be designed to supply whatever base current is required for the necessary collector current. Tolerances must, of course, be considered. However, for the transistor which is cutoff, the divider network must supply the base with a reverse current which is equal to the total leakage current * from the base at the highest operating temperature. Otherwise, the circuit may develop instability with temperature changes. Moreover, the impedance level of the divider must be low enough that the leakage current from the base does not appreciably affect the divider. Alternatively, the reverse voltage to which the base is driven can be large enough to accept the perturbations induced

* This is the so-called I_{co}, the leakage current from collector to base with the emitter open-circuited, plus the leakage current from base to emitter.

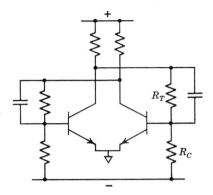

Figure 8.37. The symmetrical transistor toggle.

by leakage. This corresponds to overdriving a grid beyond cutoff. In each case, the point is to maintain the cutoff condition.

The transpose capacitors are nominally for the purpose of improving the frequency response of the resistance-capacitance network which couples the two sides of the toggle. However, in order to reduce the turn-on delay of the transistor, it is desirable to temporarily overdrive the base. Hence, the transpose capacitor, in addition to all its other functions, can be the source of charge which is delivered to the base during turn-on. It obviously plays the inverse role during turn-off; it can accept charge from the base region of the transistor. In a given circumstance, it may be a ticklish problem to make these capacitors not only double in brass, but in strings as well. Conceivably they could balance the attenuator, supply charge to the base, and provide temporary storage for a complementing mode in the toggle.

The transistor may or may not go into saturation. It depends upon the collector load line and the amount of base current. It is conceivable that with all parameters at nominal values saturation does not occur, but that parameter drifts will lead to saturation. If such effects occur, the response time of the toggle may change significantly.

Because of carrier storage delays, the normal toggle configuration may be modified to prevent saturation. In a sense, it is important to recognize that such changes are for the benefit of the transistor. Anti-saturation measures improve the performance of the transistor in the circuit and, therefore, the performance of the circuit, but they do not modify the basic behavior of the circuit as a toggle. Figure 8.38 shows a symmetrical grounded-emitter toggle which incorporates a standard technique for preventing saturation.

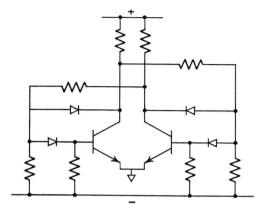

Figure 8.38. The symmetrical transistor toggle with an antisaturation measure.

If the transistor is allowed to saturate, and if the circuit is designed always to be in saturation, then the collector voltage during conduction is well determined. In this sense, the collector of the transistor toggle is more suitable for an output terminal than the plate of a tube toggle.

Related to the problem of leakage current variation with temperature is the possibility of thermal runaway. It is possible that increasing leakage current increases the internal junction temperature to the point that the leakage increases still further and thermal destruction occurs. The internal temperature is, of course, related to the collector voltage which in turn depends in part on the load line of the transistor. The load line will change position as parameters of the circuit (resistors, supply voltages) fluctuate, and conceivably thermal destruction can result from drifted components. Here again, there is a strong interaction between the components of the circuit and the performance and behavior of the transistor. Such problems, of course, must be considered part of the design.

In some transistors,* the saturation voltage of the collector is so low that the resulting voltage, when applied between the base and the emitter of a second transistor, does not permit the second one to conduct appreciably. For appropriate transistors, therefore, it is possible to use the much simplified symmetrical circuit shown in Figure 8.39 (12). The design of this circuit requires some special consideration. For example, the base of the non-conducting transistor is not

* For example, surface barrier transistors.

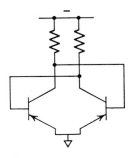

Figure 8.39. The direct-coupled symmetrical transistor toggle.

reverse biased. Therefore, leakage currents may limit the permissible temperature of operation. In this circuit, the collector swing is unusually small—a few tenths of a volt. During conduction the collector is at the saturation voltage; when out of conduction the collector is at the base-emitter voltage of the opposite transistor. Hence the circuit may be strongly susceptible to electrical noise.

So far as input and output terminals are concerned, the situation is just like our gen-

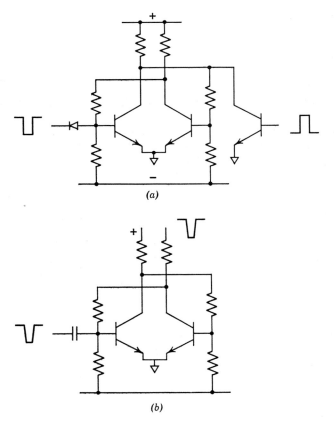

Figure 8.40. Typical triggering methods for transistor toggles.

eral discussion. The base terminal, because of the implicit diode to the emitter, defines one level of base voltage extremely well. The collector, if saturated, also defines its voltage closely. Triggering can be done by any of the methods previously discussed. Current can be injected into the toggle either conductively through a diode, resistor, or transistor, or as displacement current through a capacitor. Since a transistor in conduction requires a particular value of base charge, the input trigger must be capable of neutralizing this charge, if it is to turn off the conducting transistor. If the trigger is to turn on the non-conducting side, it can be used to inject the necessary base overdrive. Hence capacitively coupled triggers have an advantage in this respect. Figure 8.40 shows some triggering possibilities.

OTHER TOGGLE CONFIGURATIONS

The Self-biased Toggle

So long as the relative voltage differences between $E+$, $E-$, and ground are preserved, the symmetrical toggle can be placed anywhere on an absolute voltage scale. In particular the lower ends of R_C can be returned to ground, provided $E+$ is made $E++$ and the two emitters are fixed at an intermediate level. One way to develop the emitter potential is to pass the device current through a resistor; this leads to the *self-biased* version of the *symmetrical toggle* (Figure 8.41) (13). One obvious trade the designer has made if he elects the self-biased toggle, is a single, bigger power supply plus an extra component in each toggle in exchange for two power supplies, each smaller.

Most of the previous discussion from the grounded-emitter symmetrical toggle completely applies to this toggle. The emitter resistor helps to keep the loop gain low in the stable states, so that control current may not be needed. In the case of tubes it may, in fact, be

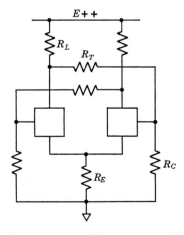

Figure 8.41. The symmetrical self-biased toggle.

difficult to design this circuit for grid current. The cathode will tend to follow the grid positively rather than permitting the grid to rise above it. The only possibility is to starve the tube for plate voltage so that the current required through the cathode resistor cannot all be supplied from the plate. In the case of transistors, the emitter also follows the base, but of course base current must flow for any internal conduction at all. One nice feature of the grounded-emitter toggle is gone; no longer is the upper control level nicely clamped by an implicit diode. In fact, explicit clamp diodes are often added to the self-biased circuit to standardize its levels.

The previous triggering methods are all still valid although the triggering properties are different. Suppose that a negatively going signal is applied to the control of the conducting device. As the control moves downwardly, the emitter, instead of staying fixed, moves downwardly with it. The emitter behaves exactly as it would in a follower. The device, therefore, does not begin to cutoff at all, but simply changes its current by the small amount necessary to let the emitter "keep down" with the control. The larger the emitter resistor is, the less is the change in device current per increment of control change. After all, negative feedback (in the form of the emitter resistor) is supposed to stabilize a circuit against changing characteristics; this is exactly what is happening.

The control input terminals to this toggle are "stretchy"; the triggers have to be much larger than for the grounded-emitter version. Eventually, of course, the circuit must flip. The downgoing control is moving toward the other one; the device current is decreasing slightly so that the collector voltage (and the other control to which it is coupled via R_T) is moving upward toward the downcoming control. Finally, the controls will intersect and the circuit will transition. The increased trigger requirement is another characteristic which ought to be priced in considering this particular toggle configuration.

Offhand, it would seem that a capacitor at the emitter would cure this triggering difficulty. Presumably the capacitor can be chosen large enough so that its voltage (and, therefore, the emitter level) will not change appreciably during flipping. It does help, but only at the expense of creating another possible difficulty. Because of the follower-like property in this toggle, there is little to control the upper level of the control swing. Therefore, it is quite possible for the upper reach of the control to be quite different on the two sides. Assume that the quiescent upper level of the left control is +15 volts; but of the right one, +13 volts. This much difference can come from drifted resistors. Suppose the toggle has stayed with its left-side conducting long enough for the emitter to follow the control to +15 volts;

accordingly, the emitter capacitor is charged to +15 volts. If the emitter time constant is large enough to relieve the triggering problem, the emitter level will not change appreciably during the transition interval. When the upcoming control arrives at +13 volts, it finds itself facing 2 volts of negative bias relative to the +15 volts emitter. If this were a tube, it may be that with 2 volts of bias, the tube cannot draw sufficient current to keep the toggle in its intended new state! If this were a transistor, it would not even be in conduction. The triggering problem dictates a large emitter capacitor; the possible asymmetry of the circuit demands a small one. Depending upon what compromise is made in the selection of the capacitor, it may be necessary to control asymmetry of the resistor network by using more stable resistors and voltage sources, and/or it may be necessary to test and select devices to control the asymmetry of the pertinent characteristics, and/or it may be necessary to guarantee a trigger wide enough to span the time required for the emitter potential to change to its new level. In a tube case, it may even be desirable to design such that the toggle will operate with some specified amount of negative bias. This in turn specifies the limit of asymmetry which is acceptable in the circuit.

An important point is emerging from this discussion. There are a large number of possible tradeoffs in choosing one circuit over another. In the case of the self-biased toggle versus the grounded-emitter toggle, the negative power supply with its associated distribution and stabilization problems is to be weighed against such things as extra components in each toggle (at least a resistor, perhaps also a capacitor and some diodes), a trickier design problem, possibly more closely controlled components, possibly more expensive components, taller or wider trigger signals, etc. A designer cannot make choices blindly; he must have an adequate background on each circuit contender for a given application, and he must know their strengths and weaknesses. To get this background, he may even have to create trial designs of several kinds of, say, toggles as well as experimental models. Because any one kind of circuit may appear a very large number of times in a digital system, large economic gains or * losses can depend on a designer's early decisions.

The Asymmetrical Toggle

So far the two feedback couplings required by our toggle have been symmetrically chosen. A possible coupling between the two halves

---

* The exclusive OR, obviously.

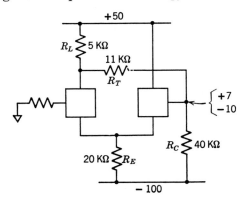

Figure 8.42.   The asymmetrical toggle.

of the circuit is the common emitter connection; we can discard one
of the crossover networks for it.   In effect, a grounded-control amplifier has had its output connected to its input.   The resulting *asymmetrical* or *Schmitt toggle* is shown in Figure 8.42 (14).

   This toggle has several distinctly different features.   First, is it even
a bistable arrangement?   Assume that the left side is conducting; the
emitter will, therefore, be very close to the potential of the left control—ground.   If the R_L, R_T, R_C, $E+$ and $E-$ are taken to be those
of the original grounded emitter version (Figure 8.3), then the right-
most control is about -10 volts which is well below the zero potential
of the emitter.   Thus the right side is cutoff; this is one stable state.
Now assume the left side is cutoff; the resistor network will bring the
right control to about $+7$ volts, and the common emitter will follow it
there.   Thus the grounded left control faces an emitter 7 volts above
itself; the left side is cutoff as assumed.   This is the other stable state.
Since the right collector does not have to provide a signal for the internal operation of the toggle, it need not have a load impedance.
More of this later.

   If the left device is conducting, a sufficiently large negative control
signal will make the common emitter go down to meet the right control,
and the circuit will flip (much like the self-biased toggle).   If the
right device is conducting, a sufficiently positive signal can take the
control up to meet the common emitter (and, therefore, the right control) and transition will again occur.   The left control is a "stretchy"
input terminal in the same sense that the self-biased toggle has
stretchy input control terminals.   The left control is quite similar to
the handle of a mechanical toggle switch; it is one terminal accepting

two kinds of input signals. Clearly the right control can also be operated on. Collector triggering will also work, as will a signal at the top end of R_L. There is a new input terminal—the emitters (Figure 8.43). Raising the emitter positively is equivalent to driving the left control negatively and will accomplish the same result. The only thing that will not work is operating on the right collector; it takes no part in the toggle action.

Output terminals are the left collector, the right control, or the common emitter. Because of the lowish impedance of the emitter (R_L prevents it from being as low as it would be in a follower), this toggle can provide an output terminal which is lower in impedance than any of those of previously discussed toggles.

The right collector of the asymmetrical toggle is "free" in the sense that any impedance can be put there to develop any sort of desired output signal subject only to this restriction:

The instantaneous collector voltage of the right device must never fall so low that it prevents the device from supplying the current required of it. At the same time, for tubes, this current must be supplied without current into the right grid, and for transistors, without excessive base-current demand.

A delayed output may be obtained from the free collector; a pulse which appears only when the toggle flips may be obtained from a suitable impedance; and so on.

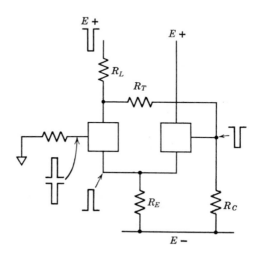

Figure 8.43. Possible input triggers to the asymmetrical toggle.

This particular toggle is intrinsically a fast one because the emitter coupling is rather low impedance, and it consequently introduces very little loop delay. Furthermore, if there is no load impedance in the right collector, there is no capacitance enhancement there, and compensation (by means of C_T) can be very precisely adjusted. Since the left control does not move in potential, there is no capacitance enhancement at the left collector, either. This toggle also has the advantage of having fewer components. If the design happens to be such that the emitter potentials are very far from ground, a possible difficulty for tubes is heater-cathode leakage and insulation problems. Many points previously developed apply to this toggle, e.g., clamp diodes to stabilize levels or absorb tolerances, a crossover capacitor to speed transition.

The Dynamic Toggle

In all of the forms of toggle considered so far, there exists two distinct patterns of current which can persist in the network; they represent the two stable states of the circuit. Equally good from the standpoint of the logical property required of the toggle (two-statedness) would be one current pattern (or kind of activity) and one condition of no current or no activity. This observation leads to the class of *dynamic toggles* (15).

A toggle must be able to flip from one state to the other in response to an external signal, and the duration of this signal is short and probably unrelated to the interval in which the toggle is to stay in a given state. The toggle must be able to stay in either state after the external signal has ceased. Therefore, some form of feedback must be included in the dynamic circuit configuration. The state of complete inactivity clearly needs no feedback; almost any circuit is able to stay inactive once it initially gets that way. The activity state is another question however, and for it, some form of positive feedback must operate.

From these remarks we can develop the general form of a dynamic toggle. There must be a feedback loop, and since it will inevitably have losses, there must be a gain element to supply these and other losses. There must be a way to excite initial activity in the circuit so that the feedback loop can become effective. Lastly, there must be a way to interfere with the feedback process so that the state of inactivity can be obtained. The circuit also must reject spurious noise signals.

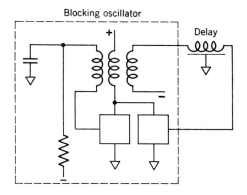

Figure 8.44. A primitive dynamic toggle.

One obvious possibility for the dynamic toggle is some form of a sinusoidal oscillator which has an arrangement for getting it into or out of the oscillating state. This particular form of a dynamic toggle has not yet been exploited, but a form which utilizes the blocking oscillator as the gain element does exist. The primitive form of this circuit is shown in Figure 8.44.

While it is true that the blocking oscillator itself has a positive feedback loop for its own purposes, it is sufficient in this discussion to consider it as a device which emits a pulse-type signal in response to an input signal; the output is an amplification of the input. The output signal of the blocking oscillator is routed through a suitable feedback path, and used to retrigger the oscillator. Therefore, the state of activity for this dynamic toggle is that of a recirculating pulse. The minimum length of the feedback loop is determined by the recovery time of the blocking oscillator.

If the dynamic toggle is in the state of activity, the other state can be achieved by simply opening the feedback loop. Since a blocking oscillator has a natural immunity to spurious noise signals, the circuit will remain in its inactive state until a trigger of sufficient amplitude and width is introduced into the blocking oscillator. If the feedback loop is closed, the circuit will remain in its state of activity with a pulse circulating around the loop. Since the design of this type of toggle hinges essentially on the design of a blocking oscillator and of a delay element, and since neither of these is particularly confined to the digital computing art, no detailed discussion of design will be given. However, see page 10.2 for some remarks relevant to the design of a blocking oscillator for digital use.

There are some logical problems of the dynamic toggle which must be discussed. Given a large number of dynamic toggles, the statistical distribution in the characteristics of the delay element and in the triggering properties of the blocking oscillator implies that the recirculation rate will differ from one toggle to the next. This can complicate intercommunication between toggles, especially if the transfer of information from toggle to toggle is to be via a pulsed signal rather than through a quasi-static non-pulse signal. For this reason among others, we generally decide to keep all the dynamic toggles in a system *synchronous* with respect to each other. Therefore, some timing signal common to the whole system must be introduced into each toggle in such a way that the precise triggering time is controlled by this synchronizing or *clock* signal.

We will see later (Chapter 9, page 9.10) that a circuit which implements the Boolean AND property, produces an output only during the time interval in which all input signals are present. Therefore, if the signal from the clock and from the feedback network are ANDed and the output of the AND circuit is used as the retrigger, all dynamic toggles will operate in unison.

It turns out that this input arrangement also compensates for a problem which arises from the non-ideal delay element. Practical delay lines are not perfect all-pass structures, either in phase or in amplitude. The output signal from such a line is attenuated relative to the input, and has a less steep edge than the input. If the signal out of the line were used as the retrigger, its lazy leading edge would enhance the triggering uncertainty of the blocking oscillator. Fortunately the distorted output of the delay line will also be somewhat broader than the input due to attenuation and phase shift of the high-frequency components. If the delay element is slightly shortened so that the feedback signal arrives in advance of the clock signal, the output of the AND gate can be made to have essentially the rise time and amplitude of the clock signal. Thus the input AND gate establishes a retrigger which has a well-defined time position and a well-defined shape.

When it is desired to set such a toggle into its activity state, the signal to accomplish this must also be ANDed with the clock. Otherwise, the first signal returned by the feedback loop might not occur at the proper time, and therefore the ANDing of the recirculating signal with the clock might not occur properly. The toggle would, therefore, fall back to its state of inactivity due to the failure of the recirculation loop to catch. Since the blocking oscillator must respond to the *set*

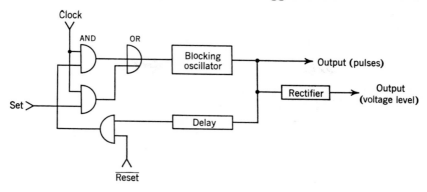

Figure 8.45. A typical dynamic toggle based on the blocking oscillator.

signal or to the recirculate signal, it is necessary to include also an OR decision element.*

How does recirculation ever get stopped? How can the toggle be reset to inactivity? The easiest way to accomplish this is to open the feedback loop; this will prevent the retrigger action, and all activity will promptly cease. Thus another AND gate is inserted into the feedback path. Its two inputs are the feedback signal and one which causes the AND gate to be unsatisfied when the reset action is desired. The second input, therefore, must be $\overline{\text{Reset}}$, a signal whose true state makes the AND gate unsatisfied. The $\overline{\text{Reset}}$ signal must completely overlap the time interval spanned by the clock signal. Otherwise a small sliver signal might leak through the AND gate and cause recirculation to continue.

We see that the particular form of the dynamic toggle described has two input terminals which are in one-one correspondence with the two stable states. As an output signal, it provides a chain of pulses to indicate the activity state; but it provides no output at all for the quiescent state. If desired, a D-C level-type signal can be manufactured by rectifying the pulse chain. Figure 8.45 summarizes these ideas and shows a typical circuit.

* This would seem to be the exclusive OR. However, if the toggle has already been set, another input signal conveys no new information. Furthermore, if the toggle is inactive, the trigger signal is the only input to the OR gate. Therefore, it is sufficient to use an inclusive-OR decision element. This is an example of a particular logical situation which can arise in a machine. If, say, the two inputs of an inclusive OR are prevented by other reasons from ever co-occurring in time, the output of this inclusive OR behaves to all intents and purposes as an exclusive OR of the two inputs.

Other Forms of Dynamic Toggles

Given the basic organizational notion of the dynamic toggle, we easily conceive of other circuit configurations. A particular one makes use of a simple triode, plate loaded with a resonant resistance-inductance-capacitance circuit which provides a signal for recirculation (Figure 8.46). The details of this circuit are available in the literature and need not be repeated here (16). It is seen that the feedback signal (a D-C voltage obtained by rectification), is ANDed as before with a clock signal, and the resulting trigger acting through the triode excites the resonant circuit. A follower output is provided for convenience, and a second kind of clock signal (Reset) is used to reset the rectification capacitor (C) during each recirculation. This guarantees that the output signal will promptly be at its "no activity" level in case recirculation suddenly ceases.

In weighing the dynamic toggle against others, we ought to make some accounting of the several input AND and OR gates. On the other side of the ledger, however, the dynamic toggle may have only one active element.

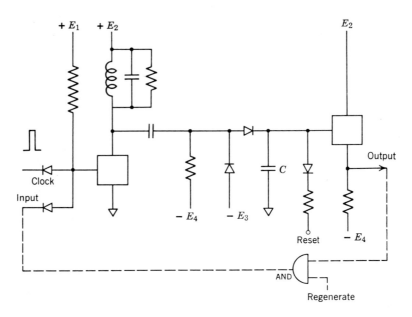

Figure 8.46. A dynamic toggle based on a resonant circuit.

Alphabetic Toggles

Sometimes a toggle is referred to as an "r-s-t" or a "j-k" toggle (17). This signifies a logical description of the toggle and specifies nothing about the circuit configuration. Such a designation implies that a truth table exists which relates the present state of the toggle and the input signals to the next state of the toggle. The circuit details which realize a given logical behavior may well vary from one designer to the next.

Toward the Ultimate

As we observed before, there are two rather distinct properties of a toggle which are of interest—the ability to transition from one stable state to another, and the ability to maintain a stable state. As we have also observed, the usual design compromises in order to utilize the same active and passive elements for both functions. The penalty, other than performance degradation due to compromise, is the steady consumption of power, even while a toggle is only maintaining a given stable state. The preferred situation would be a configuration which consumes no power unless in the transition phase. To a considerable extent, toggles using magnetic structures approach this ideal; once put into a particular state of magnetization, no further expenditure of energy is required to maintain it. The energy required for the transition comes from some source external to the toggle proper.

EXAMPLE

A magnetic material can exhibit a highly non-linear relation between the impressed magnetic field and the resulting flux in the material. This non-linear relation is generally a two-valued curve and is the well-known hysteresis loop. For zero impressed field, there are two values of remanent flux which can exist in the material (Figure 8.47). Once a remanent flux is established, no input of power from the outside is required to maintain it.

One kind of magnetic toggle could be a suitable magnetic material formed into an appropriate geometric shape. Windings are provided to establish either value of remanent flux; one value of remanent flux corresponds to the 1-state and the other, to the 0-state. Power is consumed only during the transition interval.

There is obviously a problem of sensing the state of the toggle. One pos-

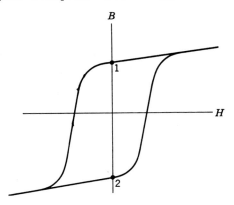

Figure 8.47. A typical hysteresis loop.

sibility is a special geometry such as the transfluxor (18) or a method of imposing a sampling field (19) such that the internal field which is representing the information state is not permanently disturbed. Another possibility is to *destructively read* the toggle by driving it to a standard state (say, the 0-state). If it is already in the 0-state, there is no change of internal flux and no induced voltage in an output winding. If the initial state were the 1-state, driving to the 0-state will generate a large change in the internal flux. The output winding will perceive an induced voltage, but the initial state of the toggle will have been destroyed. One possibility is to use the output signal not only for information purposes but also to rewrite the initial state of the toggle. It might do this by acting through suitable gain and, if necessary, delay elements.

Since the output from a switching magnetic flux is necessarily a pulse signal, magnetic toggles in a system almost have to be operated synchronously with each other.

Especially in the non-destructive sensing schemes, the output voltage is very small and supplementary amplification may be necessary. Accessories such as this must be costed when considering a particular kind of toggle for an application.

The technology which uses magnetic devices for toggles and other computer circuits is an extensive one unto itself (20). It has only been illustrated here.

Another step toward lower dissipation in the toggle is the low-temperature cryotron device (21). In it, superconducting material presents so little resistance to current flow that power consumption is vanishingly small. The standby power required to maintain a state still exists but is enormously reduced.

EXAMPLE

Superconducting materials (e.g., tin) have the property that at a critical temperature (typically 4° Kelvin), internal resistance vanishes. However, the superconducting state also responds to an applied magnetic field. At a fixed temperature, a material can be switched into and out of superconductivity by controlling a magnetic field. Consider the structure of Figure 8.48.

Except for the cross-hatched regions, the conducting material is such that at the operating temperature, it is superconducting (a "soft" superconductor) for no applied magnetic field. The magnitude of current in any conductor is such that it generates a magnetic field of sufficient magnitude around the conductor that this field can drive a neighboring conductor out of superconductivity. The cross-hatched regions are "hard" superconductors which continue to be superconducting for the magnitude of the fields which will switch the soft materials. Suppose that a current flows through the "set" input; the material beneath (point B) will go out of superconductivity (i.e., become normal); the other path through the network (L) is all superconducting, and current, therefore, will flow through L. This current will force another section of path R to become normal (point A), and therefore the triggering "set" current may now vanish. One stable position of the toggle

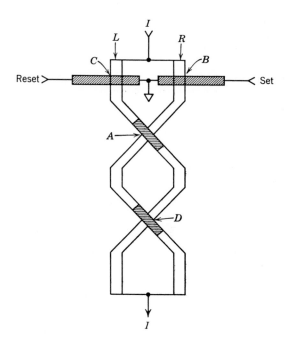

Figure 8.48. A cryogenic toggle.

is with current in the L path. If now a "reset" current appears, a normal region will be created in path L at point C; current will decrease in L and the normal region in path R (at A) will disappear. Therefore, the current will switch from path L to path R and in so doing, will create a normal region in path L at point D. Thus the toggle is locked in its other stable state.

n-Statedness

In principle, the notion of a 2-stated toggle is extensible to an n-stated version (22). Such a, say, 10-stated toggle would be of value in building a computer to operate in the decimal number system. (Remember? We presently build such machines to operate in a binary-coded-decimal representation which amounts to a pseudobinary machine.) Such n-stated devices suffer from practical problems. The resistor network required to guarantee that only one of n-active elements conducts is beset with tolerance problems. Furthermore, the lack of suitable techniques for storage devices of higher statedness, plus the efficiency of the binary system in representing information has tended to minimize the attractiveness of n-stated toggles, and their development has not prospered.

COLLATERAL READING

1. Lo, A. W., Some thoughts on digital components and circuit techniques; *IRE Transactions on Electronic Computers,* vol. EC-10, September, 1961; pp. 416–425.
2. Eccles, W. H. and F. W. Jordan, A trigger relay utilizing three electrode thermionic vacuum tubes; *Radio Review,* vol. 1, October, 1919; pp. 143 *ff.*
3. Siegel, P., *Understanding digital computers;* John Wiley and Sons, New York, 1961; pp. 139–140.

   Millman, J. and H. Taub, *Pulse and digital circuits;* McGraw-Hill Book Co., New York, 1956; chapter 5.

   Richards, R. K., *Digital computer components and circuits;* D. Van Nostrand Co., Princeton, N.J., 1957; pp. 64–99.

   Pettit, J. M., *Electronic switching, timing and pulse circuits;* McGraw-Hill Book Co., New York, 1959; pp. 117–130.

   Murphy, J. S., *Basics of digital computers;* John F. Rider Publisher, New York, 1958; vol. 2, pp. 7–10, 73–75.

   Bartee, T. C., *Digital computer fundamentals;* McGraw-Hill Book Co., New York, 1960; pp. 81–86.

   Scott, N. R., *Analog and digital computer technology;* McGraw-Hill Book Co., New York, 1960; pp. 410–441.

Smith, C. V. L., *Electronic digital computers;* McGraw-Hill Book Co., New York, 1959; pp. 107–114.

4. Rubinoff, M., Further data on the design of Eccles-Jordan flip-flops; *Electrical Engineering,* vol. 71, October, 1952; pp. 905–910.

   Paivenen, J. O. and I. L. Auerbach, Design of triode flip-flops for digital computer applications; *IRE Transactions on Electronic Computers,* vol. EC-2, June, 1953; pp. 14–26.

   Ritchie, D. K., The optimum DC design of flip-flops; *Proceedings of the IRE,* vol. 41, November, 1953; pp. 1614–1617.

5. Bode, H. W., *Network analysis and feedback amplifier design;* D. Van Nostrand Co., Princeton, N.J., 1945; chapters 3, 4.

6. Miller, J. M., *Dependence of the input impedance of a three element vacuum tube upon the load in the plate circuit;* National Bureau of Standards Science Paper 351.

7. Kreuder, N. L., The dynamics of toggle action; *Proceedings of the 1958 Western Joint Computer Conference,* Los Angeles, 6–8 May, 1958; pp. 46–50.

8. Phelps, B., Dual-triode trigger circuits; *Electronics,* July, 1945; p. 110 *ff.*

9. Most of the discussion in the references under items 3 and 4 above deal with vacuum-tube toggles.

10. Grabbe, E. M. *et al., Handbook of automation, computation and control;* John Wiley and Sons, New York, 1959; vol. 2, chapter 16.

    Hurley, R. B., *Junction transistor electronics;* John Wiley and Sons, New York, 1958; pp. 424–435.

    Smith, C. V. L., *Electronic digital computers;* McGraw-Hill Book Co., New York, 1959; pp. 117–125.

    Ledley, R. S., *Digital computer and control engineering;* McGraw-Hill Book Co., New York, 1960; pp. 672–679.

    Bartee, T. C., *Digital computer fundamentals;* McGraw-Hill Book Co., New York, 1960; pp. 87–95.

    DeWitt, D. and A. L. Rossoff, *Transistor electronics;* McGraw-Hill Book Co., New York, 1957; pp. 297–300.

    Pressman, A. I., *Design of transistorized circuits for digital computers;* John F. Rider Publisher, New York, 1959; chapter 11.

    Harris, J. R., Direct coupled transistor logic circuitry; *IRE Transactions on Electronic Computers;* vol. EC-7, March, 1958; pp. 2–6.

    Lynn, D. K. and D. C. Pederson, Switching and memory criteria in transistor flip-flops; *IRE Convention Record,* pt. 2, 1960; pp. 3–10.

    Silicon transistor flip-flop circuits; Texas Instruments, Inc.; application note, June, 1960.

    Hockenberger, R. W., Novel design technique for transistor digital circuits; *Electronics,* 24 August, 1962; pp. 42–44.

    Konkle, K. H., Circuits for the FX-1 computer; *Proceedings of the 1962 Western Joint Computer Conference,* San Francisco, 1–3 May, 1962; pp. 101–112.

11. *A discussion of storage time;* Texas Instruments, Inc.; application note, October, 1960.

    Pressman, A. I., *Design of transistorized circuits for digital computers;* John F. Rider Publisher, New York, 1959; chapter 4.

12. Beter, R. H. *et al.*, Surface barrier transistor switching circuits; *IRE Convention Record*, vol. 3, pt. 4, 1955; pp. 139–145.

13. Wanlass, C. L., Static-dynamic design of flip-flop circuits; *IRE Transactions on Electronic Computers;* vol. PGEC-1, December, 1952; pp. 6–18.

    Alrich, J. C., Engineering description of the Electro-Data digital computer; *IRE Transactions on Electronic Computers,* vol. EC-4, March, 1955; pp. 1–10.

    Millman, J. and H. Taub, *Pulse and digital circuits;* McGraw-Hill Book Co., New York, 1956; pp. 144–146.

14. Chu, J. C., The Oak Ridge automatic computer; *Proceedings of the Association for Computing Machinery,* Toronto, 8–10 September, 1952; pp. 142–148.

    Schmitt, O. H., A thermionic trigger; *Journal of Scientific Instruments,* vol. 15, January, 1938; pp. 24–26.

    Millman, J. and H. Taub, *Pulse and digital circuits;* McGraw-Hill Book Co., New York, 1956; pp. 164–173.

    Horn, I., An emitter-follower-coupled high speed binary counter; *IRE WESCON Convention Record,* pt. 4, 1958; pp. 54–61.

    Hurley, R. B., *Junction transistor electronics;* John Wiley and Sons, New York, 1958; pp. 412–416.

15. Elbourn, R. D. and R. P. Witt, Dynamic circuit techniques used in SEAC and DYSEAC; *IRE Transactions on Electronic Computers;* vol. EC-2, March, 1953; pp. 2–9.

    Greenwald, S. *et al.*, SEAC; *Proceedings of the IRE,* vol. 10, October, 1953; pp. 1308–1310.

    Elbourn, R. D. and R. P. Witt, Dynamic circuit techniques used in SEAC and DYSEAC; *Proceedings of the IRE,* vol. 10, October, 1952; pp. 1380–1387.

    Vogelsang, J. H., Transistor pulse amplifier using external regeneration; *Proceedings of the IRE,* vol. 10, October, 1953; pp. 1444–1450.

    Smith, C. V. L., *Electronic digital computers;* McGraw-Hill Book Co., New York, 1959; pp. 138–143.

16. Ross, H. D., Arithmetic element of the IBM 701; *Proceedings of the IRE,* vol. 10, October, 1953; pp. 1288–1289.

    Millman, J. and H. Taub, *Pulse and digital circuits;* McGraw-Hill Book Co., New York, 1956; pp. 416–418.

    Richards, R. K., *Digital computer components and circuits;* D. Van Nostrand Co., Princeton, N.J., 1957; pp. 99–106.

    Smith, C. V. L., *Electronic digital computers;* McGraw-Hill Book Co., New York, 1959; pp. 133–134.

17. Phister, M., *Logical design of digital computers;* John Wiley and Sons, New York, 1958; pp. 121–131.

18. Rajchman, J. A. and A. W. Lo, The transfluxor; *Proceedings of the IRE,* vol. 44, March, 1956; pp. 321–332.

19. Richards, R. K., *Digital computer components and circuits;* D. Van Nostrand Co., Princeton, N.J., 1957; pp. 392–395.

20. Grabbe, E. M. *et al.*, *Handbook of automation, computation, and control;* John Wiley and Sons, New York, 1959; vol. 2, chapter 15.

    Richards, R. K., *Digital computer components and circuits;* D. Van Nostrand Co., Princeton, N.J., 1957; chapter 5.

Ledley, R. S., *Digital computer and control engineering;* McGraw-Hill Book Co., New York, 1960; pp. 689–711.

Meyerhoff, A. J., *Digital applications of magnetic devices;* John Wiley and Sons, New York, 1960.

21. Matthias, B. T., Superconductivity; *Scientific American;* November, 1957; pp. 92 *ff. passim.*

    Ittner, W. B., III and C. J. Krause, Superconducting computers; *Scientific American,* July, 1961; pp. 124 *ff. passim.*

22. Siegel, P., *Understanding digital computers;* John Wiley and Sons, New York, 1961; p. 147.

    Mackay, R. S. and R. MacIntyre, Ternary counters; *IRE Transactions on Electronic Computers,* vol. EC-4, December, 1955; pp. 144–149.

EXERCISES

The exercises and problems of this chapter and of chapter 9 and 10 which require explicit circuit technology can be solved either in terms of the vacuum tube or the transistor. If you elect vacuum tube technology, use the type 5844 twin triode whose characteristic curves follow. Design for positive supply voltages of 125 to 150, negative supply voltages of 200 to 300, grid swings in the range of 25 to 30 volts, plate swings in the range of 60 to 70 volts, and plate currents in the range of 5 to 8 ma. If you elect transistor technology, use the PNP type 2N404 whose characteristics follow. Design for positive supply voltages of 10 to 12, negative supply voltages of 10 to 12, base current swings of about 1 ma, and collector current swings of about 10 ma. For direct-coupled circuits, design for a collector voltage of about ½, and for other circuits, a collector voltage in the range of 2 to 6.

Since our intent is to learn to design circuits with a minimum of entanglement with those aspects of device behavior which become important only at extreme circuit speeds, design your circuits to operate in the general range of a few microseconds. For instance, design the toggles so that a trigger width of the order of 1 μsec is sufficient, and so that all internal transients of transition will have decayed in 2 to 5 μsec. This avoids such problems as lead inductance in vacuum tubes and internal delays in an adequately fast transistor.

The 5844 and 2N404 are representative of the active element which is used in the design of digital circuits. Not all aspects of the transistor designs can be treated. Specifically, no characteristic information has been included on the delay phenomena of the transistor—turn-on time and carrier storage time. These effects are of prime importance in circuits intended to operate in the fractional microsecond or nanosecond range, but of correspondingly less importance in the speed range for which we are designing.

Another aspect of design peculiar to the transistor (and the diode) is the change in characteristics with ambient temperature, and/or the necessity to derate the internal dissipation rating with increasing ambient temperature. The internal capacitance can also depend on the current level through the device.

Characteristic data has been included to enable you to make transistor designs which will operate over an extended temperature range.

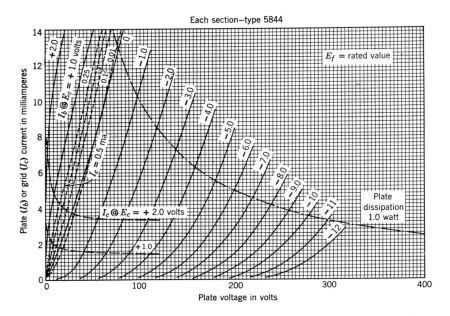

Figure 8.49. *Average 5844 plate characteristics.* (*Courtesy General Electric Co.*)

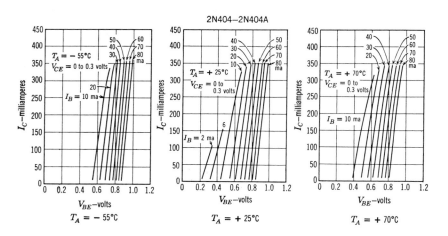

Figure 8.50. *Typical 2N404 base-emitter characteristics.* (*Courtesy General Electric Co.*)

2N404–2N404A

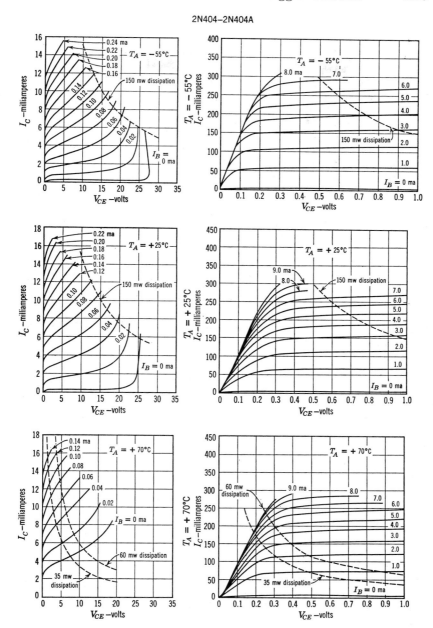

Figure 8.51. Typical 2N404 collector-emitter characteristics. (Courtesy General Electric Co.)

8.1. In addition to those mentioned on pages 8.1 and 8.2, list several other physical phenomena in terms of which binary information might be represented. In each identify the two states to be used.

8.2. To develop general insight into the behavior of resistance-capacitance circuits, determine the output voltage (e_0) of a circuit having a series resistor (R) followed by a shunt capacitor (C), when driven by the following inputs for the conditions shown. The initial voltage on the capacitor is $e_c(0)$ and the time constant of the exponential input voltages is τ.

(a) A step voltage of amplitude E; $e_c(0) = \pm E$.
(b) A rising exponential of amplitude E—$E(1 - \epsilon^{-t/\tau})$—for $RC = \tau$, $RC < \tau$, and $RC > \tau$, and $e_c(0) = \pm E/2$.
(c) The same as (b) above except that $e_c(0) = 0$.
(d) A ramp voltage rising at a rate of α volts per second—αt—for $RC < E/\alpha$, $RC = E/\alpha$, $RC > E/\alpha$, and $e_c(0) = -E$, 0, $+E$.
(e) A semi-trapezoidal voltage (it has no trailing edge but remains at the plateau level) of amplitude E whose positive going leading edge rises at a rate of α volts per second. Take $e_c(0) = 0$ and for a given RC and α, calculate and plot e_0. Deduce an expression which gives the maximum value of e_0 as a function of α. Plot a curve showing the variation of the maximum of e_0 with a suitable dimensionless parameter involving α. What physical significance has this parameter?

8.3 Why is it suggested on page 8.11 that two resistors in series (rather than in parallel) be used for R_c? (*Hint:* consider the reliability problem.)

8.4. Repeat the argument on pages 8.12 through 8.15 for either a vacuum tube or transistor situation as you wish. Use the characteristic curves given above, and design for the nominal case. Identify the "worst case" situation so far as each control and each collector is concerned. Verify your deduction by letting all resistors fluctuate $\pm 5\%$, all supply voltages $\pm 3\%$, and check each of the situations which can arise. (There are six resistors and two supply voltages involved. Each can drift in either direction independently of the others. Hence there are 2^8 different circumstances. Perhaps some of these can be eliminated by inspection, but several will probably have to be actually calculated.)

Find the variation on the control and collector levels. In this exercise, do not be concerned about modifying the toggle design in case it does not withstand all tolerance situations.

8.5. Modify the empirical design approach (pages 8.11 ff.) to accommodate each of the additional constraints given as examples on pages 8.17–8.18.

Will it be possible to accommodate all three of these in one design procedure?

8.6. Can the symmetrical toggle possibly be designed so that one side is always conducting; i.e., it has only one state? Defend your answer.

8.7. Consider a symmetrical toggle which manages to get into a state with both sides conducting. Can it stay that way? Are there special circumstances in which such a situation might be a point of stability?

8.8. For the toggle you designed in exercise 8.4, calculate the loop gain in the stable states. What assumptions are you making about the gain of the tube or transistor when it is cutoff? If your circuit appears to be unstable, modify the original design to provide stability. (Keep in mind that stability must be maintained in spite of parameter drifts.) If the design is changed, recalculate the nominal and extremal values of the control and collector levels.

8.9. Calculate and reproduce the curves of Figures 8.5-a and 8.5-b.

8.10. For the toggle which you have designed in exercise 8.8, calculate and plot the transfer and loop gain characteristics. Assume that all parameters are at nominal value. Verify the analysis of exercise 8.8.

Superpose two of the transfer characteristics and verify the voltage levels of the controls and collectors as previously calculated (exercise 8.8).

8.11. Suppose that explicit clamp diodes have been added to the collector circuits of the symmetrical toggle. Both levels of each collector are to be clamped. For the toggle that you have designed in exercise 8.8, pick diode supply voltages such that all resistor and supply voltage tolerances will be absorbed by the clamps.

8.12. Reconsider the clamped-collector symmetrical toggle of the previous example. Pick the diode supply voltages to be equal to the nominal collector levels; i.e., all parameters will have design center values. Now redesign the toggle—changing resistors and supply voltages as necessary—so that the tolerances cited in exercise 8.4 are completely absorbed. Under worst-case situations, clamp current must just continue to flow.

8.13. For the clamped-collector design in the previous exercise, deduce and plot the transfer and loop gain characteristics.

8.14. Why in Figure 8.8, is the 45° line the locus of points-of-no-return?

8.15. Verify that the transconductances given on page 8.29 are correct.

8.16. For the toggle which you have designed (exercise 8.4) and perhaps modified to be stable (exercise 8.8), find the amplitude of trigger required to slowly bring the toggle to the point-of-no-return. Repeat the above for the clamped design of exercise 8.12.

8.17. For the clamped design of exercise 8.12, what is the largest noise signal that the control can accept but not have the toggle transition? Repeat the calculation for a noise signal coupled into the collector.

8.18. Why not trigger the symmetrical toggle by coupling the signal to a control through a resistor? Like the diode, a resistor provides a conductive path into the toggle. After all, the collector triggering (or clearing) scheme couples the trigger in through a resistive path. Does this imply that the trailing edge of the collector clearing signal is subject to some constraint?

8.19. For the stable toggle which you have designed (exercise 8.8), draw the circuit diagrams for all ways of triggering it. For each case, specify the current demand on the trigger source. Repeat above for the clamped design (exercise 8.12).

8.20. In the toggle of exercise 8.8, assume that the emitter-collector capacitance is 5 mmf and that there is a stray capacitance of 3 mmf at each collector and at each control. Estimate the leading-edge transition time required of a trigger to be coupled through a capacitor to the control. Estimate the size of the input capacitor. Justify your answers. Estimate the trailing-edge transition time that the trigger must have to avoid retriggering.

8.21. For the toggle of exercise 8.8, estimate the amount of enhancement of the collector-emitter capacitance during transition. Justify your answer.

8.22. Without doing a detailed calculation, but using estimates based on the time constants of the circuit, deduce and sketch both control and both collector waveshapes during the transition of the toggle in exercise 8.20. What assumption have you made about the method of triggering and the rise time of the trigger? Estimate the dead time (pages 8.52 and 8.56) of your design, for both design center and worst-case situations.

8.23. For the designs of exercises 8.8 and 8.12, estimate the value of the crossover capacitor that should be used to speed up transition. Keep in mind that the control must not overshoot the voltage which it is approaching even though all parameters have drifted to the worst-case situations.

8.24. For the designs of exercises 8.8 and 8.12, calculate the amplitude of the signal that must be coupled to the collector supply to reduce the collector voltage to zero. Calculate the voltage levels for the waveshapes in Figure 8.36 for each of the given designs.

From the time constants of the designs (see exercise 8.20), decide what value the crossover capacitors should have. Estimate the transition time required on the leading edge of the trigger. Sketch in detail that part of the waveforms during which the two controls are drifting toward a common asymptote. Calculate the rate of drift, and hence, determine a reasonable estimate of the width of the trigger.

8.25. Deduce some other schemes for giving the symmetrical grounded-emitter toggle a complementing input. In each case, sketch the waveshapes of the toggle during transition, and identify any special constraints on the triggering source.

8.26. Is the quasi-D-C scheme of triggering a toggle a particularly bad choice for the transistor toggle? Why?

8.27. Design a direct-coupled transistor toggle (Figure 8.39) using the 2N404.

8.28. Deduce an analytic expression for the loop gain of the symmetrical grounded-emitter transistor toggle. Use the appropriate equivalent circuit for the transistor.

8.29. Deduce the transfer and loop-gain characteristics of the self-biased toggle.

8.30. Convert the clamped-collector design of exercise 8.12 to the self-biased version. Determine the maximum amplitude that the control-applied trigger must have to guarantee transition.

8.31. In view of the asymmetry problem in the self-biased toggle having an emitter capacitor (page 8.77), can the transistor version be designed? If so, how? What special constraints need be imposed on the circuit? What precautions need be taken?

8.32. In the asymmetrical toggle, why is the restriction levied that the right side not draw excessive control current?

8.33. Deduce the transfer characteristic of each side of the asymmetrical toggle. Deduce the loop gain characteristic.

8.34. Deduce an analytic expression for the loop gain of the self-biased toggle. The asymmetrical toggle.

8.35. Convert the designs of exercises 8.8 and 8.12 to the asymmetrical version. Identify all of the various triggers which might be applied to the circuit. For each, there is an amplitude which will guarantee transition. Calculate this amplitude for each trigger. (In practical circumstances, it might be possible to use somewhat less amplitude.) Keep in mind that the trigger amplitude must be sufficient even though the circuit parameters have drifted. (Use the tolerances suggested in exercise 8.4.)

Assuming the capacitances suggested in exercise 8.20, determine the value of the transpose capacitor required to speed the transition. (Keep in mind tolerances.) Actually calculate the waveshape of the right control when the drifts are such as to optimize speedup and when the drifts are worst so far as speedup is concerned. Determine the fastest and slowest response time of the toggle. Use a trigger applied to the left collector. (Its amplitude has been determined above; assume that its leading edge is a step function.)

8.36. For the self-biased toggle, deduce and sketch the waveshapes of all points in the toggle during transition. Identify each region of behavior (in the spirit of Figure 8.24), and identify the appropriate time constants in each region.

Repeat for the asymmetrical toggle.

8.37. Extend the notion of the symmetrical grounded-emitter toggle to a 3-state circuit. There must be sufficient feedback paths to guarantee that only one element can conduct at a time.

Now consider the 5-stated version. Justify the statement on page 8.88 that the resistor networks have serious tolerance problems. Might clamp diodes suitably deployed about the circuit assist with tolerances? Discuss.

PROBLEMS

The following problems may seem to resemble the exercises closely. The intent is to do the design with considerably more care and in greater depth. Detailed calculations should replace what were previously estimates or educated guesses.

8.1. Design completely a symmetrical grounded-emitter toggle for the static situation. Use either vacuum tube or transistor technology as you wish, but follow the general voltage and speed range suggested above, and use the characteristic curves given above. The circuit must tolerate $\pm 3\%$ drift on supply voltages, $\pm 5\%$ drift in resistance values, and $\pm 25\%$ drift in current capability of the active elements.

Specify the nominal and two extremal values of each voltage in the toggle. The dissipation within the element must not exceed 50% of the rated dissipation, and resistors are to be derated on power by 50%. The current capability of the device is not to exceed 75% of the rated characteristics. If you select transistor technology, design to operate over the temperature range of $-55°C$ to $+70°C$.

8.2. Derive the transfer and loop characteristics of the toggle designed in problem 8.1.

8.3. Consider the symmetrical toggle designed in problem 8.1, and assume that it is to be triggered through an auxiliary triode. Calculate the trigger current necessary to make the two controls equipotential. (This is a lower bound for the current which will actually flip the circuit.)

Now let all resistors drift $\pm 5\%$, all voltages $\pm 3\%$, and the current capability of the active element $\pm 25\%$. Let the tolerances be such as to require more triggering current, and then such as to require less. In each case, find the triggering current required to make the two controls equipotential. Hence, determine the guaranteed minimum current that must be supplied to the toggle to make the controls equipotential.

8.4. Suppose that the toggle in problem 8.3 is driven by increasingly large amounts of triggering current. For each value of current, a minimum trigger width is determined that will just cause the toggle to transition. How would you expect the minimum trigger width to depend on trigger amplitude? Would the width be independent of amplitude? Sketch the curve which illustrates the dependence. Support your answer with an appropriate discussion of the interaction between triggering current and toggle behavior.

8.5. Consider the symmetrical toggle designed in problem 8.1. Use the approximations outlined on pages 8.53 *ff.* to calculate and draw the actual collector and control waveshapes of this toggle during transition. Assume that the statically measured collector-control capacitance is 10 mmf, and that there is a stray capacitance of 3 mmf at each collector and at each control.

Repeat the above, but assume that all components have drifted in such a direction as to make the toggle slowest, and then fastest to transition in a given direction. (Use the tolerances given in problem 8.1).

8.6. Consider the toggle and its waveshapes from problem 8.5. Assume that each component has its nominal value. Calculate a curve which shows the dependence of transition time on
(a) E−, as it alone varies from −3% to +3% about its design center;
(b) E+, as it alone varies from −3% to +3% about its design center.
Repeat parts (a) and (b) but assume that all resistors have drifted 5% in the worst direction. State what criterion you have used for specifying transition time.

8.7. Convert the toggle designed in problem 8.1 to a self-biased version. Determine the amplitude of the triggers that must be supplied to the controls to effect a transition. Recalculate the required trigger amplitudes after all resistors have drifted 5%, and the supply has drifted 3%, all in the worst direction.

8.8. Convert the toggle designed in problem 8.1 to the asymmetrical version. Calculate the amplitudes of all the different triggers that might be applied to this toggle to cause it to transition in either direction. Include the emitter as an input terminal. Recalculate all trigger amplitudes after all resistors, supply voltages, and active elements have drifted in the worst direction. (Use the tolerances specified in problem 8.1.)

8.9. Repeat problems 8.2, 8.5, and 8.6(b) for the self-biased toggle of problem 8.7, and the asymmetrical toggle of problem 8.8.

8.10. Indicate some schemes for providing the asymmetrical toggle with a complementing input. Discuss the details of each situation and show that it can work properly. Sketch the waveshapes of all points in the toggle during transition. Identify the temporary memory in each situation.

8.11. Why might the asymmetrical toggle transition more slowly if some impedance is inserted into the "free" collector?

8.12. A circuit which implements the Boolean functions f_8 (Figure 4.5, page 4.19) is called the NOR circuit. Using the two-input NOR (f_8) as a building block, construct a toggle.

Extend the notion of the NOR to a three-input device. Write down its truth table. Use it as a building block and construct a 3-state toggle. (It may be helpful to postpone this problem until Chapter 9, especially pages 9 28 *ff.*, has been studied.)

8.13. Consider the symmetrical grounded-emitter toggle, and assume that a follower has been inserted in the transpose path to provide current gain between the halves of the toggle. Draw the circuit diagram of this toggle. Redesign the toggle from problem 8.1 to fit this case. Maintain the same nominal collector and control voltages, but increase the current through R_T and R_C by a factor of 3. Recalculate the extremal values of all voltages in the circuit as the components assume the tolerances indicated in problem 8.1.

Is the technique outlined on pages 8.52 *ff.* for calculating transition time likely to give a better answer for this current-boosted toggle than for the ordinary symmetrical toggle? Why? Calculate and draw the collector and control waveshapes during the transition phase.

8.14. Would current gain in the transpose path of the asymmetrical toggle increase its speed as much as the same amount of current gain inserted in both transpose paths of the symmetrical toggle? Why?

8.15. The symmetrical toggle designed in problem 8.1 is driven on the control through a diode by a trigger whose amplitude is twice that necessary to make the controls equipotential. Calculate the amplitude of the trigger.

This toggle is then driven at the collector and then driven at the supply end of R_L. In each case the amplitude of the trigger is such as to cause the amplitude of the signal at the control to be the same as the directly applied control trigger. Calculate the amplitude necessary at the collector and at the upper end of R_L to fulfill this requirement.

For each of the three ways of triggering the toggle, calculate the current supplied by the trigger and hence the peak power that must be delivered by the trigger. For each of the three ways of triggering the toggle, calculate the transition time. State the criterion you have used to specify the transition time.

Define a figure-of-merit for a triggering scheme which is to increase as a toggle transitions faster, and as the peak power that must be supplied decreases. Calculate this figure-of-merit for each of the three schemes.

8.16. Four collector clamp diodes are inserted in the toggle of problem 8.1. Select the diode supply voltages equal to the nominal design center collector levels. Redesign the toggle with all the conditions of problem 8.1 so that all component drifts are absorbed by the clamps.

Now repeat problems 8.2, 8.5, and 8.6 for the redesigned toggle.

8.17. Repeat problem 8.16 except that four additional clamp diodes are added for the two controls. Draw the circuit diagram. Since these new diodes will absorb tolerances in the control voltages, it is no longer necessary to overswing the control as much. Shorten the collector swing (and hence the control swing) so that the control levels correspond to conduction and 25% beyond cutoff. Set the supply voltages of the control clamp diodes to these values. Now design the resistor networks and supply voltages so that with the tolerances stated in problem 8.1, the clamp currents just approach zero for the corresponding worst-case situation.

Now repeat problem 8.5, and determine how much faster the new circuit is than the original one of problem 8.1. Also compare the total power dissipation in the two circuits. Further speed up the circuit by adding first transpose capacitors, and then current gain in the transpose network. At each stage, do whatever redesign is necessary, and determine how much faster each circuit is. Hence develop insight into how significantly various schemes contribute to the speed of a toggle versus their cost in components or power.

8.18. Draw the circuit diagram of a toggle using gate elements only; i.e., find an arrangement of AND, OR, and NOT circuits which behaves like a toggle, has two stable states, and corresponding inputs.

8.19. Draw the circuit diagram of a symmetrical relay toggle. Find an arrangement of relays which has two stable states, and two inputs which correspond to the two states.

nine

Gates

A large part of a digital computer may be regarded as an ensemble of information storing devices (toggles) which communicate with each other via a switchable communication (*gating*) network. Some of the toggles directly control the switches (*gates*) of this network, and these toggles will themselves receive information from the network to determine future switching configurations. Other toggles may only receive information from the network or deliver information to the network.

As shown in Chapter 4 it is possible to define the behavior of such a switching network in terms of Boolean expressions. Provided that circuits—the *gates*—can be developed which implement the fundamental Boolean connectives, the transition from the algebraic description of the network to its circuit configuration is a relatively straightforward procedure. Because of the prominence of the AND, OR, and NOT connectives in Boolean procedures, most of our development here will deal with these three.

GROUNDWORK

In what sense do we say: A gate realizes the Boolean AND, or a voltage represents a Boolean variable? A variable of the Boolean algebra may have only two values; for convenience, call them true ($= 1$) and false ($= 0$). Each electrical signal will be considered as having only two levels, one of which will be identified as representing true and the other, false. Which is which is up to the designer, but once he makes his choice, he must abide by it or find that the circuits do not implement the expected logic. We will postpone until later the problem of how component tolerances might influence this constraint of two-valuedness (see pages 9.14, 9.18; Figure 9.58).

Once an assignment of meaning has been made for each of the two levels of the input and output signals of a circuit, the logical description of the circuit follows from its behavior. If the output is in the true state only when, say, input A *and* input B are each in the true state, then the circuit implements the Boolean AND. If some change in the definition of the input or output states is made, then this same circuit will implement some different Boolean function.

EXAMPLE

Suppose that a circuit has inputs A and B, and output C. For some definition of the three variables, further assume that it implements the AND connective. The algebraic description of the circuit is

$$A \cdot B = C.$$

Now invert the logical sense of both inputs and the output. What was the false state of each signal is now redefined to be the true state and vice versa. Algebraically, this amounts to the substitution:

$$A \rightarrow \bar{A}$$
$$B \rightarrow \bar{B}$$
$$C \rightarrow \bar{C}.$$

The circuit is then described by the expression

$$\bar{A} \cdot \bar{B} = \bar{C}$$

or

$$\overline{(A + B)} = \bar{C}$$

or

$$A + B = C.$$

What was an AND circuit has become an OR circuit, although the circuit itself is no different. This is simply a De Morgan theorem at work in the physical world.

GATE TO GATE

Since Boolean expressions can be compounded of ANDs, ORs, and NOTs (e.g., $P = AB + \bar{G}C + DE\bar{F}$), gates in general will have to communicate with each other as well as with toggles. Offhandedly, the optimum gate technique would seem to be one in which the information representing signal is uniform throughout. Specifically,

1. there is no logical inversion through the gate (i.e., if the true state is represented by a voltage which is positive relative to the voltage which represents the false state at the input, the same is true of the ouput);

2. the two absolute levels of true and false are the same at input and output (i.e., if true is represented by $+10$ volts and false by -10 volts at the input, so it is at the output); and

3. the difference between the true and false levels is the same at input and output (i.e., if the amplitude of the input signal is 20 volts, so also is the output).

Otherwise, D-C level shifting, amplification, or complementing of the logical meaning of the signals may occur.

Some gate circuits fit the requirements exactly as billed. Others do not, yet this is not to say that they are not useful. For example, the transistor NOR circuit (see page 9.28), contains a logical inversion; there is also a voltage shift between input and output; and the output is larger than the input. Yet under some circumstances, the NOR is very useful. Often negations are required by the logical expressions, and gates which incorporate a negating operation provide it, so to speak, free. Sometimes it will be necessary to implement expressions in which a combination of variables occurs in more than one place; e.g.,

$$P = AB(C + D) + AB(E + F + G) + ABR.$$

It would be very desirable to have the AND gate which implements the AB be able to drive three other gates—in this case, three ANDs. Practically, therefore, it may be very convenient to have gates which contain voltage or current amplification.

SWITCHES AND BOOLEAN VARIABLES

Consider the single-pole, single-throw toggle switch normally used to control a motor. Define the true (or "1") state of the switch to correspond to its contacts being closed. Since the switch has only two positions, automatically the false (or "0") state corresponds to its

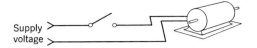

Figure 9.1.   **A simple motor circuit.**

contacts being open. Define the true state of the motor to be represented by rotation of the armature. In the circuit of Figure 9.1, the state of the motor depends on the state of the switch according to the following truth table:

Switch	Motor
open	standing still
closed	rotating

In a different notation,

X	$f(X)$
0	0
1	1

where X is the state of the switch and $f(X)$ the functional dependence of the state of the motor on the switch. Since the state of the motor depends directly on whether the circuit is open or closed, it follows that the Boolean algebraic description of the single-pole, single-throw switch in this situation is $f(X) = X$.

This functional dependence will change to $f(X) = \overline{X}$ if the correspondence of the two states of the switch with 0 and 1 is changed. It also follows that for a single-pole, double-throw switch, two functionals are required, one for each output contact. Clearly these are

$$f_1(X) = X$$

and

$$f_2(X) = \overline{X}$$

Thus a simple switch can represent a Boolean variable, and therefore we expect that an arbitrary Boolean function can be realized from some combination of switches. Because a truth table (which is a definition of some unique Boolean function) can be realized as a switching network, and because we also hope to discover circuits which will realize a truth table, a gate is often referred to as an *electronic switch.*

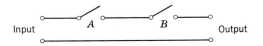

Figure 9.2. The AND *circuit.*

ANDs and ORs from Switches

Consider two single-pole, single-throw switches connected in series
(Figure 9.2). There exists a closed circuit through this network
($= 1$), if switch A and switch B are simultaneously closed ($= 1$).
Since each switch can take either position independently of the other,
there are four (2×2) entries in the truth table which describes the
behavior of this arrangement.

A	B	$f(A, B)$
0	0	0
0	1	0
1	0	0
1	1	1

Since the circuit is closed only when A *and* B are closed, $f(A, B)$ is 1 only
when A and B are each one. From the verbal description as well as from
the truth table, it follows that

$$f(A, B) = A \cdot B.$$

Consider now two switches in parallel (Figure 9.3). There is a closed
circuit if A *or* B *or both* is closed; this is precisely the description of the
inclusive-OR connective. The truth table describing the situation is

A	B	$f(A, B)$
0	0	0
0	1	1
1	0	1
1	1	1

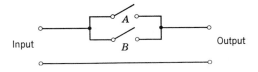

Figure 9.3. The OR *circuit.*

from which it follows that the functional form is

$$f(A, B) = A + B.$$

EXAMPLE

Consider the problem of controlling a hall light from upstairs and down-stairs. If the light has been turned on downstairs, it must turn off if the upstairs switch is thrown from one to the other position. We want a closed circuit to the light if A is closed or B is closed but not both. The truth table is

A	B	$f(A, B)$
0	0	0
0	1	1
1	0	1
1	1	0

for which one form of the functional relationship is

$$f(A, B) = (A + B)\overline{(AB)}$$
$$= (A + B)(\bar{A} + \bar{B}).$$

This corresponds to the circuit of Figure 9.4 in which it is understood that if contact A is closed, $\bar{A}$ is open and vice versa. This appears to require two double-pole, double-throw switches, although simply redrawing of the circuit (Figure 9.5) shows that two single-pole, double-throw switches will suffice. The dashed lines identify the physical location of switches A and B. As indicated by the dotted alternate wires, this configuration permits the circuit to begin and end at either physical location or begin at one and terminate at the other. The price for this flexibility is three wires connecting the two switches together. This particular point is relatively unimportant for switch or relay nets because the contacts are bilateral; i.e., the contact will conduct in either direction, or in different words, information can flow in either direction. For switching networks which use unilateral devices (e.g., diodes), there is but one direction of information flow, and such flexibility might sometimes be of importance.

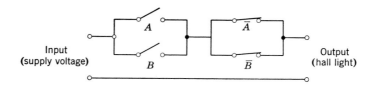

Figure 9.4. One form of an exclusive OR *switch circuit.*

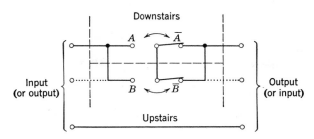

Figure 9.5. A second form of the exclusive OR *switch circuit.*

Further algebraic manipulation of the initial expression leads to the alternate representation

$$f(A, B) = A\bar{B} + \bar{A}B$$

for which the circuit is that of Figure 9.6. As before, the dashed lines identify the two physical locations. There are now only two wires between the switches, but the circuit must begin at one physical location and terminate at the other! Otherwise an extra wire is needed.

There are many and divers reasons in a given case why some particular algebraic description of a circuit may be preferable to all others.

RELAY GATES

If we think of the switches of the previous section as the contacts of a relay, it is clear that the same arguments and techniques apply. The input information which causes a switch to change its state is

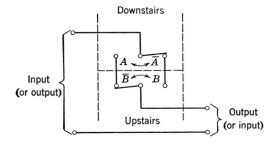

Figure 9.6. A third form of the exclusive OR *switch circuit.*

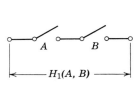

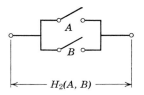

Figure 9.7.   The hindrance AND.

Figure 9.8.   The hindrance OR.

mechanical motion of its handle; for the relay, the input signal is electrical energization of the coil.

There is a dual development which can be made for the switch or the relay, and since it is customary in telephone switching problems to think of the relay in the dual manner, we will include the alternate discussion (1). Again we will see the basic duality of Boolean algebra which the De Morgan theorems express.

Instead of phrasing the argument in terms of the conditions for a closed circuit, let us define a term *hindrance* * (H) which measures the opposition of the circuit to current flow. It is natural to identify the closed circuit with a 0 value for H, since $H = 0$ implies no opposition to current flow. Since H is a bivalued variable, the 1 value then corresponds to an open circuit. This is opposite to the previous convention in which the closed position of a switch or pair of contacts was taken as the 1-state which implies the closed circuit, which in turn implies that the hindrance through it is 0. We expect that the analytical expressions which previously described the series and the parallel circuits will interchange because we are now inquiring into the 0's rather than the 1's of the Boolean functions.

In the series circuit of Figure 9.7, the hindrance is 0 only when both switches have zero hindrance, and hence the truth table is

A	B	$H_1(A, B)$
0	0	0
0	1	1
1	0	1
1	1	1

from which it follows that

$$H_1(A, B) = A + B.$$

* This term was used by Shannon in his first paper on the use of Boolean algebra in relay network design. See reference 7, Chapter 4.

This is the functional form which makes $H_1 = 0$ only if A and B are both 0. Previously the series circuit was described by the algebraic operation of $\cdot$.

Similarly, for the parallel circuit of Figure 9.8, the truth table is

A	B	$H_2(A, B)$
0	0	0
0	1	0
1	0	0
1	1	1

from which it follows that

$$H_2(A, B) = A \cdot B,$$

which is again opposite to what was previously found for the parallel circuit.

So say the De Morgan theorems: When the variables are complemented, the AND and OR operations interchange, although the circuits stay the same.

The general theory of relay network design is well documented and need not be further discussed here (1).

GATES

As in our development of toggles, there is the problem of what active element to choose for the discussion. Some kinds of gate circuits utilize triode elements, and therefore our generalized active element from Chapter 8 will do. In vacuum-tube technology, however, there are pentode tubes which have two input terminals to control the internal current. In particular, either control element can switch off the current so far as the output (plate) is concerned; the pentode tube behaves much like two simple switches in series. Let us imagine a second kind of generalized active element which is just like the one of Chapter 8 except that it has a second control input. Either control element can switch off the output current.

To implement the Boolean connectives of AND and OR, we need an element with two input terminals. Perhaps we can discover ways in which to combine one-input devices to do the job, but for the moment let us assume the two-input generalized element. Each control signal (A, B) can be at one of two levels. One level permits internal current so far as one of the controls is concerned, and the other level denies internal current. These two levels will be assigned to the 0- and 1-states as a designer's choice. For convenience in the following discussion, refer to the two levels simply as upper and lower; in the diagrams, the head of a vertical arrow will indicate whether the 1- (or true) state corresponds to the upper or lower level.

The output variable of our device can be either collector current or collector voltage. If current, then the two states are zero current and some current, and will be assigned to represent the two logical conditions. If collector voltage is the output variable, there are two levels which correspond to zero current and some current, and again the two levels will be assigned to represent the logical states.

The AND

Assume that the output variable is current. Let the upper control levels represent true and the presence of current represent true (Figure 9.9). Collector current exists only if control A (C_A) and control B (C_B) simultaneously are true. Algebraically this is

$$F(A, B) = A \cdot B$$

which is the Boolean AND.

Now consider the output variable to be collector voltage, and define its lower level to represent true (Figure 9.10). The collector voltage is in its lower state (true or 1) if and only if C_A and C_B are simultaneously in the upper state (true or 1). Again this is the Boolean AND, but notice the inversion of the logical convention between input and output.

In each of the above descriptions, it was required that the input variables be simultaneously true. If the two input signals which represent the variables are not of equal time duration, the output

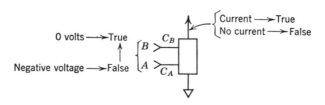

Figure 9.9. The AND *with a 2-input device*

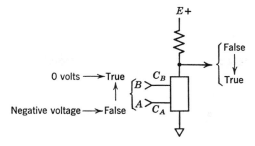

Figure 9.10. A second AND *with a 2-input device.*

signal will be in its true state only for the interval during which the inputs are simultaneously in their true state. Hence, if signal A is a broad pulse, but signal B a narrow one completely contained within the width of A, the output pulse will have the width of signal B. Gate circuits must operate this way; otherwise, they would not faithfully implement the logical connective.

The OR

From duality, we would expect that if the conventions of Figures 9.9 and 9.10 were all inverted, the same circuits would represent the Boolean OR (Figure 9.11). For example, if no collector current represents true and the lower level at each control represents true, then the collector current is 0 (true) if C_A is true *or* C_B is true *or both* are true. This is precisely the Boolean inclusive OR which is represented algebraically as

$$F(A, B) = A + B.$$

Figure 9.12 also implements the inclusive OR, but there is an inversion of the logical convention between input and output.

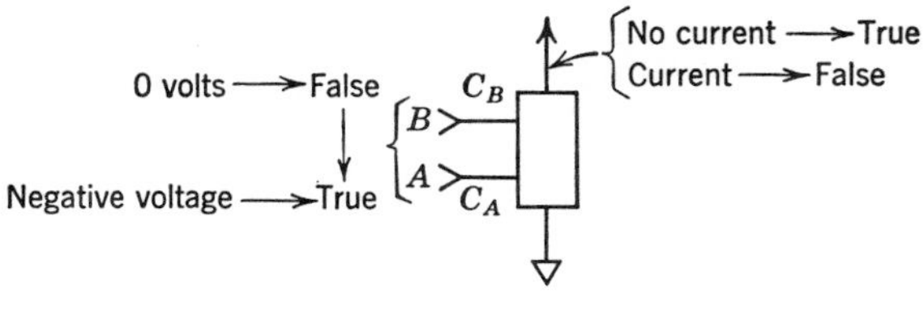

Figure 9.11. An OR *with a 2-input device.*

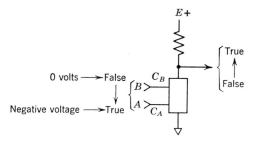

Figure 9.12.   A second OR *with a 2-input device.*

Other Gates

If some of the conventions of Figures 9.9, 9.10, 9.11, and 9.12 are inverted, a complementing operation is introduced into the gate.

EXAMPLES

1. In Figure 9.13, the output is not in its true state if C_A and C_B are in true states.   This is the so-called AND-NOT or NAND gate described by the truth table

A	B	$F(A, B)$
0	0	1
0	1	1
1	0	1
1	1	0

and the analytic expression

$$F(A, B) = \overline{(AB)}.$$

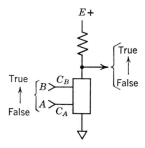

Figure 9.13.   The AND-NOT *with a 2-input device.*

2. In Figure 9.14, the output is not in its true state if C_A or C_B or both are in true states. This is the inclusive OR-NOT or NOR gate described by the truth table

A	B	$F(A, B)$
0	0	1
0	1	0
1	0	0
1	1	0

and the expression $F(A, B) = \overline{(A + B)}$.

3. In Figure 9.15, the output is in the true state if C_B is not true or C_A is true or both obtain. This gate has no particular name, but its description is given by the truth table

A	B	$F(A, B)$
0	0	1
0	1	0
1	0	1
1	1	1

or the algebraic expression

$$F(A, B) = A + \bar{B}$$
$$= \overline{(\bar{A}B)}$$

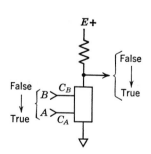

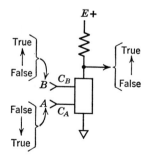

Figure 9.14.   The OR-NOT *with a 2-input device.*

Figure 9.15.   The function $(\overline{\bar{A}B})$ *with a 2-input device.*

Thus we see that one particular circuit can implement many different logical operations, depending upon how the designer chooses to define the logical states at input and output terminals.

The gate discussed here and implemented by the generalized element, has an interesting property. For a consistent logical convention (e.g., true is represented by the upper level at inputs and output), the gate includes a negation operation. Consider a long cascade of such gates. If every other logical level in the chain is assumed to have the opposite convention, the resulting logic is alternately the AND and the OR. In some cases, additional negation operations may need to be used in case the final output has the wrong convention.

Depending upon how the input and output conventions are selected, the two-input gate implements one of the sixteen Boolean functions of two variables.

Pentode Vacuum-Tube Gates

Since the control and suppressor grids of a pentode are each a high impedance point and require signals at the same D-C level, they are usually the input terminals of a pentode gate (2). The screen grid could be used as an input but would require a relatively low impedance source at a D-C level different from that appropriate to either the control or suppressor grids. Likewise, the cathode might be used as a low impedance input. One level of an input signal will usually be such that the plate current is cutoff and the other level, such that some particular value of plate current exists. The output variable of a pentode gate can be either plate current or plate voltage. Depending upon how the logical conventions are established at the input and output, the pentode gate will implement one of the sixteen Boolean functions of two variables.

There is a characteristic of the pentode gate which may make it unsuitable for some kinds of gating networks. There is a shift in D-C level between input and output which is troublesome. The output signal is not at the proper voltage position for the input signal of a following similar stage. This can be overcome at the expense of additional components as shown in Figure 9.16, but the tolerances of the resistors R_1, R_2, and R_3 will reflect in imprecisely determined true and false levels. As shown in this figure, the levels will become bands of finite width—meaning that any circuit to which such a gate communicates must be able to accept any level within a band as representing the logical state of that band. The tolerance problems of the circuit have destroyed the hoped-for two-valued behavior.

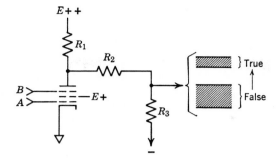

Figure 9.16.   Tolerance problems in a pentode gate.

EXAMPLE

Suppose that in Figure 9.16, the actual output levels of the true state were 0 to −2 volts, and that the output goes to the grid of a tube whose cathode is grounded (Figure 9.17).   As R_1, R_2, and R_3 or the supply voltages fluctuate over time, the true level at the following grid can range from −2 to 0 volts. The following stage will have to be designed to accept this fluctuation without malfunctioning itself.   A two-volt change in grid signal will result in a much larger change in the lower level of the plate signal in the grounded-cathode stage.

Because of the tolerance problem, other precautions such as diode limiters may need to be used between stages of pentode gating.   Occasionally it may be convenient to capitalize on the D-C shift through the pentode.   For example, the circuit of Figure 9.18 uses the pentode not only to do logic but also to serve as a trigger tube for the toggle.

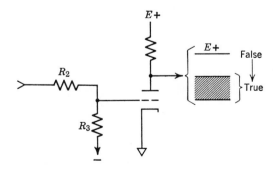

Figure 9.17.   The amplification of tolerance problems.

More involved forms of pentode gates in which the screen or the cathode is manipulated can be sometimes useful.

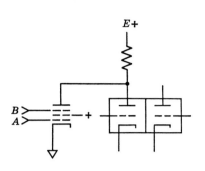

Figure 9.18. A pentode combination gate and trigger tube.

The usual cautions about derating plate dissipation and cathode current apply to the pentode gate. We have a new problem because the plate current transfers to the screen if the suppressor grid goes to cutoff, but the control grid does not. Since a screen usually does not have a large dissipation rating compared to the plate, the screen is basically the limiting factor in the pentode gate. If one input signal is a sequence of pulses but the other is non-periodic, the screen will be favored by using the control grid as the input for the pulse signal. The duty cycle of the pulse sequence then is favorable to screen dissipation.

TRIODE GATES

Since both vacuum-tube and transistor triodes are available, we will do the following discussion in terms of our anonymous active element. As in Chapter 8, our assumed device resembles a triode vacuum tube or an NPN transistor. Particulars for the tube or transistor follow the general discussion.

Since our device is considered to have only one high-impedance input (the control), either more than one triode must be used, or the emitter must be used as a relatively low-impedance input. The latter form is sometimes referred to as the *degenerate triode gate*. A typical version of this is shown in Figure 9.19 in which the output is true if *A* and *B* are each true; it implements the AND. By redefining some or all of the conventions, the single triode gate can perform other logical functions.

The simple form of triode gate—as will some others—also suffers from logical inversion through the gate and a D-C level shift at the output. It is oftentimes convenient to take advantage of the D-C level shift and to combine a logical operation and toggle triggering in

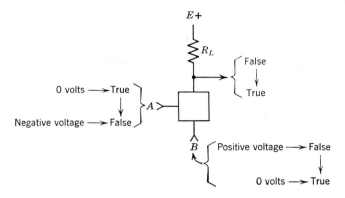

Figure 9.19.   The degenerate triode AND *gate.*

one circuit (see Figure 9.18 which illustrates this point for the pentode gate).

The Collector-Coupled Triode Gate

If more than one triode is to take part in a gate function, one of its elements must be connected to the corresponding one of the others. Since the controls are to be reserved as inputs, either the collectors will be connected together or * the emitters. Figure 9.20 illustrates a typical triode gate with a common collector resistor. For the configuration shown, the output is true if *A* is true or *B* is true or both are true—the OR gate. Note in passing that there is still a logical inversion and a D-C level shift—which may be used, or avoided by putting a resistance voltage divider at the output (cf., Figure 9.16).

There is a new and different problem which appears for the first time. Because the two devices may not have precisely the same characteristics, the true level of the output will be different depending upon whether *A* or *B* is true. Furthermore, if both *A* and *B* are true, the output will be at some third and lower level because the two together draw more current than either alone. Quite aside from the output signal tolerance due to parameter fluctuations, there are three distinct output levels, all of which represent true. This situation effectively adds a noise component to the signal and will be called *logical noise* because it exists as a result of the logical operation which

* This connective is the exclusive OR.

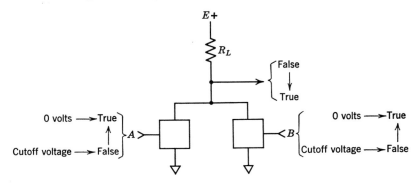

Figure 9.20. The collector-coupled triode OR *gate.*

the circuit performs. Clearly, it arises because of the finite impedance of the device when in the conducting state. Put differently, it exists because the switch element is not ideal; i.e., it does not have zero impedance in the conducting state. The same kind of situation is also present in a relay circuit, but contacts approximate the ideal switch so well that there is generally no practical difficulty.

Figure 9.21 demonstrates the logical noise problem, where B has been assumed to have a slightly lower impedance than A. This par-

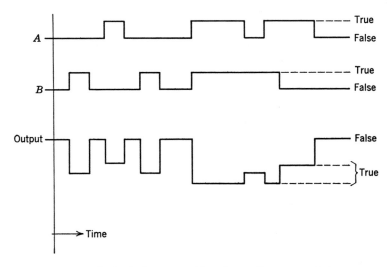

Figure 9.21. The logical noise problem in a collector-coupled OR *gate.*

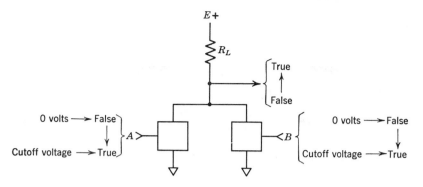

Figure 9.22.   The collector-coupled triode AND *gate.*

ticular circuit does not have logical noise on the false state; however the AND circuit of Figure 9.22 has noise on the false state but not the true.   To the logical noise we must add whatever long- and short-term drifts are contributed by component tolerances and voltage supply drifts.

More than two triodes can be connected to a common resistor.   The circuit of Figure 9.23 realizes the 4-way inclusive OR;

$$F(A, B, C, D) = A + B + C + D.$$

In this circuit the logical noise is larger because the total current through the resistor varies by a larger increment.   Figure 9.24 shows an approximate representation of such circuits, where r_c is the internal device resistance in its conducting state.   Assuming that all triodes have the same

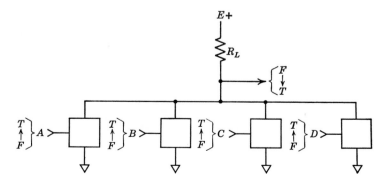

Figure 9.23.   The 4-input collector-coupled OR *gate.*

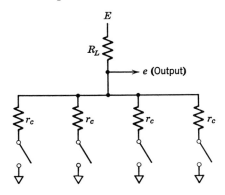

Figure 9.24. An approximate equivalent for collector-coupled gates.

r_c and that r_c does not change too much with collector voltage, the output voltage is given by

$$e = \frac{E(r_c/n)}{R_L + (r_c/n)}.$$

This function has the general characteristic shown in Figure 9.25.

If the initial step from E to $E \cdot r_c/(R_L + r_c)$ is large enough compared to

$$\frac{Er_c}{R_L + r_c} - \frac{E(r_c/n)}{R_L + (r_c/n)},$$

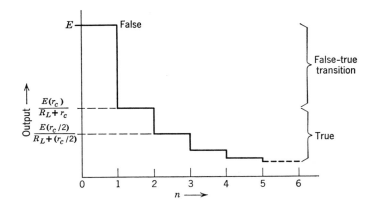

Figure 9.25. The output of a collector-coupled gate as a function of the number of inputs.

the logical noise will be small compared to the signal representing the true-to-false transition. If this is the case, even though a band of voltages represents the same state, some other circuit can still satisfactorily discriminate between the true and false levels. The combined effect of logical noise and tolerances establishes a limit to the number of inputs that a practical gate can have, because each increases the amount of noise and hence worsens the signal-to-noise ratio. By way of observation, notice that a control on which one state is represented by a voltage below the cutoff level readily rejects noise on one side of the input information signals.

As with the simple pentode gate, the collector-coupled triode configuration can implement the AND-NOT, the OR-NOT and others. Pentode gates can also utilize a common plate resistor configuration.

The Emitter-Coupled Triode Gate

Figure 9.26 is a typical form of the emitter-coupled gate. Notice that it is two followers connected together, and that the common emitter will follow whichever control is more positive. Therefore, the output will follow input A up to its true state, or it will follow B, or it will follow them both—the inclusive OR function. This is the first configuration which we have discussed that does not have a logical inversion; furthermore, the D-C level shift is just the control-emitter voltage rather than the control-collector voltage. Unfortunately, there is no companion configuration which performs the AND operation for the same logical convention, i.e., for true up.

If all three conventions are reversed, the gate does become the AND

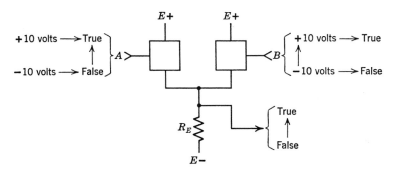

Figure 9.26. The emitter-coupled triode OR *gate.*

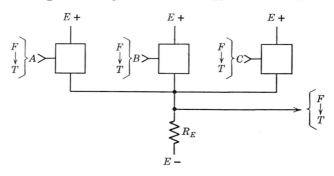

Figure 9.27. The emitter-coupled 3-input triode AND *gate.*

(Figure 9.27), and if some of the conventions are reversed, it contains one or more negations. Clearly, more than three sections can be combined to provide n-way AND or OR functions.

There is a practical aspect of the emitter-coupled gate which is sometimes convenient. Since it is effectively a follower, the common connection is low impedance and will tolerate a certain amount of loading. Therefore, the parts of the gate can be physically separated by some distance; this may help span the finite dimensions of a machine. In a split-gate configuration the design problems of the follower itself must be considered (Chapter 10, page 10.3).

The usual derating policies are applicable to this circuit, but there is one new feature to watch. All of the current through the emitter resistor may flow through one device, or it may be shared by two or more. The current capability of one device, therefore, strongly influences the choice of the common resistor.

The circuit also exhibits logical noise. The current through the emitter resistor depends principally upon the resistor itself and the voltage across it and, therefore, stays reasonably constant in either logical state. As each additional section of the gate comes into conduction, the current divides roughly equally among all sections and diminishes in previously conducting sections. Since the control potentials are fixed, the emitter must change in potential by an amount which is sufficient to establish a bias which is appropriate to the diminished value of current per section. This shifting of emitter potential to adjust the control-emitter voltage results in a noise component on the output signal.

To the extent that the characteristics of the devices differ, the current will not divide equally among the conducting sections. Furthermore, the levels of all controls (i.e., the input signals) may not be alike which can also cause unequal current distribution. Such things influence the logical noise.

The first section of the OR gate of Figure 9.26 which reaches the true condition conducts a current i_e which is approximately

$$\frac{E_{\text{True}} - E_1}{R_E}.$$

As the second section becomes true, the current in the first diminishes to $i_e/2$ which corresponds to an increase in the emitter voltage of $i_e/2\gamma$, where γ is a transconductance relating input voltage and output current of the device. As the third input becomes true, the current in all three devices becomes $i_e/3$ which corresponds to a further increase in emitter voltage of $i_e/6\gamma$; the total logical noise is $i_e/2\gamma + i_e/6\gamma$ or $2i_e/3\gamma$. The increase in logical noise as the number of inputs to the gate increases may limit the number of inputs which can be used in a practical case.

Although the D-C level shift (the control-emitter bias) is small, it cannot be ignored if there is a long cascade of emitter-coupled gates. Suppose that the level shift is just 1 volt and that the total signal is 10 volts (from -10 to 0). Five gates later, the output swing is at best -5 to $+5$ and five more gates later, the lower level is where the upper level ought to be. The situation is really even worse because the gain through the emitter-coupled gate is less than unity. Therefore, in large assemblages of such gates, amplification and standardization of level may be necessary at particular places in the network.

Vacuum-Tube Triode Gates

Except for some relabeling of terms, the general discussion of triode gates applies to vacuum-tube versions (3). The input is usually considered to be the grid although sometimes it is convenient to drive the cathode as an input. In such a case, a source of suitably low impedance must be available as a driver, e.g., a cathode follower. Triode vacuum tubes can be combined in the cathode-coupled or plate-coupled configuration, but the magnitude of the logical noise increases rather quickly as the number of inputs to the gate structure increases. This follows from the observation that the internal impedance of a tube while conducting is, roughly speaking, the same order of magnitude as the circuit impedances.

One feature of the vacuum tube is its high-impedance input terminal. The design, therefore, of the cathode-coupled gate must allow one triode of the group to provide all of the current required by the cathode resistor, while maintaining negative bias. Otherwise, grid current may result and the source of an input signal be perturbed. If negative bias is maintained, the cathode output terminal is always more positive than the most positive of the inputs. Hence there is a voltage rise through the common-cathode gate. Since gain through each level of such a gate is slightly less than unity, in a long cascade of such gates, it may be necessary to restandardize signal level or amplitude.

As the number of inputs which are, say, true in the cathode-coupled gate change, the current through the remaining conducting sections changes. Since the plate-cathode voltage does not change appreciably, the resulting shift in cathode potential (assuming that the grid level does not change) is the incremental plate current divided by the transconductance (g_m). (The γ of the argument on page 9.23 becomes g_m.)

Transistor-Triode Gates

Transistor versions of the common-element gates also exist (4). The bases of the transistors are relatively low impedance and, therefore, will require current. However, this is a problem of the design of the input drivers rather than a problem of gate design. Moreover, the drivers must tolerate the rather wide variation in impedance of the base. For example, consider the emitter-coupled OR gate, and assume that one input (A) is true; driver A must supply a certain current. Now suppose that input B becomes true, but that its true voltage level is more positive than that of input A. The first transistor, even though in the true state, will cease conducting, and driver A will be relieved of its load. If the impedance of the driver is not sufficiently low, a logical change in one gate can be reflected as a logical noise on an input signal, and hence coupled spuriously into other gates. On the other hand, the impedance of a conducting transistor—especially if saturated—is small compared to other circuit impedances. Hence in the collector-coupled configuration, the logical noise inherent in the gate is likely to be very small.

In the emitter-coupled gate, there is a voltage drop from the base to the emitter because of the drop through the forward-biased emitter junction. However, since this is the drop of a semi-conductor junc-

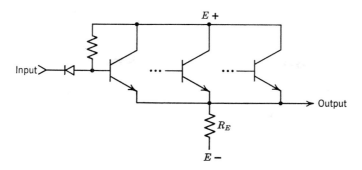

Figure 9.28. Offsetting base-emitter drop in transistor emitter-coupled gates.

tion in forward current, it can, in principle, be offset by an equal but opposite drop in a similar semi-conductor junction in forward current (i.e., a conducting diode). Since it can be expected that the two drops will behave similarly with current, the emitter drop can be reasonably well neutralized. Figure 9.28 is a typical way of dealing with this problem.

The logical noise problem in the emitter-coupled gate is likely also to be small because the transistor is so much better a switch than the vacuum tube. However, it can be estimated as follows. For a given increment in the emitter current, there is a corresponding increment in base current of $1/(1 + \beta)$ as much. This incremental base current flowing through the emitter-diode characteristic will be reflected in an incremental base-emitter voltage. What may be more serious is the change in source voltage as the incremental base current flows through the source resistance. Because β can fluctuate widely from one transistor to the next, the division of current in an emitter-coupled circuit can be unequal. There may be some contribution to logical noise from this effect.

The peculiarities of the transistor must also be considered. For example, the transistors of the collector-coupled circuit are switching between conduction and no current. Hence there is a turn-on and a turn-off delay, for which particular base driving methods (e.g., over-drive) are favorable. It may be necessary to take precautions against leakage currents. It may be desirable to take precautions against saturation under some circumstances. In the emitter-coupled circuit, the base current, of course, flows through the emitter resistor, and account may have to be taken of it.

Figure 9.29 shows some typical common-element gates.

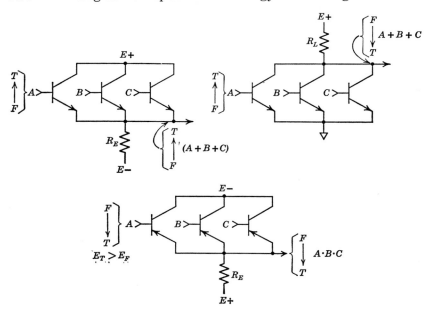

Figure 9.29.   Typical transistor common-element gates.

Direct-Coupled Transistor Gates

Because of the different characteristics of the transistor compared to the vacuum tube, new circuit configurations are possible (5). Some transistors * have the property that the collector-emitter voltage during conduction is very small, and if applied to the base-emitter of a second transistor, no appreciable conduction in it occurs. Hence it is possible to utilize the collector-coupled configuration, but omit any voltage divider between stages. Such an arrangement is really a current-operated circuit rather than voltage-operated, because the current in the load resistor is switched either into the collector of one transistor or into the base of one or more others. Figure 9.30-a shows one kind of gate circuit in *direct-coupled transistor logic*. Because the collector-emitter voltage is so low, transistors can be stacked in series to provide the gate circuit of Figure 9.30-b. The logical convention, of course, determines which connective each of these circuits implements. The DCTL circuit obviously operates in saturation, and therefore low storage time in the transistor is necessary if fast

* For example, the surface barrier transistor.

circuits are to be designed. In such circuits, the collector swing is very small and is the difference between the saturated collector-emitter voltage and the base-emitter voltage. The collector swing can be allowed to be larger if series resistors are inserted into the base connections, but the circuit then tends to become voltage operated rather than current operated.

It is often convenient for one stage of logic to drive several others. If transistor uniformity is not sufficiently good, it may be difficult to get the collector current switched reasonably equally into several bases. A series base resistor will, of course, improve this situation. However, as voltage swings become larger, the demands of capacitances increase, and one problem is relieved at the expense of another.

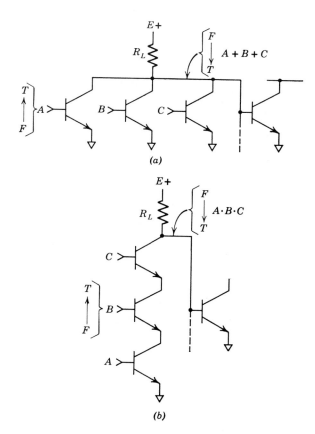

Figure 9.30. Direct-coupled transistor gates.

The NOR Gate

The circuit of Figure 9.31 implements the NOR connective; it is also called *resistor-transistor logic* (RTL) (6). For an NPN transistor, the false level of the input signals is very nearly zero volts. The first variable which rises to a suitable positive voltage brings the transistor into saturation. The impedance of the conducting base is very small compared to the series input resistors, and therefore the crosstalk back through the resistor network to the input terminals is minimized. The resistor to the negative return voltage offsets the collector-leakage current, but it can also help sweep charges from the base during turn-off, and of course it helps in the voltage divider action from the collector source. The larger the current in this resistor, perhaps to speed turn-off, the larger must be the current into the input, and hence the total dissipation of power in the circuit rises.

The trick of adding shunt capacitance around the base resistors to improve the transistor delays unfortunately is of limited usefulness. If the capacitors are large enough to assist with the injection of charge into the base, it may be that if, say, two of three inputs change state, sufficient displacement current is injected into the transistor to produce a spike output signal. For example, in the NOR circuit, even though two of the three variables may change to false, the gate should remain satisfied and in the true state. The slug of current from the two capacitances can momentarily drive the transistor out of conduction and produce a spurious output signal. To make matters worse, this spike may propagate through a chain of gates because all of the input circuits are of relatively low impedance to the spike. Hence, if

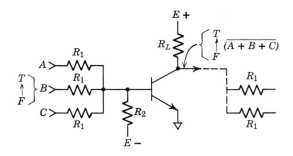

Figure 9.31. The resistance-coupled transistor NOR gate.

capacitors are used, the number of inputs to the NOR is often limited to two.

The output signal from the collector of the NOR is the input to the summing resistors of similar stages. Because of the gain of the transistor, it is possible to drive several loads. Hence it is essential for interaction between the input terminals to be small. Otherwise, a spurious coupling between the several inputs of one gate can be coupled via common signal sources to many other gates. The low impedance of the conducting base takes care of the problem at one level of input, and the low impedance of the saturated collector (as a source) takes care of the problem at the other level of input. Hence it is only required to pick the series resistor so that it is relatively large compared to the impedance of the saturated collector.

There is no serious logical noise in this circuit because of the saturation of the collector. Hence one level of collector swing is well defined. Techniques can be developed for designing machines around this circuit (7), and since there is only one kind of switching circuit in the logical parts of the machine, manufacturing and design economies result.

Diode-Coupled Gates

The input resistors can be replaced by diodes to produce the *diode-coupled logic*. There are two different ways in which the circuit can be operated, the voltage and current switching mode. The voltage switching mode (Figure 9.32) is essentially a normal diode AND gate * driving an inverting transistor amplifier (8). This introduces a negation into the logic of the stage but provides the ability to drive a multiplicity of outputs. The gate, therefore, implements the NAND connective; like the NOR, it may require that the sense of the logical convention be inverted in successive stages of logic. The collector circuit is sometimes clamped in order to provide a well-defined level of voltage which is independent of the number of loads driven. The shunt capacitor provides the overdrive on turn-on and turn-off, and the resistor to the negative return compensates for the collector leakage current. The outputs from the collector drive the inputs of corresponding circuits.

The switching mode of Figure 9.33 is sometimes called *current-operated logic* (9). As in DCTL, the current from the supply is

---

* The details of diode logic are developed on pages 9.39 *ff*.

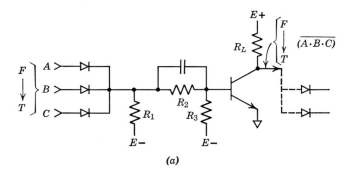

(a)

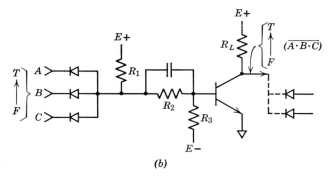

(b)

Figure 9.32. Two diode-coupled transistor NAND *gates.*

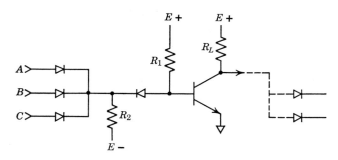

Figure 9.33. The diode-coupled low-level transistor gate.

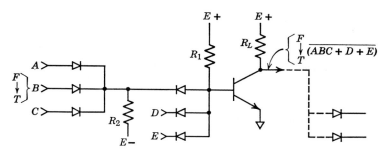

Figure 9.34. A current-operated AND-OR-NOT *gate.*

switched between the collector of one transistor and the input diode network of another. The gate still includes a negation and hence can be used to implement either NAND or NOR connectives depending on the sense of the logical convention. The collector resistor (of the previous level) and the resistor in the gate are so chosen that the voltage delivered to the series diode at the base is somewhat positive; hence it is reverse biased. Therefore, the base input current is determined solely by the base resistor returned to the positive voltage, and the transistor performance is independent of the number of logical inputs. The voltage drop in the diodes of the logic circuit is in the opposite sense to the drop in the series diode to the base. The base of the transistor must be guaranteed to reach zero or a slightly negative voltage in order to cutoff. Since the collector does not quite reach zero volts, a slight level shift is necessary between the input terminal and the base of the transistor. One way to arrange this is to use silicon diodes for the input logic but a germaniun diode for the base diode.

If the logical convention is chosen so that the circuit implements the NAND, it follows that an OR * gate can be constructed at the base of the transistor by adding additional series diodes to new input networks (Figure 9.34). Thus the circuit can be made to implement the AND-OR-NOT, or by reversing the convention, the OR-AND-NOT.

As in all current-switching circuits, the voltage excursions are small. The capacitance effects are minimized, and hence fast circuits can be designed.

* This point may be obscure until the behavior of diode gates has been studied; see page 9.39 *ff*.

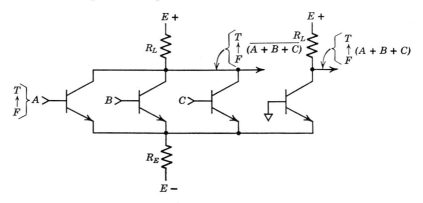

Figure 9.35. A current-mode transistor OR *gate.*

Current-Mode Gates

In *current-mode logic,* the transistors are inserted in a constant current circuit, which, therefore, prevents them from saturating (10). Consider Figure 9.35. This is a hybrid collector-coupled and emitter-coupled circuit driving a grounded-base amplifier.* It is clear that as the inputs move about ground potential, current is steered from one or more of the logic transistors into or out of the grounded-base amplifier. For example, if all three inputs are negative, the current through the emitter resistor must flow into the amplifier transistor. If any input moves to slightly above ground, the common-emitter connection follows the highest base, and hence current switches out of the amplifier transistor into the logic transistor whose input is most positive. It is clear that both the direct and negated outputs are available. Very fast switching circuits are possible with this configuration.

Miscellaneous Tricks

Since both PNP and NPN transistors exist, they can be used alternately to shift a D-C level first one way and then the other in a cascade of gates (11). For example, consider the current-mode logic of Figure 9.36. There is a negative D-C level shift at X but a corresponding positive shift at Y. Hence to the extent that the currents switched

* This circuit is similar to the current switch described in Chapter 10, page 10.12.

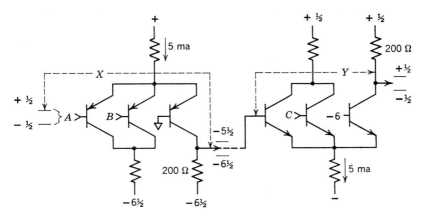

Figure 9.36. Level shifting in cascaded transistor gates.

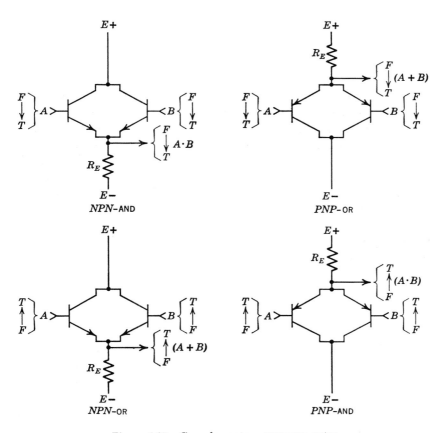

Figure 9.37. Complementary NPN-PNP gates.

are equal, the final output is at the same D-C level as the inputs *A* and *B*. Input *C* must be at a D-C level different than *A* and *B*. If *C* were initially at the same level as *A* and *B*, it must be shifted negatively by the amount of the voltage shift at *X*. This is conveniently done by first routing *C* through another similar PNP stage.

For the particular logical configuration in which an NPN emitter-coupled gate implements the AND connective, the PNP emitter-coupled gate implements the OR. For the opposite convention, the NPN is the OR and the PNP, the AND. This is an extra degree of flexibility which is sometimes useful (Figure 9.37).

A DIODE CIRCUIT WITHOUT CAPACITANCE *

For our immediate purposes, assume that we have a perfect diode device. When forward biased, it has zero internal impedance; when reverse biased, infinite impedance. Eventually, we will let it take on shunt capacitance, and later, a finite back impedance and a non-zero forward impedance. This back-impedance chararacteristic will distinguish the vacuum diode from the semiconductor diode.

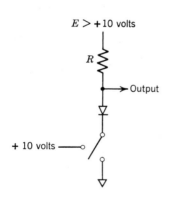

Figure 9.38. A simple diode switching circuit.

Consider first the behavior of a single diode in the circuit of Figure 9.38. If the switch is set to the ground position, current will flow from the positive supply through the resistor *R* and the diode to ground. For the perfect diode, the output potential is zero, and the current is E/R. Now assume that the switch is instantaneously flipped to the +10 position. The plate of the diode must also move up to +10. Assume that it did not. No current could flow through the back-biased diode, and therefore none could flow through the resistor. There could be no voltage drop across the resistor, and hence both ends of the resistor (and the diode plate) must be at $E+$ volts, which is inconsistent with the assumption that the plate voltage did not change. The diode

---

* Much of the insight to be developed in this section will be applicable also to the design of tube and transistor gate circuits.

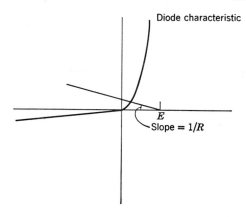

Figure 9.39. Graphical determination of the diode voltage.

plate must rise to the voltage at which conduction resumes. Diode current changes to match the new magnitude of the current in R (i.e., $(E - 10)/R$). For a practical diode with non-zero forward imped-ance, a graphical construction can be used to determine the current in the circuit (Figure 9.39).

If the switch is suddenly changed back to the ground position, the diode suddenly finds itself with more voltage than the amount of current flowing requires. The only way it can adjust to this situation is to lower the plate voltage, thereby increasing the current through R. The output returns to zero volts.

Just as the output of a follower follows the input up and down, so the diode plate follows its cathode up and down. Similarly, in Figure 9.40, the cathode is obedient to the motion of the plate.

With Capacitance

Now introduce capacitance into the circuit (Figure 9.41). Assume that the switch is in the ground position. The output is at 0 volts and the voltage across the capacitor is also zero. Now move the switch instantaneously to the +10 position. The plate is reluctant to move because the capacitor will not alter its voltage unless it can acquire charge. At the instant that the switch changed position, there was a current of E/R * flowing in the circuit. If the voltage across the

* Jump back to the preface and read the note about units.

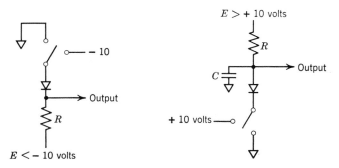

Figure 9.40. A second
simple diode switching
circuit.

Figure 9.41. A simple diode
switching circuit with capacitance.

resistor does not change, this current must continue to flow. The
only sink for it is the capacitor, which therefore can begin to acquire
charge and to change its voltage according to the relation

$$\frac{de}{dt} = \frac{I}{C}.$$

The current E/R therefore switches from the diode into the capacitor
and causes the initial rate of change of voltage across it (and hence
the voltage of the diode plate) to be E/RC.

The only influence acting on the capacitor is the current available
through the resistor. For the moment, the presence of the diode is
unfelt because it is back biased and cannot conduct. Thus the capacitor C begins to change toward E volts through the resistor R; this
is a description of the well-known exponential change of voltage in
a resistance-capacitance circuit. The asymptote toward which the
capacitor charges is E because there is no way for it to know of the
diode's presence.

Were is not for the diode the capacitor would, in fact, eventually
reach E. As the capacitor—and with it the diode plate—reaches
+10 volts, the diode ceases to be back biased and begins to conduct
again (Figure 9.42). It now is the sink for the current through R;
there is no more current for the capacitor, and no further voltage
changes occur in the circuit.

Clearly this is an equilibrium position. If the capacitor voltage
were to move more positively, it could do so only by borrowing current from the diode. However, a decrease in diode current is incon-

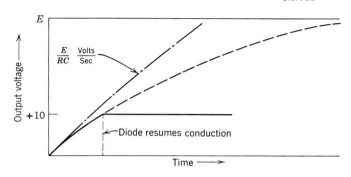

Figure 9.42. The output voltage of Figure 9.41.

sistent with an increase in its voltage—diodes just are not that way. Therefore, no such assumed positive voltage change can occur. Conversely, were the capacitor voltage to move negatively, it could do so only by dumping current. The only sink for this current is the diode, and again the supposed increase in diode current is inconsistent with the supposed decrease in voltage, and the assumed perturbation cannot occur.

Figure 9.43 summarizes the situation. At the instant the switch changes, the output voltage starts to exponentially rise toward *E* volts. As the output passes through +10 volts, the diode resumes conduction and all motion ceases.

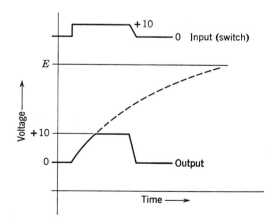

Figure 9.43. The complete behavior of Figure 9.41.

What happens when the switch suddenly returns to the ground position?   So to speak, the diode finds that the cathode has been knocked right out from under its plate. Again, the capacitor cannot alter its voltage unless it can change its charge. This time, the voltage is required to move negatively, and therefore the current must flow out of the capacitor to some point which is negative relative to $+10$ volts. The only such place in the circuit is through the diode and switch to ground.

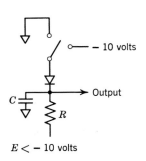

Figure 9.44. The dual circuit to Figure 9.41.

Therefore, while the positive-going edge of the output signal is determined by the ability of E and R to furnish current to the capacitor, the negative-going edge of the output is determined solely by the ability of the diode to remove current from the capacitor (Figure 9.43).   In a practical case, the switch will be some source with finite but low impedance, and its ability to accept current from the capacitor will help to determine the trailing edge.

For the circuit of Figure 9.44, the same argument leads to the graphical result in Figure 9.45.

Notice that in contrast to, say, pentode tube gates, diode circuits

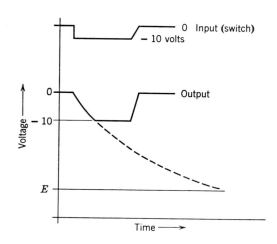

Figure 9.45. The complete behavior of Figure 9.44.

present a low-impedance input. Therefore, signals for such circuits must come from suitably low-impedance sources.

Now we're ready!

DIODE GATES

The Diode AND Gate

Consider the circuit of Figure 9.46 for the logical conventions given there. Suppose that both A and B are initially at 0 volts. The current flowing through the resistor will split equally between the two diodes. If input A moves to $+10$ volts, the output cannot move positively. If it did, this would imply decreasing current through the resistor (and, therefore, diode B), which is inconsistent with the assumed increase in voltage across the diode (its cathode has not moved). All of the resistance current, therefore, switches to diode B. Since the forward impedance of these diodes is zero, the output voltage does not change. If input B now switches to $+10$ volts, the output will exponentially rise to $+10$ volts at which time both diodes resume conduction. The output reaches its true state if input A *and* input B are each true; this configuration realizes the AND connective.

If one of the inputs now returns to false, the output will return to false as it should. The problem of discharging the capacitor falls on whichever of the inputs (or both) resumes the false state first.

This is a good time to consider the current in each diode. With

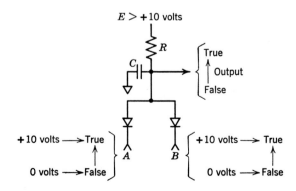

Figure 9.46. The first 2-input diode AND *gate.*

both inputs in the false state, each diode current is half the resistance current—$\frac{1}{2}(E/R)$ in this case. With one input in the true state, the other diode current is the full resistance current (E/R). With both inputs in the true state, each diode current is $\frac{1}{2}[(E-10)/R]$. As one input is just leaving the true state, that diode current is $(E-10)/R$ plus whatever current the capacitor is discharging. The capacitive component will depend on the rate of change of voltage across the capacitor, which in turn depends on the rate of change of the input signal between the true and the false states.

From a consideration of available components plus some derating schedule, the designer will have established some maximum current for his diodes. It may be necessary to control the rates of change of the signals to the logical networks in order to guarantee that transient values of current do not exceed the selected rating.

Since the diode B current in this example changes by 2-to-1 during the false-to-true transition of A, it is clear that with practical diodes having finite forward resistance this circuit will exhibit logical noise on the false level of the output. Just as we found before, this results from an imperfect switching element; in this case the fault is the non-zero forward impedance.

Clearly, more than two diodes can be joined together to provide an n-way AND gate. For such a case the current extremes through any one diode become worse; the logical noise also increases, and the signal-to-noise ratio worsens. This situation helps to determine a practical limit to the number of logical inputs to a gate stage.

Another Diode AND Gate

Consider the circuit of Figure 9.47. The output reaches the true state when A *and* B are each true. The transient and quiescent currents can be determined in the manner outlined for the previous diode AND gate.

The Diode OR Gate

In the circuit of Figure 9.48, the output reaches the true state if A reaches true *or* B reaches true *or both* do. This circuit implements the inclusive-OR operation and, moreover, has the same logical conventions as the gate of Figure 9.46. The transient and quiescent currents

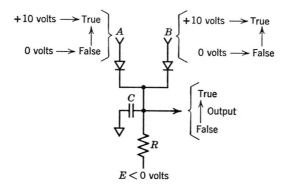

Figure 9.47. The second 2-input diode AND *gate.*

are readily determined. There is an important difference between the AND and OR gates of the same logical convention. In the AND gate, the false-to-true transition is determined by the time constant of the circuit while the true-to-false transition depends on the characteristics of the input signal; in the OR gate, the false-to-true transition depends on the external signal, and the true-to-false on the time constant of the circuit.

The OR circuit will exhibit logical noise on the true level. Furthermore, more than two diodes can be used to provide an *n*-way OR gate. The current variation in each diode becomes worse with increasing *n* as does the logical noise. This factor sets a practical limit to the number of logical inputs to a gate of this kind.

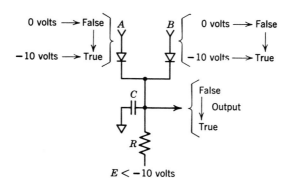

Figure 9.48. The first 2-input diode OR *gate.*

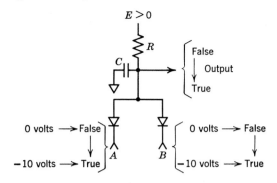

Figure 9.49. The second 2-input diode OR *gate.*

The Second OR Gate

The circuit of Figure 9.49 also realizes the inclusive-OR function and uses the same logical conventions as the AND gate of Figure 9.47. By this time it is clear how to analyze this circuit for behavior.

Diode-Gate Recap

There are two pairs of diode gates which are complements of each other (12). The following observations apply to either pair:

1. There is no logical inversion through any of these gates.

2. In either of the pairs there is both an AND and an OR gate with the same logical convention. Therefore, it is easy for the two members of a pair to communicate with one another.

3. Subject to limitations imposed by component capability, the n-way OR or the n-way AND can be implemented.

4. The input terminals are relatively low impedance, which implies that driving sources must be capable of providing or accepting current.

5. Logical noise may exist on the false level, or on the true level, or in combination AND-OR circuits on both levels.

6. Since practical diodes do not have zero forward impedance, the output levels will be slightly displaced relative to input levels; there is a D-C shift, although small. In a long chain of gates this may require standardization of levels at intervals through the chain.

7. The internal impedance of the diode and the resistor in the gate form a voltage divider. Therefore, the output is slightly attenuated

from the input. This may require amplification at intervals in a long chain of gates.

8. Since diodes tend to have lower capacitances, it becomes possible to construct gating networks at low current levels. However, capacitance will control the behavior of the circuit and must be considered as an integral part of the design problem.

DESIGN OF THE SINGLE-LEVEL DIODE GATE

The principles concerned in designing a single AND are precisely the same as for a single OR gate; for definiteness, consider the AND of Figure 9.50. For the logical conventions shown, the rising front edge of the output will be determined by the natural time constant of the circuit, but the falling trailing edge will depend on the impedances of the input sources. The capacitance C will include any stray capacitance due to wiring and connections, the shunt capacitance of the diodes, and any capacitance which the load may present. For the moment, assume that the load does not present a resistive component, and that the diodes are ideal—zero forward impedance and infinite back impedance.

The principle part of the design is to choose the resistance (R) and the voltage (E) so that some pre-

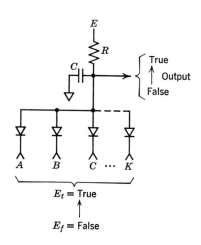

Figure 9.50.   The   many-input diode AND gate.

scribed rise time of the output occurs. The required rise time of the output may be set by such factors as the following:

1. Overall time scale of the machine. A system in which most signals are a few microseconds in duration will require rise times of fractions of a microsecond.

2. Nature of the load. Particular methods of triggering toggles require specified rates of rise on the signal; the gate might have such a load.

To start with, we have given the rise time, the characteristics of the diode, the voltage levels of the input signals, and an estimate of the stray capacitance—which we note depends on the precise details of the circuit packaging. Two parameters—R and E—are to be determined.

Observe first that the output can rise no faster than the input signal; the diode plate cannot get ahead of the cathode in time. On the other hand, so far as the capacitor is concerned, the maximum current available in the circuit should be switched into it; this will guarantee that it moves as rapidly as possible. This demands that the input signals rise just slightly faster than the expected rise time of the output because under this circumstance, all of the current flowing through R will be available to the capacitor. If one of the diodes does not completely cutoff because of a slowly rising input, the current which it conducts will be part of that which is flowing through R. This, in turn, implies that less current is available to change the capacitor, and it will, therefore, change its voltage more slowly.

The argument begins by assuming that all inputs switch to the true state rapidly enough to leave all diodes completely non-conducting. It is not necessary that all input transitions occur at the same instant; so long as one input remains false, the output will remain false.

At the time the last input switches to true, there is a current of $(E - E_f)/R$ flowing through R; E_f is the input level corresponding to the false state. This current (I) will cause the capacitor to change its voltage at a rate of I/C; if ΔE is the amplitude of the input signal, an estimate of the rise time of the output is

$$\left(\frac{RC}{E - E_f}\right) \Delta E.$$

If this argument is used backwards, it leads to an indeterminate situation. There are two parameters to be determined—E and R—but there is only one equation.

In a more rigorous treatment, an exponential is to be fitted to the given data. We know that the output is at E_f at time t_0, and that it must be at E_t at time t_1. However, the equation of the exponential which passes through the point t_0, E_f and one other arbitrary point t_1, E_t is:

$$E_t = E_f + (E - E_f) [1 - \epsilon^{(t_1 - t_0)/\tau}]$$

which still contains two parameters (τ, E). The problem of fitting an exponential to the desired behavior of the output is, therefore, an indeterminate problem.   Either there is one free choice, or an additional constraint is needed to resolve the situation.

What Other Constraint?

Perhaps some particular voltage is favored, or a large stock of an appropriate resistor is available.   If so, the proper value of the remaining parameter can be calculated.

If $E = E_t$, the output will take forever to reach the true state, and it cannot ever satisfy the specified rise time.   It is clear that E must be greater than E_t, but how much greater?   The voltage E is the asymptote toward which the capacitor is charging; therefore, the greater that E is, the faster can be the rise of the output signal.   The greater that E is, the more dissipation there will be in R.   This is one more example of a tradeoff available to the designer; power dissipation can be exchanged for speed of response.

How can this tradeoff be measured and a sensible choice made?

How Big the E?

The signals of interest in the diode network start at E_f at time t_1 and arrive at E_t at time t_2.   Since the voltage is exponentially approaching E which is greater than E_t, there is very little rounding of the corner when the signal reaches E_t.   It is, therefore, convenient to regard the rise time as $t_2 - t_1$ which is a slightly different definition than often used for pulse signals.*

If $E = E_t$, the rise time is clearly infinite.   If E is infinite but E/R is finite, then the rise time is

$$t_R = (E_t - E_f)\frac{C}{I}$$

$$= (E_t - E_f)\frac{RC}{E}$$

where $I = E/R$ is the current available to the capacitor.   Subject to the constraint that the initial current available to the capacitor remains constant as E varies (i.e., $(E - E_f)/R$ is a constant), then the variation of rise time with E is shown in Figure 9.51.   The family of exponentials

---

* Frequently the rise time is measured between 10% and 90% of the signal amplitude.

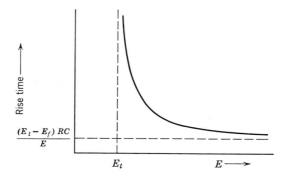

Figure 9.51. Variation of rise time with E if $(E - E_f)/R$ is a constant.

which correspond to this curve is shown in Figure 9.52. It is clear that the decrease in rise time is rather rapid at first, but the curve flattens. It is clear that each additional investment in a larger E buys less and less decrease in rise time. But each investment in a larger E costs power dissipation in the resistor.

So far as dissipation is concerned, there is some uncertainty how to measure it. Part of the time the resistor dissipates $(E - E_f)^2/R$ watts but the rest of the time it dissipates $(E - E_t)^2/R$. Since the duty cycle between the two situations is not known, a rigid decision cannot be made. If E is sufficiently larger than E_t, one choice is as good as the other

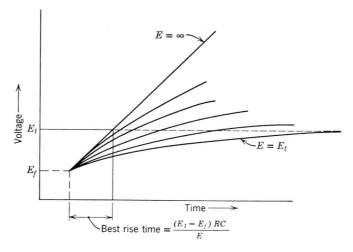

Figure 9.52. The family of exponentials corresponding to Figure 9.51.

(i.e., $E - E_f \approx E - E_t$). It is a little more convenient to select the first because the rule of our game is that $(E - E_f)/R$ is a constant. Therefore, the power dissipated in R increases only linearly with $E - E_f$.

One choice is to continue to increase E so long as the relative decrease in the rise time exceeds the relative cost in power dissipation. The designer may also, of course, terminate the game prematurely if he discovers that playing it too far forces him to use, say, a half-watt resistor rather than a quarter-watt one.

Linearity

Another choice for consideration is the linearity of the output signal. Figure 9.53 shows a number of exponentials, all of which pass through the given time-voltage points and, therefore, meet the rise-time requirement. Clearly, they become less and less linear as the asymptote moves downward toward E_t. This time, R is being chosen so that for a given E, the exponential passes through the second point; $(E - E_f)/R$ is not the same for each curve.

It may be that the load requires a signal of specified linearity. If so, the second constraint may be a specification of linearity, coupled perhaps with the requirement that the dissipation in R be minimum.

How Much C?

The total capacitance in the gate structure is composed of the load component, the stray component, and the diode component. Each

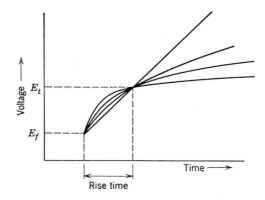

Figure 9.53. Changing linearity for a constant rise time.

diode can contribute its shunt capacitance; whether it does or not depends on how the input signals behave.

If every input to the gate rises just slightly faster than the output, there is very little change of voltage across any diode. The displacement current is correspondingly small, and there is very little apparent capacitance. At the other extreme, every input can rise very rapidly compared with the output rise. In this case one side of each diode is effectively held at a constant voltage by the low impedance driving source. Therefore, the full output swing is developed across each of the back-biased diodes, and the apparent capacitance contributed by the diodes is the sum of the statically measured shunt capacitances.

The ultraconservative choice is to pick the worst case and to include all of the diode shunt capacitance. This means that the rise time may often be faster than required, but there is a guarantee that the rise time will always be at least as fast as required. In gates with only a few inputs, perhaps the inclusion of all diode capacitances may be too conservative.

Finite Back Impedance

Our design technique must now be adjusted to accommodate those real-life diodes which do not exhibit infinite back impedance. On one hand, the finite back impedances may never be noticed during transitions if the input signals change at such a rate that the voltage across the diode never changes significantly. On the other hand, the inputs may change very rapidly to the true state. In this case, Figure 9.54 shows the situation at the instant the inputs change. Each input can contribute an additional current of $(E_t - E_f)/r_b$ to the capacitor; the output, therefore, rises a little faster than expected, because the capacitor can obtain extra current. It almost looks as though finite back resistances were desirable. The extra current must come from the several signal drivers.

Consider an intermediate case—Figure 9.55. Every input but one has changed to the true state. The remaining diode must handle not only the current through R (as it always had to) but now it has the extra burden of a current of

$$\frac{(n-1)(E_t - E_f)}{r_b}$$

which flows from E_t through the back impedances of the $n - 1$ back-biased diodes. Notice, furthermore, that if all inputs are true, the one

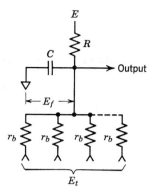

Figure 9.54. The back impedance situation at the beginning of the true-false transition.

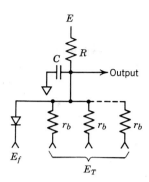

Figure 9.55. The back impedance situation prior to changing of the last input.

which goes false first has to handle the back impedance current of all other diodes in addition to the current from the capacitor and the current through R.

The effect of the finite back impedance is to widen the range of current which can flow through any diode. Therefore, each diode must work harder, and the logical noise will be increased. As back impedances change with time, the logical noise will also change. The finite back impedance also reflects a need for lower impedance sources; this point will become particularly obvious in the design of cascaded AND-OR networks.

The number of inputs to a gate structure may very well be limited in some cases by the effect of finite back impedance.

Recap

Design of the single level but many-way gate proceeds as follows:

1. Input-signal swing and desired output rise time are given.
2. Total capacitance is estimated from a knowledge of the load, experience with packaging, and the shunt capacitance of the diodes.
3. From these data plus one of the constraints discussed previously (or a free choice), E and R are selected.
4. The current distribution through the network can be calculated for all combinations of the inputs.

5. The ability of the chosen diode type to handle these currents can be verified.

6. Logical noise can be determined from a knowledge of the forward impedance of the diodes.

7. The effect of the finite diode back impedances can be calculated, and any adjustment of previously selected parameters can then be made.

8. All component parameters—including the forward and back impedance of each diode—are now allowed to take on prescribed tolerance shifts and the design checked or revised as necessary.

9. Finally, the current capability of the diode will determine the fastest switching time of the trailing edge (for the AND gate) or the leading edge (for the OR gate) of the input signals.

AND-ANDs or OR-ORs

A two level AND-AND and a two level OR-OR gate are shown in Figure 9.56. There is also another AND-AND and another OR-OR which can be made by using logical conventions opposite to those shown in this figure.

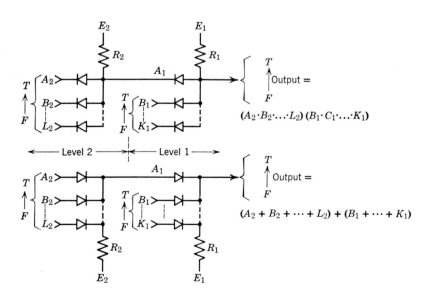

Figure 9.56.   The 2-level AND-AND *and* OR-OR *diode gates.*

The design starts from the output and works toward the left. Assume that the signal from level 2 (which feeds diode A_1) is just slightly faster than the rise time expected of the final output. The two levels of the gate structure are effectively uncoupled for the rising edge of the AND-AND or the falling edge of the OR-OR. Level 1 can be designed according to the technique already developed. The designer might possibly exclude the shunt capacitance of diode A_1 because the assumed behavior of the level-2 signal implies very little change of voltage across this diode. Level 2 can then be independently designed by the same techniques to provide the speed of response originally assumed from it.

There is only one new twist. Suppose that the AND-AND gate is in its true position; all inputs are, therefore, in the true state. If one of B_1, C_1, . . . , K_1 is the first to go false, the corresponding driver and diode must accomodate just the current of R_1, the capacitance current, and the back impedance current—just as in the one-level gate. If one of A_2, B_2, . . . , L_2 is the first to go false, the corresponding driver and diode must accomodate a larger current which consists of the R_2 component, the R_1 component, a larger back impedance component, and the capacitance current.

The capacitance to be discharged in the latter case consists of the load capacitance, the stray capacitance from level 1, the stray capacitance from level 2, shunt capacitances from all diodes of level 1 except A_1, and shunt capacitances from all diodes of level 2 except the one having the false-going signal. As we saw before, if more than one input changes at the same time, the capacitance current situation could be somewhat more favorable.

The back impedance current situation also depends on the number of inputs which change simultaneously. In the worst case in which only one input from level 2 goes false, the corresponding driver must supply back current to all diodes in the structure except two—A_1 and the one in level 2. With the back and forward impedances of the diodes, the resistor values, the voltages and the tolerances on each given, the current distribution for any configuration of input signals can be calculated.

The corresponding discussion for the OR-OR gate is readily constructed. For either AND-AND or OR-OR, the extension of the design method to more levels is also straightforward. The current through the diodes increases significantly at each level. This is the effect of the low-impedance characteristic of the basic diode gate; level 2 must be capable of driving the low-impedance input of level 1. The current growth from level to level is usually the factor which limits the number of levels in a cascaded structure.

The AND-OR or OR-AND

A new design aspect appears in the AND-OR or the OR-AND structure (13). It arises because level 2 must be designed to supply the necessary current to level-1's low-impedance input terminal. For definiteness, consider the OR-AND of Figure 9.57; the argument for the AND-OR of Figure 9.58 can then be constructed easily. The duals of these two networks also exist. The problem is to select values of E_1, R_1, E_2, and R_2, given input voltage levels representing the true and the false state, a desired rate of change of the output signal, the charactistics of the diodes, and the stray and load capacitances.

Assume that all inputs are false; so is the output. If B_1, C_1, . . . , K_1 all go true, the output will continue false until A_1 goes true, which in turn implies that some one or more of A_2, B_2, . . . , L_2 have gone true. Whichever of the set $[A_1, B_1, . . . , K_1]$ is the last to become true determines when the output becomes true. The node N transitions from false to true at a rate determined only by the ability of a driver to change the capacitance C_2. For the moment assume that N moves from false to true more rapidly than we expect of the output. Make the same assumption about the other inputs B_1, C_1, . . . , K_1.

Under these circumstances, the capacitance C_1 is charged by the current through R_1, and the design of the AND level proceeds as though

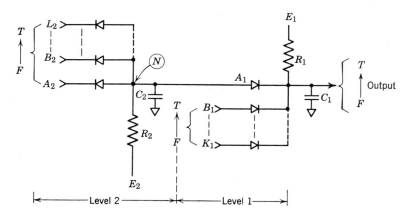

Figure 9.57. The OR-AND *diode gate.*

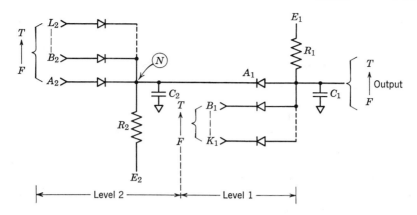

Figure 9.58. The AND-OR diode gate.

the OR level did not exist. This problem has already been discussed, and a technique developed for the design of a single-level AND gate. Values for E_1 and R_1 can, therefore, be selected.

As in the single-level gate, C_1 consists of the load capacitance, the stray capacitance, and the shunt capacitance of all the diodes A_1, B_1, . . . , K_1. If, say, K_1 is the first input to return to false, its driver will have to accomodate the capacitance current from C_1, the resistive current from R_1, and the resistive current through the back impedances of all the level-1 diodes except K_1.

Assume now that the output is true because A_2, B_1, C_1, . . . , K_1 are all true. Consider the situation as A_2 returns to the false state, and assume that it changes rapidly compared to the expected rates of change of the output. Both capacitors C_1 and C_2 have been charged to the true level; somehow they both must find a sink for their charge, or the output never will move to false. For the moment, ignore the back impedance of the diodes. We see that the only possible sink for the charge is the voltage source E_2 to which the capacitor charge is conveyed by the current in R_2.

Before seeking a design procedure for E_2 and R_2, look at the physics of the situation. The equivalent circuit is shown in Figure 9.59. None of the diodes A_2, B_2, . . . , L_2 appear, since they are all back biased; temporarily their back impedances have been assumed infinite. Just prior to switching from true to false, the current flowing through R_1 partly is divided in some way among the diodes A_1, B_1, . . . , K_1, and partly contributes to the current in R_2. Just after

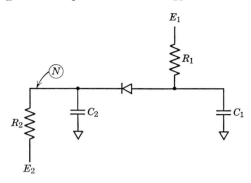

Figure 9.59. The equivalent circuit of Figure 9.57 for the true-false transition.

switching, the node N has moved slightly below the true level; diodes $B_1, C_1, \ldots, K_1$ all become back biased, and the total current through R_1 now flows through A_1 into R_2. If the current in R_2 just matches that in R_1, node N will never move; R_1 and R_2 will constitute a voltage divider in equilibrium. Therefore, the current in R_2 must exceed that in R_1.

Prior to switching, A_2 was true. Part of the current in R_2 came through A_1 from R_1, and the rest of it came through A_2 from a driver. After switching, A_2 is false. Part of the current in R_2 comes through A_1 from R_1; the excess of current in R_2 over that in R_1 is available for discharging the capacitance $C_1 + C_2$. At switching time current must become available for diversion into the capacitance, if node N is to change its voltage position.

As node N moves downwardly, the voltage across R_2 and, therefore, the current through it decreases; but the current through R_1 is increasing. Progressively, less and less current will be available for the capacitance which, therefore, will change its voltage more and more slowly. Finally (if none of the diodes $A_2, B_2, \ldots, L_2$ have resumed conduction), the currents through R_1 and R_2 will become equal and all motion of the node will cease. It is clear that the asymptotic voltage which $C_1 + C_2$ exponentially approaches is not E_2 but rather is a voltage lying between E_1 and E_2 and determined by the values of R_1 and R_2. Because a voltage divider in equilibrium has equal currents in the two resistors, it follows that the asymptote is exactly the voltage determined by R_1 and R_2 considered as a voltage divider connected between E_1 and E_2.

This can be seen in another way by applying Thévenin's theorem

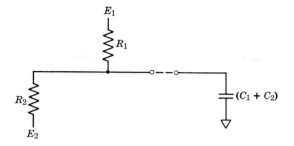

Figure 9.60. Figure 9.59 redrawn.

(Figure 9.60). So far as the capacitor is concerned, the network of two resistors and two voltages can be replaced by one voltage and one resistor. The one voltage is the open circuit voltage of the original network and the one resistor, the parallel value of R_1 and R_2 (Figure 9.61).

The voltage of the node is (except for the small drop across A_1) the same as the output voltage. There will be a prescribed rate of fall for the output signal, and E_2, R_2 must be chosen to meet this requirement. Now the design argument of the single-level gate begins all over: Where should the asymptote be relative to the desired end voltage, which in this case is the false level? The asymptote must be below the false level or the output will never get to false. How far below though? The set of possible constraints considered for the single-level gate is available. Perhaps linearity, perhaps dissipation in R_2, perhaps a preferred value

$$E_1 - \frac{(E_1 - E_2)R_1}{R_1 + R_2}$$

$$\frac{R_1 R_2}{R_1 + R_2}$$

$(C_1 + C_2)$

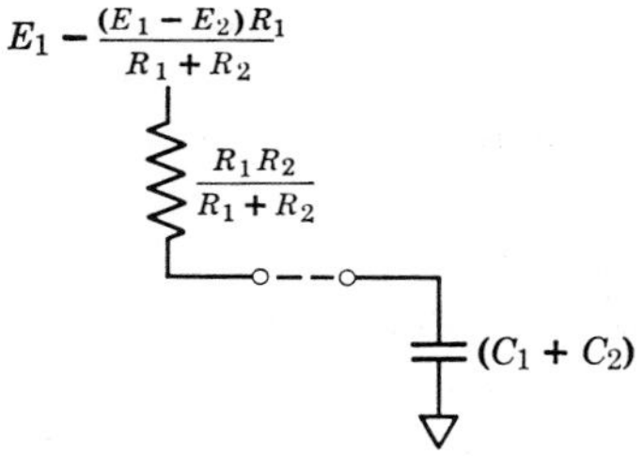

Figure 9.61. The Thévenin equivalent of Figure 9.60.

for E_2 or R_2, or a combination of these will be used to either position the asymptote or determine the time constant. The other parameter is then completely determinate. There is no requirement that the additional constraint used to resolve the uncertainty be the same for both trailing and leading edges.

What about the effect of finite back impedances? Again assume that A_2 has become false very rapidly, that B_2, . . . , L_2 remain false, and that B_1, C_1, . . . , K_1 remain true. The equivalent circuit is shown in Figure 9.62; E_t is the voltage level corresponding to the

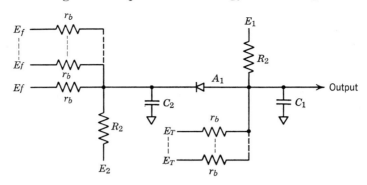

Figure 9.62. The back impedance situation for a particular configuration of inputs.

true state; and E_f, to the false state. Initially, the back impedances r_b which are connected to E_f will assist R_2 to discharge $C_1 + C_2$. Later in the transition cycle, the r_b's which are connected to E_t will oppose the discharge of $C_1 + C_2$. Thévenin's theorem can be used to reduce the complex network to a single resistor and a single voltage, and the capacitance behavior can be determined. It may be more convenient to regard the effect of back impedances as a perturbation on the original design than to include the effect in the initial design.

The components of C_1 have already been identified. C_2 consists of the stray capacitance at the node plus the shunt capacitance of the diodes. The ultraconservative choice, of course, is to include the capacitance of all diodes within the level.

It is clear that the drivers associated with inputs A_2, B_2, . . . , L_2 must be more powerful than those associated with B_1, C_1, . . . , K_1. Suppose that A_2 goes true but that all other inputs stay false. Driver A_2 must handle the current of R_2, plus capacitance current of C_2, plus the back currents of all diodes in level 2 except A_2. Since the current in R_2 is greater than that in R_1, the total current required of the level-2 driver is greater than that of the level-1 driver. Therefore, the current capability of diode A_2 will limit the rise time of input A_2.

Current Build-up

The above argument can easily be extended to a three-level AND-OR-AND structure. We would find that the current in the R_3 (of the third level) will be greater than that in R_2. There will always be some logical configuration of the inputs which requires one diode to accept all the current from the resistor in its own level. Thus the increase of current from level to level in a gating network may well limit the number of levels which can be used practically because of the increased burden on the diodes.

To get some insight into the problem, consider an approximate solution to the design of a multilayer gate. Given a total capacitance in the level 1 of C and a desired voltage change of Δe in time Δt, the current required in R_1 is

$$I = C \frac{\Delta e}{\Delta t}.$$

If the trailing edge must change in the same Δt, the *excess* current in R_2 (over that of R_1) must also be $C(\Delta e/\Delta t)$; this implies that the total current in R_2 is $2C(\Delta e/\Delta t)$. However, the capacitance being discharged by R_2 is greater because of the stray and diode capacitance from level 2. If the new total capacitance were, say, $C' = 1.5C$, then the current in R_2 would have to be $2.5C(\Delta e/\Delta t)$. In the third level, the current might be 4 to 6 times $C(\Delta e/\Delta t)$.

From this discussion we see the extreme importance of minimizing the capacitance in a gate structure and also in the load. Therefore, packaging techniques which have low stray capacitances and diodes with small shunt capacitances are favorable choices.

Tolerances

Having completed the preliminary design of an AND-OR, we must make a final check to determine the fine structure of the circuit behavior. There are several important points. First of all, the expected drift in value of each resistor and in the supply voltages will have an effect on the currents in the circuit and, therefore, on rise times. These effects can be calculated straightforwardly. Next, the forward impedance of the diodes can be inserted, and the calculated voltage shift and signal attenuation through the circuit can be determined. In this connection, the cascade of an AND and the OR is more favorable than the cascade of AND-AND or OR-OR. The voltage shift in the AND is toward one supply potential, whereas in the OR, it is toward the other one. Hence the two shifts have opposite senses in the AND-OR whereas in the two-of-a-kind cascade the shifts are in the same direction. This is a good example of a situation in which the choice of the form of a Boolean expression can minimize the problems of the circuit designer.

Any noise components which are present on the input signals to a gate circuit will, of course, be felt at the output. These effects can be calculated readily. Hence, when the final design is finished, the circuit will be guaranteed to produce output signals of certain amplitude, voltage position, and rise time. The tolerances on each characteristic of the output signal will be known, and will depend in part on the tolerances of the input signal characteristics and in part on the expected drifts in the component parameters.

NOT CIRCUITS

These are unusually easy to implement since the truth table for negation is simply

A	$f(A)$
0	1
1	0

Therefore, any inverting circuit can function as a NOT if the signal which represents a negated variable is the reflection of the one which represents the original variable. The NOT circuit must turn a signal upside down while preserving its shape, its amplitude, and (usually) its D-C position.

If information is contained in the form of pulses rather than voltage levels, a transformer can negate; level shifts due to a changing duty cycle may cause trouble. A one-stage amplifier is also a NOT circuit;

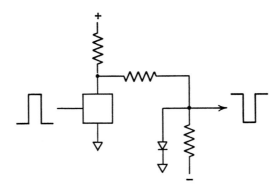

Figure 9.63. A simple NOT *circuit based on the symmetrical toggle.*

its only problem is the D-C shift between input and output. There often is an output voltage divider to restore the level, plus clamp diodes to define precisely the level. If present, the clamp diodes can, of course, absorb the tolerance drifts of the resistors, the supply voltage, and the tube or transistor. Figure 9.63 will be recognized as one-half of the symmetrical grounded-emitter toggle and is clearly an inverter. Sometimes a gate which contains a polarity reversal can be used to provide the NOT connective.

It might be that a true state were represented by, say, a positive signal of given width, but that a false state were represented by a positive signal of different width. In such a circumstance the negation circuit would have to be more complex than a simple inverting circuit.

FINAL WORDS

In the end, a gate will have to communicate with other gates, with toggles, and perhaps with other kinds of circuits. A gate structure may have logical noise on either or both of its output states; furthermore, it will have a long term uncertainty of level in the output states due to component aging and drifts. The ambiguous zone must be maintained wide enough so that the loads driven by the gate have no trouble deciding which logical state exists (see Figure 9.64).

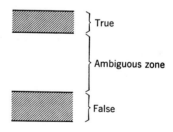

Sometimes it is convenient from a production standpoint to design a standard gate package which contains a number of inputs and outputs and performs some fairly extensive logic. Only those inputs and outputs will be

Figure 9.64. The signal-to-noise problem in gates.

used which are needed at a particular place in the machine. For such a standardized logic package, it is necessary to know how many loads of what kinds each output can drive. Frequently the standard package contains several ANDS, several ORS or severals NORS (or a mixture of these but not connected to each other). For a simple one-connective gate, the term *fan-out* is often used to describe the number of outputs which can be driven: sometimes the term *input-output ratio* describes the same thing. Sometimes the term *fan-in* is used to describe the number of inputs which can be accepted by a simple gate.

Direct-Coupled versus Pulse Logic

All of the gate design techniques which have been developed have been implicitly slanted towards gating networks that are completely direct coupled; i.e., there are no series capacitors in signal carrying wires. Such *direct-coupled logic* has the significant advantage that the duty cycle of the signals is immaterial. Generally speaking, the duty cycle of a logical signal (i.e., the ratio of time in one state to the time in the other state) is nearly unpredictable; therefore, networks which are direct coupled tend to be more desirable.

EXAMPLES

1. Some toggle in a machine will be the master go-stop toggle. So long as the machine is actually running, this toggle will be in the go position. Depending upon the particular batch of problems, the output of this toggle to a gating network may change every few seconds, every few fractions of a second, perhaps in microseconds, or perhaps every few hours.

2. The logical networks which implement the adder will respond to the particular information being processed; therefore, the duty cycle of such signals will be substantially unknown to the designer.

It is possible to use pulse signals rather than voltage (or current) levels to represent logical states. Under such circumstances, information about the duty cycle may be available, and the designer can implement pulse-logic networks. Obviously, he must have some knowledge of duty cycle or he cannot select appropriate values of coupling capacitors. A risk of pulse logic is the degradation of pulse shape through a network; this can result in accumulated time delays, which in turn might make gates malfunction or operate marginally.

Sometimes a pulse signal is injected into an otherwise direct-coupled network in order to make the output signal appear as a pulse.

EXAMPLE

A toggle is to be triggered from a gating network, and a capacitance-coupled triggering scheme has been selected. One possibility is to make the layer of logic nearest the toggle an AND and to make one of the inputs to this AND be a pulse signal. This pulse signal can be carefully shaped to meet the requirements of the toggle and will be transmitted without significant degradation through a properly designed one-level gate.

OTHER GATING ELEMENTS

As we look back over the discussion of switching devices, we observe that the elements have all exhibited a highly non-linear voltage-current characteristic. In the final analysis, the problem of deciding between two logical states is, in most cases, exactly the problem of amplitude discrimination. It could also be discrimination in phase, in frequency, or in some composite characteristic. To assure proper discrimination, the true and false levels must be separated far enough, and the logical noise must be small enough. As the switching element becomes more and more nearly linear, the logical noise increases and satisfactory discrimination becomes progressively more difficult.

Generally speaking, any element with a non-linear input-output characteristic is a candidate for a gate. We have not discussed, by any means, all of the gate structures which are in existence; we have only considered many common ones. The tube, transistor, and diode structures can function from the slowest speeds to very high speeds (e.g., from seconds to milliseconds to microseconds to nanoseconds); other gates might function only in a particular speed range because of some limitation of the element.

EXAMPLES

1. Certain resistance materials exhibit highly non-linear voltage-current characteristics (Figure 9.65). This characteristic is generally similar to that of a diode but does not have the sharp knee. Gating networks from such elements can be expected to have large logical noise (14).

2. Consider a magnetic material which has the rectangular hysteresis loop of Figure 9.66; consider some closed magnetic structure of this material which has four windings—three input and one output (Figure 9.67) (15). Let the sense of the current in two of the windings (A and B) be such that it tends to drive the magnetic material toward positive saturation. The third winding (C) carries a steady bias current which positions the material one unit of current to the left of the lower remanence point (point 1 in Figure 9.66). The fourth winding (D) is an output. If the currents in A and B

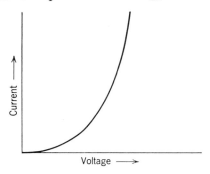

Figure 9.65. A non-linear resistance material.

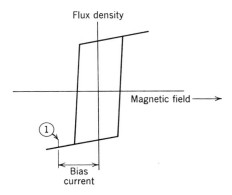

Figure 9.66. A material with a rectangular hysteresis loop.

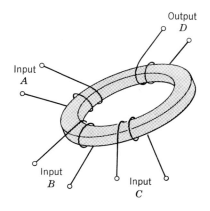

Figure 9.67. A magnetic gate element.

are each equal in amplitude to the bias, it is obvious that the magnetic material will transit from the lower saturation level to the upper only if *A and B* are present simultaneously. If signals *A* and *B* are pulses, the steady bias current will reposition the material to the point 1 after *A* and *B* have disappeared (Figure 9.66). The output signal is, therefore, also a pulse.

The NOT is easy: two windings of opposite sense.

The OR is also easy; set the bias current to zero! This raises an interesting possibility. If the bias current is regarded as a threshold, and the input currents have a value of $+1$, then this same magnetic structure is an AND for a threshold of -1 but an OR for a threshold of 0. It is intriguing to speculate about the possibility that one element might implement a wide variety of Boolean functions, depending upon the value of one or more thresholds.

Magnetic components are suited for frequencies up to the lower megacycle range. At high operating rates, heating due to hysteresis and eddy current losses may cause a degradation in magnetic properties or even cause the magnetic material to pass through the Curie point. Generally speaking, magnetic elements tend to be very rugged and reliable.

3. Certain materials exhibit the property that at sufficiently low temperatures (approximately 4° Kelvin) they lose resistance and become *superconducting* (16). The temperature at which superconduction sets in depends on an applied magnetic field; therefore, at a fixed temperature, an element may be flipped into and out of superconduction by controlling a magnetic field. The conductor which carries the current to establish the control field can be made of a material which will remain superconducting at a field strength which is sufficient to alter the state of a controlled element. The structure of Figure 9.68 implements the 3-way AND; the resistance through the structure is zero only if currents *A* and *B* and *C* are all zero. If any one current is present, part of the structure will be resistive. Similarly,

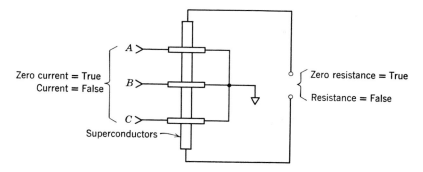

Figure 9.68.   A 3-input superconducting AND *gate.*

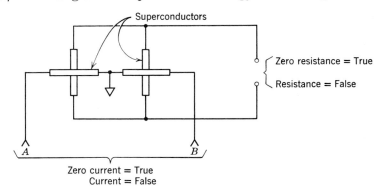

Figure 9.69. A 2-input superconducting OR *gate.*

the structure of Figure 9.69 implements the 2-way inclusive OR; the through-resistance is zero if current A is zero or B is zero or both are zero.

Notice the similarity between *cryogenic elements* and relay contacts. The true state is generally regarded as that of zero resistance; thus the concept of a hindrance function is appropriate. All techniques and tricks for designing relay networks are applicable.

Because of the low resistance of the cryogenic structures, the total dissipation even in large networks tends to be very small. Cryogenic elements offer the advantage that they can be fabricated by deposition techniques; complicated structures can be built all at one time by means of multilayer deposition.

COLLATERAL READING

1. Keister, W., A. E. Ritchie and S. H. Washburn, *The design of relay switching circuits;* D. Van Nostrand Co., Princeton, N.J., 1951.
2. Richards, R. K., *Digital computer components and circuits;* D. Van Nostrand Co., Princeton, N.J., 1957; pp. 106–111.
3. Siegel, P., *Understanding digital computers;* John Wiley and Sons, New York, 1961; pp. 130–132.

   Bartee, T. C., *Digital computer fundamentals;* McGraw-Hill Book Co., New York, 1960; pp. 73–76.

   Scott, N. R., *Analog and digital computer technology;* McGraw-Hill Book Co., New York, 1960; pp. 388–392.

   Smith, C. V. L., *Electronic digital computers;* McGraw-Hill Book Co., New York, 1959; pp. 88–91.
4. Pressman, A. I., *Design of transistorized circuits for digital computers;* John F. Rider Publisher, New York, 1959; chapter 4, pp. 257–263, 273–277.

   Richards, R. K., *Digital computer components and circuits;* D. Van Nostrand Co., Princeton, N.J., 1957; chapter 4.

Bartee, T. C., *Digital computer fundamentals;* McGraw-Hill Book Co., New York, 1960; pp. 54–59.

Wanlass, C. L., Transistor circuitry for digital computers; *IRE Transactions on Electronic Computers,* vol. EC-4, March, 1955; pp. 11–16.

Goldstick, G. H., Comparison of saturated and non-saturated switching circuit techniques; *IRE Transactions on Electronic Computers,* vol. EC-9, June, 1960; pp. 161–175.

Smith, C. V. L., *Electronic digital computers;* McGraw-Hill Book Co., New York, 1959; pp. 97–101.

Hurley, R. B., *Junction transistor electronics;* John Wiley and Sons, New York, 1958; pp. 393–400.

5. Pressman, A. I., *Design of transistorized circuits for digital computers,* John F. Rider Publisher, New York, 1959; chapter 9.

Bartee, T. C., *Digital computer fundamentals;* McGraw-Hill Book Co., New York, 1960; pp. 106–110.

Beter, R. H. *et al.,* Surface barrier transistor switching circuits; *IRE Convention Record,* vol. 3, pt. 4, 1955; pp. 139–145.

Githems, J. A., The Tradic Leprechaun computer; *Proceedings of the 1956 Eastern Joint Computer Conference,* New York, 10–12 December, 1956; pp. 29–33.

Harris, J. R., Direct coupled transistor logic circuitry; *IRE Transactions on Electronic Computers,* vol. EC-7, March, 1958; pp. 2–6.

Angell, J. B., Direct coupled logic circuitry; *Proceedings of the 1958 Western Joint Computer Conference,* Los Angeles, 6–8 May, 1958; pp. 22–27.

6. Pressman, A. I., *Design of transistorized circuits for digital computers,* John F. Rider Publisher, New York, 1959; chapter 8.

Ledley, R. S., *Digital computer and control engineering;* McGraw-Hill Book Co., New York, 1960; pp. 669–672.

Cole, C. T. *et al.,* A transistorized transcribing card punch; *Proceedings of the 1956 Eastern Joint Computer Conference,* Philadelphia, 10–12 December, 1956; pp. 80–83.

Rowe, W. D., The transistor NOR circuit; *IRE WESCON Convention Record,* pt. 4, 1957; pp. 231–245.

Design of a NOR circuit; Texas Instruments, Inc., application note, February, 1961.

Scott, N. R., *Analog and digital computer technology;* McGraw-Hill Book Co., New York, 1960; pp. 419–431.

Marcovitz, M. W. and E. Seif, Analytical design of resistance-coupled transistor logical circuits; *IRE Transactions on Electronic Computers,* vol. EC-7, June, 1958; pp. 109–119.

Finch, T. R., Transistor resistor logic circuits for digital data systems; *Proceedings of the 1958 Western Joint Computer Conference,* Los Angeles, 6–8 May, 1958; pp. 17–22.

Chao, S. C., A generalized transistor logic circuit and some applications; *IRE Transactions on Electronic Computers,* vol. EC-8, March, 1959; pp. 8–12. Also a supplement to this article: *IRE Transactions on Electronic Computers,* vol. EC-9, September, 1960; pp. 371–372.

Wray, W. J., Jr., Worst case design of variable threshold transistor-resistor logic circuits; *IRE Transactions on Electronic Computers,* vol. EC-11, February, 1962; pp. 382–390.

7. Scott, N. R., *Analog and digital computer technology;* McGraw-Hill Book Co., New York, 1960; pp. 431–438.

Maley, G. A. and J. Earle, *The logic design of transistor digital computers;* Prentice-Hall, Englewood Cliffs, N.J., 1963; chapters 8, 9, 11.

Earle, J., Synthesizing minimal stroke dagger functions; *IRE Convention Record,* pt. 2, 1960; pp. 55–65.

8. Pressman, A. I., *Design of transistorized circuits for digital computers,* John F. Rider Publisher, New York, 1959; chapter 6.

9. Pressman, A. I., *Design of transistorized circuits for digital computers,* John F. Rider Publisher, New York, 1959; chapter 7.

Bartee, T. C., *Digital computer fundamentals;* McGraw-Hill Book Co., New York, 1960; pp. 67–69.

Masher, D. F., The design of diode-transistor NOR circuits; *IRE Transactions on Electronic Computers;* vol. EC-9, March, 1960; pp. 15–24.

10. Pressman, A. I., *Design of transistorized circuits for digital computers;* John F. Rider Publisher, New York, 1959; pp. 264–269.

Henle, R. A., High speed transistor computer circuit design; *Proceedings of the 1956 Eastern Joint Computer Conference,* New York, 10–12 December, 1956; pp. 64–66.

Yourke, H. S., Millimicrosecond transistor switching circuits; *IRE Transactions on Circuit Theory;* vol. CT-4, September, 1957; pp. 236–240.

Yourke, H. S. and E. J. Slobodzinski, Millimicrosecond transistor current switching techniques; *Proceedings of the 1957 Western Joint Computer Conference,* Los Angeles, 26–28 February, 1957; pp. 68–72.

Walshe, J. L., IBM current mode transistor logic circuits; *Proceedings of the 1958 Western Joint Computer Conference,* Los Angeles, 6–8 May, 1958; pp. 34–39.

Jarvis, D. B. *et al.,* Transistor current switching and routing techniques; *IRE Transactions on Electronic Computers,* vol. EC-9, September, 1960; pp. 302–308.

11. Olsen, K. H., Transistor circuitry for the Lincoln TX-2; *Proceedings of the 1957 Western Joint Computer Conference,* Los Angeles, 26–28 February, 1957; pp. 167–171.

Baker, R. H., Symmetrical transistor logic; *Proceedings of the 1958 Western Joint Computer Conference,* Los Angeles, 6–8 May, 1958; pp. 27–33.

Konkle, K. H., Circuits for the FX-1 computer; *Proceedings of the 1962 Western Joint Computer Conference,* San Francisco, 1–3 May, 1962; pp. 101–112.

12. Pressman, A. I., *Design of transistorized circuits for digital computers;* John F. Rider Publisher, New York, 1959; chapter 5.

Bartee, T. C., *Digital computer fundamentals;* McGraw-Hill Book Co., New York, 1960; pp. 65–67.

Millman, J. and H. Taub, *Pulse and digital circuits;* McGraw-Hill Book Co., New York, 1956; chapters 13, 14.

Ledley, R. S., *Digital computer and control engineering;* McGraw-Hill Book Co., New York, 1960; pp. 667–672.

Richards, R. K., *Digital computer components and circuits;* D. Van Nostrand Co., Princeton, N.J., 1957; chapter 2.

Siegel, P., *Understanding digital computers;* John Wiley and Sons, New York, 1961; pp. 128–130.

Scott, N. R., *Analog and digital computer technology;* McGraw-Hill Book Co., New York, 1960; pp. 393–399.

Murphy, J. S., *Basics of digital computers;* John F. Rider Publisher, New York, 1958; pp. 43–47.

Smith, C. V. L., *Electronic digital computers;* McGraw-Hill Book Co., New York, 1959; pp. 92–95.

Chen, T. C., Diode coincidence and mixing circuits in digital computers; *Proceedings of the IRE,* vol. 38, May, 1950; pp. 511–514.

13. Gluck, S. E. *et al.,* Design of logical OR-AND-OR pyramids for digital computers; *Proceedings of the IRE,* vol. 41, October, 1953; pp. 1388–1392.

Leondes, C. T. and M. Rubinoff, Some recent developments in logical OR-AND-OR pyramids for digital computers; *IRE Convention Record,* pt. 7, 1953; pp. 34–35.

14. Schertz, F. A. and R. T. Steinbeck, Nonlinear resistors in logical switching circuits; *Proceedings of the 1953 Western Joint Computer Conference,* Los Angeles, 4–6 February, 1953; pp. 174–186.

Smith, C. V. L., *Electronic digital computers;* McGraw-Hill Book Co., New York, 1959; p. 105.

15. Haynes, J. L., Logic circuits using square-loop magnetic devices—a survey; *IRE Transactions on Electronic Computers,* vol. EC-10, January, 1961; pp. 191–203.

Andrews, L. J., A technique for using memory cores as logical elements; *Proceedings of the 1956 Eastern Joint Computer Conference,* New York, 10–12 December, 1956; pp. 39–46.

Lockhart, N. F., Logic by ordered flux change in multipath ferrite cores; *IRE Convention Record,* pt. 4, 1958; pp. 268–278.

Smith, C. V. L., *Electronic digital computers;* McGraw-Hill Book Co., New York, 1959; pp. 101–105.

16. Matthias, B. T., Superconductivity; *Scientific American,* November, 1957; pp. 92 *ff. passim.*

Ittner, W. B., III and C. J. Krause, Superconducting computers; *Scientific American,* July, 1961; pp. 124 *ff. passim.*

Buck, D. A., A magnetically controlled gating element; *Proceedings of the 1956 Eastern Joint Computer Conference,* New York, 10–12 December, 1956; pp. 47–49.

EXERCISES

Where necessary in the following exercises and problems, use the 2N404 transistor and the 5844 vacuum tube (see pages 8.92 and 8.93 for characteristics). Use the reverse and forward current characteristics for germanium and silicon diodes on pages 9.68 and 9.69.

9.1. A panel contains a light and four toggle switches. For some combinations of the switches in the on position, the light is turned on. What experiments can be performed from the front of the panel to determine the switch wiring behind the panel? How many such experiments might have to be performed? From such experiments, could you be certain of the uniqueness of the pattern of connections? Could you determine how many poles each switch has and whether the contacts are single or double throw?

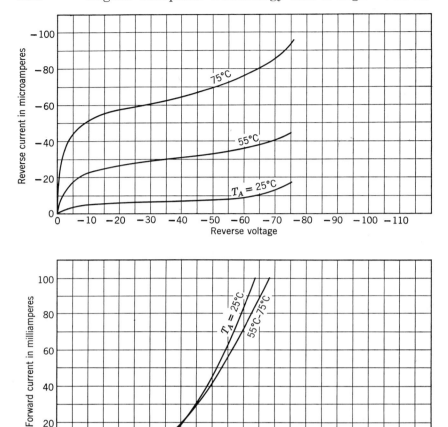

Figure 9.70. Typical germanium diode characteristics.

Could you determine the correspondence between closed contacts and the position of a switch handle?

9.2. Four lights have to be switched off and on independently, or any two on but in series. What is the least number of switches that will provide this amount of flexibility? Using Boolean methods, design a network of switches that will accomplish the desired arrangement.

9.3. Repeat the previous exercise but use relays instead of switches.

9.4. For the 2-input element of Figure 9.9, how many Boolean expressions can it realize for all choices of logical conventions at each input and output? List them.

9.5. If all possible terminals (both high and low impedance) of the pentode were used for logical inputs, how many different Boolean expressions could the single pentode circuit realize?

9.6. A 6-input AND is to be realized from 2-input pentode gates. Sketch the configuration; there is to be no logical inversion of the final output. Discuss the tolerance and logical noise aspects of the arrangement.

9.7. Derive an expression for the logical noise and signal-to-noise ratio in the n-input
      (a) collector-coupled gate,
      (b) emitter-coupled gate.
Do this in terms of the anonymous element and in terms of either the tube

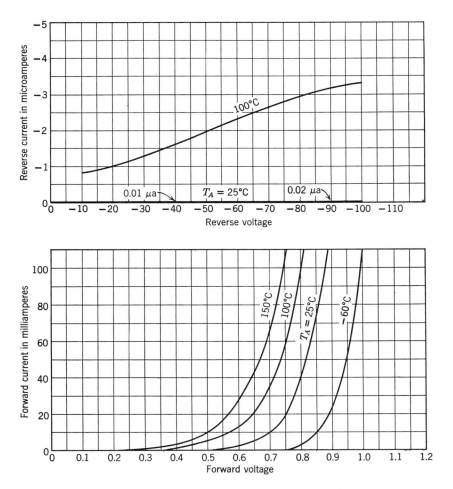

Figure 9.71. Typical silicon diode characteristics.

or the transistor. Also determine the change in current through each element of the gate structure as the inputs take on all possible logical configurations. Make this calculation for the 3-, 4-, and 5-input cases.

9.8. Must the circuit of Figure 9.28 be designed so that the input diode is
always conducting?

9.9. Consider the following tube NOR-circuit:

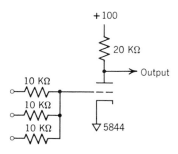

For input levels of 0 volts (= true) and −20 volts, calculate the output
voltage for each logical state of the inputs. Identify each level of the output with the proper Boolean state, and hence deduce the output signal-to-
noise ratio.

    (a) Comment on the feasibility of vacuum tube NOR's driving other
        vacuum tube NOR's.

    (b) Suppose the impedance of the input sources were 1000 Ω. Re-
        calculate the output signal-to-noise ratio.

    (c) Let all resistors vary ±10%, all voltages ±10%, and the r_p of
        the tube ±25%. Calculate the worst output levels and the worst
        signal-to-noise ratio.

9.10. Consider the following resistor-input NOR circuit. Calculate the output level for each logical state of the inputs.

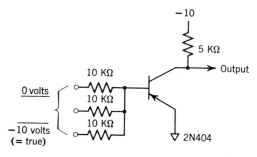

    (a) Let all resistors vary ±10% and the supply voltage ±5%. Cal-
        culate the maximum and minimum values of each output level
        and the worst signal-to-noise ratio.

    (b) If the impedance of each input source is 1000 Ω, calculate the
        actual voltage presented to each input of the NOR for each logi-
        cal state of the inputs. Find the nominal output level for each
        logical input state.

(c) As a result of the situation in (b), consider the situation in which some of the sources which drive the NOR circuit also drive other NOR circuits. Hence discuss the internal impedance of the sources as it relates to crosstalk between various NOR gates.

9.11. Consider a 3-input AND circuit of the kind shown in Figure 9.46. Assume that the diodes are ideal.

(a) As the inputs assume each of the possible logical configurations, how many different current configurations will exist in the gate?

(b) Deduce the situation in which the current in any diode is minimum. Maximum.

(c) Determine the current in each diode for each situation found in part (a). Obtain the expressions in terms of E and R. The input levels are E_t and E_f.

(d) Let the diode forward resistance be r ohms. Determine the output levels for each situation of part (a).

(e) Let the diode reverse resistance be R_b ohms. Determine the output voltage level for each situation in part (a).

9.12. Repeat exercise 9.11 for the 5-input OR gate of Figure 9.49.

9.13. For exercises 9.11 and 9.12, assume that the diodes are germanium (not ideal), $E = 50$ volts, the input levels are ± 10 volts, $R = 50$ KΩ.

(a) Find the actual currents throughout the circuit for all logical cases.

(b) Let the voltages vary by $\pm 10\%$ and the resistors by $\pm 10\%$. Let the forward characteristic of the diode vary $\pm 20\%$ and the reverse characteristic, $\pm 35\%$. Determine the minimum and maximum value of each output level.

(c) How much capacitance can be tolerated at the output if the rise and fall time is required to be 0.2 μsec?

(d) If the capacitance is actually 5 mmf, what is the actual rise and fall time? What must be the rise and fall times of the input signals?

(e) If the capacitance changes by $\pm 15\%$ in addition to the other tolerances of the circuit, what are the maximum and minimum rise times?

9.14. Let $R = 25$ KΩ and $E = +50$ volts in a 4-input version of Figure 9.48. Let the diodes be silicon and the total capacitance be 10 mmf. Determine the actual transition time of the output signal as it is determined by the gate circuit. Find the maximum current which the input drivers must handle in order to make the other transition time be the same. Hence determine the impedance of the driving sources.

9.15. In the circuits of Figure 9.46, 9.47, 9.48, and 9.49, find the nominal levels of the output voltage. Take $E = \pm 50$ volts (as the case may be), $R = 50$ KΩ, input levels to be ± 10 volts. Diodes are germanium. As the following drifts in parameters occur, find the corresponding changes in the output levels:

$R:\ \pm 10\%$ Forward impedance: $+50\%,\ -20\%$
$E:\ \pm 10\%$ Back impedance: $+10\%,\ -30\%$

Hence find the logical noise and the D-C shift contributed by the circuit as a consequence of the imperfect components and their lifetime drifts.

If each input voltage level may vary by $\pm 5\%$, find the additional drift in the output voltage. Hence find the maximum and minimum values to which each level of the output might drift as various parameters drift over time.

9.16. Consider the AND circuit of Figure 9.46. Each input signal can be $+10$ volts ($=$ true) or -10 volts ($=$ false); $R = 25$ KΩ; $E = +75$ volts. Assume that the diodes are perfect.

- (a) For all combinations of inputs, calculate the distribution of currents in the network, including the current in each diode.
- (b) Repeat (a) except that the network is a 6-input AND.
- (c) Let R have a tolerance of $\pm 10\%$. Repeat parts (a) and (b).
- (d) Let the forward resistance of the diodes be 200 Ω. Calculate the output voltage for all combinations of inputs to the 3-input AND.
- (e) Identify each level of output voltage with the proper Boolean state of the output, and hence find the signal-to-noise ratio in the circuit.
- (f) Find the maximum and minimum current that each input source must supply in part (e).
- (g) Assume that each source is a voltage source of impedance 500 Ω. In view of (f), find the voltages actually delivered to the AND circuit as input signals, and recalculate the signal-to-noise ratio at the output.
- (h) Assume that the back impedance of each diode in part (d) can be as low as 100 KΩ. Find the maximum current which must be supplied by an input source.

9.17. Repeat exercise 9.16 for the AND circuit of Figure 9.47, the OR circuits of Figure 9.48 and Figure 9.49.

9.18. Design a 3-input AND gate (Figure 9.46) for input levels of ± 10 volts, output transition times of 0.3 μsec, and an output load capacitance of 5 mmf. The shunt capacitance of the germanium diode is 2 mmf. The dissipation in the resistor is to be minimum. Assume that the input source is a step voltage in series with a resistance of 500 Ω. Calculate the maximum current to ever flow through a diode. When does this occur?

9.19. Plot in detail the curves of Figures 9.51 and 9.52.

9.20. Consider the AND-AND circuit of Figure 9.56. Determine the rise time that each input signal must have in order to allow the output signal to rise at a rate of 50 volts per μsec. For a capacitance at the output node of 10 mmf and at the interior node of 5 mmf, design the circuit for minimum dissipation. The input levels are ± 10 volts. Determine the maximum current which each input source must handle. Identify the diode which must carry the maximum current. When? Let the back resistance of the diodes be 50 KΩ. Recalculate the maximum current demanded of each driver.

9.21. Design the AND-OR circuit of Figure 9.58 for four inputs to each level. The shunt capacitance of the germanium diodes is 2 mmf; the input levels are ± 5 volts. The positive-going transition time of the output must be no slower than 0.2 μsec; the negative-going transition, no slower than 0.5 μsec. Resistors and supply voltages may vary by $\pm 10\%$ and diode characteristics by $\pm 25\%$. The load presents a capacitance of 5 mmf. The output signal is to be linear within 10%. After designing the circuit, determine:

- (a) the maximum and minimum (but non-zero) current in each diode,

(b) the maximum current to be handled by each input driver,

(c) the variation in output transition times as circuit parameters drift,

(d) the maximum and minimum values of each output level,

(e) the best and worst signal-to-noise ratios at the output,

(f) the minimum and maximum logical noise at the output.

9.22. Consider the following triode inverters:

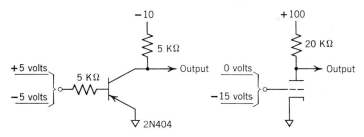

(a) Calculate the output levels.

(b) Assume that the circuit parameters drift as follows:

Voltages: $\pm 10\%$
Resistors: $\pm 5\%$
β: $\pm 50\%$
r_p: $\pm 50\%$

Find the corresponding drift in the output levels.

(c) Now modify the circuit by adding diode clamps.

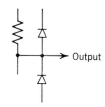

Take the diode supply voltages to be the nominal levels of the output (from part (a)), rounded to the nearest integer. Redesign the circuit by changing the load resistor and (if necessary) the supply voltage, so that the clamp diodes absorb all parameter drifts in the circuit. Determine the maximum and minimum current in each diode.

(d) Let the forward resistance of the diodes be 100 Ω and the back resistance, 250 KΩ. Find the output voltage levels.

(e) Suppose that the forward resistance of the diodes can vary $+30\%$, -20%, and that the back resistance can vary -50%, $+30\%$. Assume that the clamp voltages are regulated to $\pm\frac{1}{2}\%$. Find the resultant extreme values of the output voltage levels.

(f) Suppose that it is necessary to control the output levels more closely than found in part (e). How should the circuit be redesigned to meet the requirement?

(g) Consider the design arrived at in part (e). Suppose that each diode has a shunt capacitance of 5 mmf, and that the total all-other capacitance at the output terminal is 15 mmf. Will the circuit meet the requirement that the output must change from either level to the other in 0.2 μsec?

(h) Calculate the actual rise and fall time of the circuit for parts (a) and (c). Make whatever assumption is necessary about the rise and fall time of the input signal.

(i) If all capacitances drift by $\pm15\%$, what is the resultant change in the rise and fall times in part (h)?

9.23. Consider the following 4-input network of resistors:

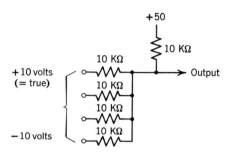

(a) Calculate the output voltage for all logical combinations of the inputs, assuming that the source impedance of the signals is zero.

(b) Assuming that the network is to implement the AND, identify each output level with the appropriate logical state.

(c) Hence calculate the signal-to-noise ratio of this network as an AND gate.

(d) Assume that each resistor can vary by $\pm5\%$. Calculate the worst signal-to-noise ratio.

(e) Assume that the network is to implement the OR. Repeat parts (b), (c), (d).

(f) Repeat parts (b), (c), (d), (e) but for the case of five inputs. Hence consider the desirability of a resistor network as a many input gate circuit.

(g) Repeat parts (a)–(f) assuming that the resistance of the input sources is 500 Ω. Hence discuss the cross-talk problem between input sources as a function of the ratio of input source resistance to the input resistance.

(h) Repeat all previous parts with the load resistor (to ±50 volts) as 1 KΩ. Is the performance of the gate any better?

(i) Repeat all parts of this exercise but for the appropriate diode networks rather than for a resistor network. Assume that the diodes are perfect. Assume that the tolerance on the resistor in the diode network is $\pm5\%$, and the resistance of the input sources is at first 0, then 500 Ω. Comment on the signal-to-noise ratio at the output of a gate as a function of the non-linearity of the switching element.

PROBLEMS

9.1. For the following 6-input common-element gates, calculate the output levels:

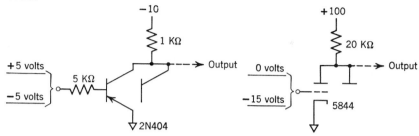

Also calculate the logical noise at the output and the signal-to-noise ratio. Let the input voltages and the supply voltages vary by ±10%, all resistors by ±5%, and the β of the transistor (or the r_p of the tube) by ±35%. Calculate the worst logical noise and the worst signal-to-noise ratio, and the worst output levels.

9.2. For the following 5-input common-element gates, calculate the nominal output levels:

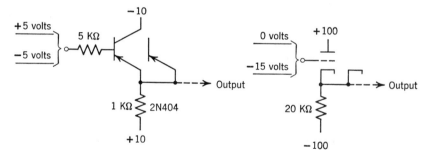

Also calculate the logical noise at the output and the signal-to-noise ratio. With the same tolerances as in problem 9.1, calculate the worst logical noise, the worst signal-to-noise ratio, and the worst output levels.

9.3. Consider a single pole 8-position rotary switch. Such a switch routes an incoming signal to 1-of-8 destinations.

    (a) Give a logical description of this switch, defining whatever Boolean functions and variables are needed. Exhibit the description in truth table form.

    (b) Sketch the gating network which realizes this switch. (Assume that there are eight inputs available, only one of which is true at a time. Such information tells in which position the switch should be.) Use, at first, collector-coupled and emitter-coupled gates, then diode gates, then NOR gates, then NAND gates.

9.4. A comparator is to give a true output if the two input binary digits are alike; a false output, otherwise.

(a) Define the logic of the comparator in truth table form.

(b) Sketch the diode gating network required.

Now assume that the comparator deals with 8-bit words. The output is to be true only if the two input words agree in all columns. Sketch the diode gating network required, and estimate the number of diodes required.

(c) Repeat the previous parts, but use the NOR gate instead of diode gates.

9.5. In transistor technology, it is common to use a shunt capacitor in the base drive circuit to improve the transistor turn-on time. In the NOR circuit of Figure 9.32 consider the implication of the capacitor on the susceptibility of the circuit to noise signals. For $C = 50$ mmf and for a triangular noise spike 0.5 volts in amplitude and 0.1 μsec wide at the base, what is the output noise signal? What would it be if the capacitor were absent?

9.6. Using a 3-input majority gate element (see problem 4.9), derive a gating network which produces the proper output for an even parity check over the 1's of a 3-bit group.

For a binary group of length 3^n, determine how many 3-input majority elements are needed to realize the even parity check.

9.7. Using Boolean methods, design a network of switches that will allow a light to be turned on and off from three locations. If turned on (off) at one location it must be able to be turned off (on) from either other location.

9.8. The circuit of Figure 9.30-b is to be used to drive other circuits of the same kind. What will determine the maximum number of inputs that can be used in such a gate? Might there be difficulties in cascading circuits of this kind? For the 2N404, considering both the tolerance problem and conservative design, what is the maximum number that you would use in such a gate?

9.9. How would your answers to problem 9.8 change if the transistors in Figure 9.30-b had base input resistors?

9.10. Design the PNP version of the circuit of Figure 9.34 for the following conditions:

E = −10 volts

Germanium diodes

2N404 transistor

Output to drive three inputs of similar circuits

Inputs to be driven from similar circuits

Make any other assumptions which are necessary.

9.11. Design an AND-OR-AND diode gating circuit (Figure 9.57). The number of inputs at each level is 4, 5, 4 respectively. The input levels are ±5 volts with a tolerance of ±5% on each level. The output is to drive up to three inputs of other circuits of the same kind. The positive-going transition time of the output must be no slower than 0.15 μsec; the negative-going, no slower than 0.25 μsec. The output is to be linear to ±10%. The forward characteristic of the germanium diodes can vary by ±25%; the back characteristic, by ±35%. Supply voltages vary by ±5%; resistors, by ±5%. Diode shunt capacitance is 2 mmf. There is a stray capacitance of 10 mmf at the output node, and of 5 mmf at the interior nodes.

(a) Calculate the maximum and minimum current through each diode and specify the logical state of the input signals which correspond to each situation.

(b) Determine the current which each input driver must handle to satisfy the transition times of the output.

(c) Specify the maximum and minimum value of each output level.

(d) Calculate the best and worst output signal-to-noise ratios.

(e) Calculate the fastest and slowest transition times (in each direction) of the output signal.

9.12. Repeat problem 9.11 for the OR-AND-OR configuration (Figure 9.58). The number of inputs at each level is 5, 3, and 6 respectively.

9.13. Write the truth table which defines the parity digit in terms of the other 4-bits of an odd parity-checked 4-bit code group. Derive the algebraic expressions, and sketch the resulting logical network.

Repeat the above, except that the code group to be checked is a 6-tuple. Hence develop an appreciation for the amount of equipment required for a parity check as a function of the length of the binary group to be checked.

Suppose that a parity check were to be applied to 36-column words. How much equipment is involved? How many layers of logic (and hence delay time) is involved? Is there any other way to derive the parity digit than from a gating network? Suppose that the digits were available serially. Would that help? If so, how fast would they have to be available in order to produce the parity digit as rapidly as with a gating network?

9.14. Consider a many-input AND gate for the arrow-up logical convention. Let the resistor be R, the total capacitance at the node be C, the required output levels E_u and E_l. Let I_{max} be the maximum current permitted through a diode. In terms of these parameters, determine the fastest rise time (T_r) that the circuit can possibly achieve. How must it be designed to achieve it?

Suppose that the rise time (t) is less than the fastest. Determine an expression which gives it, then develop an expression for t/T_r which involves only variables that represent voltage parameters of the circuit. As a measure of power (P) in the circuit, use that in the resistor when the output is at E_l. Define a reference power (P_0) as

$$P_0 = (E_u - E_l)I_{max},$$

and find an expression for P/P_0 which involves only variables which represent voltage parameters of the circuit.

What is the physical significance of P_0? Suppose that the ratios t/T_r and P/P_0 were plotted against E/E_l for various ratios of E_u/E_l. Of what use would such curves be in the design of the AND gate? Give a numerical illustrative example of their use. Demonstrate that such curves are also useful for the design of OR gates and of cascaded gates.

9.15. Consider an AND-OR gate for the arrow-up logical convention. The components of the AND gate are E_1 and R_1; of the OR gate, E_2 and R_2. The capacitance at the internal node is C_2; at the output, C_1.

Assume that the current (I_2) through R_2 and the current (I_1) through R_1 are essentially constant. If the rise and fall times in the circuit are to be equal, determine the ratio I_1/I_2 in terms of other parameters of the circuit.

Hence determine the peak and steady-state currents through the diodes of the AND gate in terms of I_2.

Let I_{max} be the maximum current ever permitted through a diode. Determine I_1 and I_2 in terms of I_{max}. In the steady-state situation indicate the current distribution in the circuit (in terms of I_{max}). Find the positive- and negative-going transition times, and show that their ratio is unity (as we originally assumed).

Assume now that only the steady-state currents are limited to I_{max}; the peak current can exceed I_{max}. Again determine I_1, I_2, the current distribution, and the rise and fall times.

Repeat the above analysis, except assume that the ratio of rise time to fall time is not unity but $1/k$.

Determine whether there is a particular design for which the current in the AND and OR diodes can be equal.

9.16. Consider an AND-OR gate. Suppose that the two supply voltages are determined by some other consideration. Where should the signal levels of the circuit (E_u and E_l) be relative to the supply voltages to make the rise and fall time equal? Take the various parameters of the circuit to be as given in problem 9.15.

9.17. In the discussion on pages 9.56 *ff.* concerning current build-up, there is an implicit assumption having to do with the relation of the actual current through a diode to the current rating of the diode.

What is this assumption? If it were violated, how would the discussion of current build-up change? Might there be special design considerations—especially logical ones—that would have to be levied?

ten

Miscellaneous Circuits

In this chapter we discuss a number of unrelated circuits, some of which are required not for the logical completeness of a machine but for practical reasons, e.g., driving capacitance loads, shaping electrical signals, and amplification. We will continue to use our generalized active element and to particularize to a transistor or a tube only where necessary.

LINEAR AMPLIFIERS

Frequently the signals from storage devices (see Chapter 12) are so low level that amplification is necessary. Such amplifiers are often, but not necessarily linear, and a wide bandwidth is required. Occasionally linear amplifiers or ones with response characteristics shaped either in frequency or in amplitude are also needed for other purposes. The design principles of such amplifiers are well documented in the literature (1). Only a few things which must be watched carefully are discussed here.

Because our designs must be conservative, some derating schedules will be used. A given design may have to guarantee a minimum gain or bandwidth or both, and therefore we will systematically have to investigate the circuit to determine how each component drift will affect these two properties. If a specific value of gain is required, negative feedback can be employed to stabilize the amplifier. Sometimes feedback can also be used to shape the frequency response. Frequently, however, the signals to be amplified are of very short duration; this may cause some difficulty in maintaining the delay in the feedback loop sufficiently short.

Sometimes amplifiers used in a storage device will be subjected to the large signals developed during writing operations (see Chapter 12, page 12.69) and will, therefore, overload. The overload and recovery characteristics of an amplifier may be of concern. Special precautions (e.g., limiters) may need to be taken; special configurations (e.g., emitter- or cathode-coupled amplifiers, direct-coupled amplifiers) have advantageous overload and recovery characteristics.

BLOCKING OSCILLATORS

The circuit of Figure 10.1 or one of its derivatives is often used as a pulse source. The design of such circuits is well known in the art (2), but there are a few important points to be watched. One is the derating schedule to be used. In some applications (e.g., radar) the blocking oscillator is designed so that both control and collector currents are many times handbook ratings. This is not consistent with the design attitude which the digital designer must adopt; we must be much more conservative with respect to the peak currents permitted in the active element. We could insist that the peak current not exceed what would be allowed for a steady-state current, or we might permit the peak current to be equal to the handbook rating.

The blocking oscillator is convenient in that it provides either polarity of output. On the other hand, it is not a direct-coupled

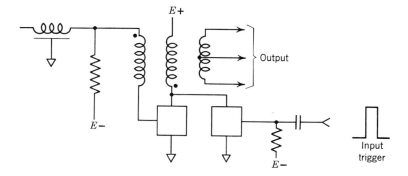

Figure 10.1. A typical blocking oscillator.

circuit, and the transformer will impose a recovery interval on it. A possible source of concern is the jitter in triggering delay. As the shape or amplitude of the input signal changes, the time required for the oscillator to start may vary. This could be especially the case if the blocking oscillator were driven from, say, an OR gate, all of whose inputs were not precisely alike in shape and amplitude.

As we have seen (Chapter 9, page 9.10), gate circuits, if they are to function properly, require that their inputs coexist in time. As we also must suspect by now, signals may arrive at a given point after having followed many different paths through a large gating network. Variations in delay due to the change in path length which occurs as the internal logical configuration changes, plus uncertainties in triggering time of blocking oscillators or other pulse sources can be a touchy problem in the design of various parts of the machine.

THE FOLLOWER

The emitter follower is important for its current gain and, therefore, for its ability to drive heavy resistive or capacitive loads. Such resistive loads could be the losses in a magnetic circuit, grid or base currents, or the input currents of diode networks. Since digital machines may be large physically, it is often necessary to drive the shunt capacitance of long wires or coaxial cables.

Small signal theory indicates that the internal output impedance of a follower is very low,* and furthermore that this is true regardless of the polarity of the signal. Since the emitter resistor represents substantial negative feedback, the follower is linear over a fairly large region; the temptation, therefore, is to conclude that the follower continues to be a low impedance source for the large signals normally found in digital equipment (3).

Let us look at the physics of the situation. Suppose that a follower is being driven by a trapezoidal signal and has a capacitance load (Figure 10.2). As the control rises linearly, the emitter is expected to follow. However, the capacitance requires current if its voltage is to change. If the input rises at the rate of $\Delta e/\Delta t$, the capacitor re-

---

* For the vacuum tube, the output impedance is approximately the reciprocal of the grid-voltage plate-current transconductance $1/g_m$. For the transistor, the output impedance is approximately the impedance of the source driving the base divided by $\beta + 1$.

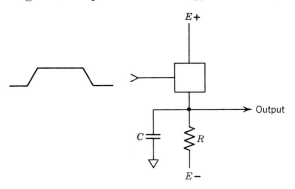

Figure 10 2. The follower.

quires a current of $C(\Delta e/\Delta t)$ if the output is to follow the input. The resistor (R) will also demand current as the voltage across it increases. The only source for both these currents is the active element.

Assume that there has been some quiescent value of current in the emitter resistor; there is some bias between the control and emitter.* After the input has begun to move, the output lags behind the input slightly until the bias has so adjusted itself that the resulting new bias permits the device to supply the additional current required by the capacitor. It can happen, for example, that a tube is unable to supply the required total current unless the grid itself goes into current; if this happens to be the case, the designer had better know it and be prepared to supply such current from a suitable source. Otherwise the source of the input signal can be rudely perturbed. For a transistor follower, the capacitance load is reflected as additional base current.

There is a small time delay through the follower which depends on the capacitance load. With increasing capacitance, the output must lag the input for a longer time to permit the larger bias adjustment implied by the larger capacitance. This time delay can be readily estimated. For a ramp signal at the input, the capacitor requires a current of

$$C\left(\frac{\Delta e}{\Delta t}\right).$$

---

* For the tube, the grid will be negative relative to the cathode normally. Sometimes a cathode follower is specifically designed for grid current, in which case the grid is positive relative to the cathode. For an NPN transistor, the base is positive relative to the emitter.

This requires an incremental change in device bias of

$$e_c = \frac{1}{g_m}\left(C\,\frac{\Delta e}{\Delta t}\right)^*$$

where g_m is the transconductance. The input is moving at the rate of $\Delta e/\Delta t$; therefore, to move e_c, it takes a time interval of

$$e_c\left(\frac{\Delta t}{\Delta e}\right)$$

and the delay through the follower is

$$\frac{C}{g_m}\,\text{sec}\,\dagger$$

if C is in farads and g_m, in mhos.

As the input voltage reaches the plateau of the trapezoidal signal, the capacitor no longer demands current, and the current required of the device decreases to only that required by the resistor. As the input begins to move negatively, trouble begins. The capacitor now must discharge current into some sink. The device cannot pass current in the reverse direction, and thus the only sink is represented by the emitter resistor and the voltage to which it is returned.

The fastest rate at which the capacitor can discharge corresponds to complete cutoff of the device. In this case the current flowing in the emitter resistor comes completely from the capacitor. If the device is not completely cutoff, some fraction of the current in the resistor will be supplied from the device; therefore, less current will be extracted from the capacitor and it will move more slowly. If the emitter circuit, considered as a simple resistance-capacitance network, does not decay as rapidly as required, there is nothing the device can do to hasten the action. Specifically, there is no impedance of low value which is effective in discharging the capacitor.

The design of the follower starts with whichever edge of the input signal is negative going. The return voltage (E) of the emitter resistor and the resistor (R) itself are chosen so that the desired rate of change of voltage occurs across the capacitor. The situation exactly

* In Chapter 8 (page 8.18), we had assumed an equivalent circuit for the generalized device which followed vacuum tube practice. The factor g_m is a transconductance which relates input voltage and output current.

† For the vacuum tube, this is the proper expression; g_m is the grid-voltage plate-current transconductance. For the transistor $1/g_m$ is replaced by $R_s/(\beta + 1)$ where R_s is the impedance of the source that drives the base.

parallels the diode gate situation. As with the diode gate design, there is an indeterminacy which can be resolved in the same way. Of course, E must be more negative than the lower level of the input.

Consider now the positive-going edge. The rate of change of this edge determines the amount of current required for the capacitor. The resistor is known, and therefore its current requirement can be calculated. The sum of these two determine the current required from the derated device. Finally, the device may be selected, and then its supply voltage.

EXAMPLE

The circuit of Figure 10.3 is to be designed. To discharge the capacitor on the trailing edge, a current of

$$I = C(\Delta e/\Delta t)$$
$$= (200 \times 10^{-12})(25 \times 10^{6})$$
$$= 5 \times 10^{-3} \text{ amp}$$
$$= 5 \text{ ma}$$

is required. Therefore,

$$R = 40/5 \times 10^{-3} = 8 \text{ K}\Omega.$$

This, of course, is an approximation since it assumes that the discharge current is constant. Furthermore, the change in control-emitter bias has been ignored which amounts to assuming that the gain of the follower is unity. An exact design would fit an exponential curve through the known beginning and end points of the voltage swing at the output, and would take into account

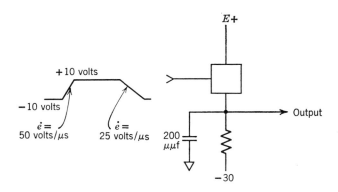

Figure 10.3. A specific follower to be designed.

the shift in bias.   These refinements can be made on an iteration of the design; the approximation is a good way to get started.

On the leading edge the capacitor requires a current of

$$(200 \times 10^{-12})(50 \times 10^{6}) = 10 \times 10^{-3} \text{ amp}$$

$$= 10 \text{ ma.}$$

Just as the input turns the corner onto the plateau, the resistance current is

$$\frac{40}{8 \text{ K}\Omega} = 5 \text{ ma.}$$

Therefore, the peak current required from the device is 15 ma.   If a 2-to-1 current derating were being used, a device capable of supplying 30 ma (handbook rating) will be selected.   The collector supply depends on the device and may in part be determined by its internal dissipation rating.

The price of providing the fast-moving negative-going edge is steady power dissipation, both in the device and in the resistor.   This is a consequence of not having a bilateral, switchable current device.   In the transistor art, the situation is more favorable because, say, a PNP can be used to pull the capacitance one way and an NPN, to pull it the other way (Figure 10.4).   The bias levels of the two transistors must be carefully watched.   If both come into conduction at once, one will pour current into the other, and the capacitance may not receive any current.   The design technique outlined above predicates that the designer wishes to meet the speed requirements for minimum current in the circuit.

Our empirical insight into follower action can be verified by a Laplace transient analysis of the circuit.   This analysis shows that

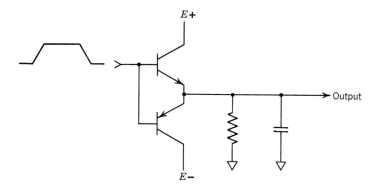

Figure 10.4.   Push-pull transistor followers.

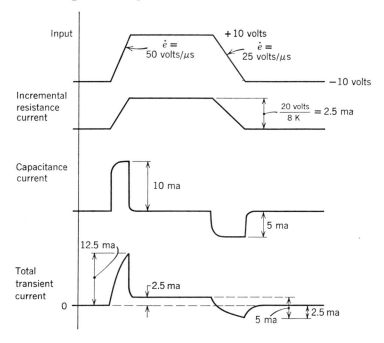

Figure 10.5. Transient current components in the follower of Figure 10.3.

there are two transient components of device current (Figure 10.5): one for the capacitor and one for the resistor. The capacitance current builds up exponentially with a time constant of the load capacitance multiplied by the internal resistance of the follower as a source. Since this time constant is very short, the capacitance current pulse is nearly rectangular. Furthermore, we clearly see that on the negative-going edge, the net device current attempts to go negative—which it cannot. This implies that there must be an additional component of resistive current equal to at least the peak value of the current to be discharged from the capacitor. This additional component is the one which we provided as standby current in the emitter resistor.

MONOSTABLE MULTIVIBRATORS

Monostable or one-shot multivibrators are sometimes used as pulse sources (4). As usual, the design must be conservative and a derating

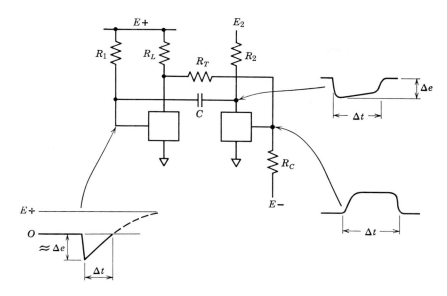

Figure 10.6.   A monostable multivibrator.

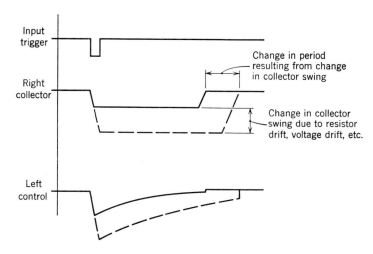

Figure 10.7.   The effect of tolerances on the period of a symmetrical monostable multivibrator.

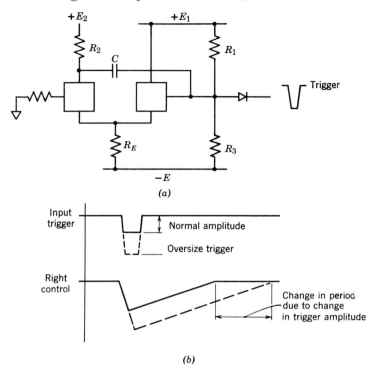

(a)

(b)

Figure 10.8. The effect of trigger amplitude on the period of an asymmetrical monostable multivibrator.

policy followed. Much of the knowledge from the design of toggle circuits can be applied directly. By replacing one of the resistive feedback paths by a capacitive one, either the symmetrical or asymmetrical toggle can be converted to monostable form. Consider Figure 10.6, which is derived from Figure 8.2. We will pick R_1 to supply the normal amount of input current to the left side; R_2 and E_2 represent the Thévenin equivalent of the original complex collector load; C is picked to give the proper timing interval. A negative pulse applied to the left control will cause the circuit to flip, and as the capacitor discharges, the left control will gradually return positively. The circuit finally reflips, at which time the capacitor recharges through R_2 and the control-emitter diode on the left side. As shown, the circuit therefore has a recovery time which depends principally on C, R_2, and E_2. Figure 10.7 shows that if the collector swing of the right side changes, the duration of the cycle changes. Such problems must be considered in determining how the width (or amplitude) of the output signal will change as various parameters drift.

Figure 10.8 illustrates another point. As before, E_2 and R_2 represent the Thévenin equivalent of the original collector network; R_1 and R_3 have been picked to position the right control at the same potential as the upper level of the right control of the Schmitt toggle from which this circuit is derived (e.g., approximately +8 volts for the circuit of Figure 8.38). A negative signal on the right control is one way of triggering this circuit (Figure 10.8-a). However, if the amplitude of this trigger is too large, it, rather than the collector swing, determines the level from which the control begins to return upwardly. Therefore, the length of the cycle will depend on the trigger amplitude (Figure 10.8-b). If the amplitude of the trigger is guaranteed to be less than the collector swing, the latter determines the lower reach of the right control. The coupling diode effectively disconnects the circuit from the effect of variable trigger height. On the other hand, unless the width of the trigger is very small compared to the natural timing interval of the multivibrator, the width of the trigger will influence the timing interval of the circuit (see exercise 10.8).

L-C PULSE GENERATOR

The circuit of Figure 10.9 can be used when a pulse of precisely controlled width is required (5). It capitalizes on the fact that the axis-

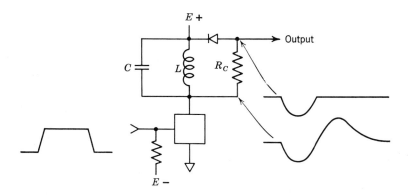

Figure 10.9. An L-C pulser.

crossings of the voltage in a parallel resonant circuit depend only on the values of the inductance (L) and the capacitance (C) and not on the amplitude of the oscillation. The device is normally cutoff; the input signal is large enough to bring it into conduction. As the device is switched on, the resonant circuit begins to oscillate. If the switched current is I, the amplitude of oscillation is $I\sqrt{L/C}$; the frequency of oscillation is $1/(2\pi\sqrt{LC})$. After the first half cycle, the phase of the oscillation begins to reverse. As it does, the diode connects a critical damping resistor across the resonant circuit. Therefore, the voltage across it cannot again recross the axis. By taking the output as shown, the overshoot (the damped second half-cycle) is deleted from the output signal.

The design of the circuit is straightforward and completely determinate. The desired amplitude, width, and available current specify L and C which in turn determine $R_C(= \frac{1}{2}\sqrt{L/C})$. ($R_C$ must still impose critical damping even if it and the L and the C have drifted!) If necessary the resonant circuit can be temperature compensated so that the width of the output is extremely stable. The maximum amplitude of the oscillation is set by the supply voltage and the least collector voltage at which the device will pass the required current. There are two characteristics of the L-C pulser which might be minor problems in particular cases. Damping the resonant circuit takes roughly one to two times the width of the first half cycle; thus the maximum duty cycle is about $\frac{1}{3}$. Since the pulse width varies as only the inverse square root of L or C, it is difficult to make the output continously variable over a range of more than about 3-to-1, because of limitations in the range of variable capacitors or variable inductances.

Further shaping of the half-sinusoidal output can be done, but care must be taken to preserve the axis-crossings since their separation is the invariant of the signal. The L-C pulse circuit might be used in the free collector of the asymmetrical toggle.

CURRENT SWITCH

The emitter-coupled amplifier of Figure 10.10 is a convenient current switch (6). If the left control is at $+5$ volts and the cutoff level of the device is somewhat less (say, 2 volts), the current of the emitter resistor flows through the left side. As this control moves to -5 volts, the current transfers to the right side. Moreover, the current in the right side is well determined. Since R_E represents a large

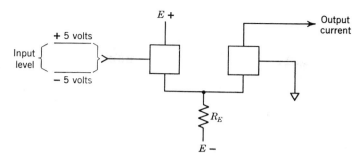

Figure 10.10. The current switch.

amount of negative feedback, the current through the device is governed almost exclusively by this resistor and by the voltage to which it is returned. The dependence of the current on device characteristics decreases with increasing R_E, which in turn implies an increasingly negative E and increasing dissipation in R_E. If E is large compared to the control-emitter bias, drifts in the bias as the device ages will influence the current only slightly.

The transistor version of this circuit can be a little tricky to design because the input base current also flows through the emitter into the R_E. Variation in the base current, therefore, results in a small variation in the switched current.

THE SLICER

This circuit (Figure 10.11-a) is an overdriven emitter-coupled amplifier (7). It can also be considered as a current switch whose output current flows through the load R_L. As in the current switch, an input signal which is at least a cutoff above the right control will steer the current of the emitter resistor into the left side. For an input signal which is at least a cutoff below the right control, the current transfers to the right side and develops an output signal across R_L. Hence the input signal is assumed to be larger than twice the cutoff of the active element. The design starts at the output. The collector resistor (R_L) is picked to provide the necessary rate of change on the rising edge. If the value is unreasonably low, the alternate load circuit (Figure 10.11-b) can be used, but it will cost standby dissipation in the resistor, an additional power supply for the clamp, as well as the

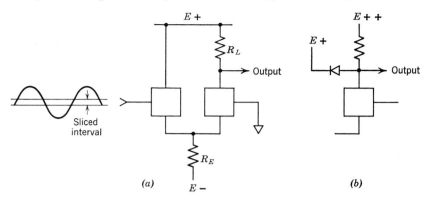

Figure 10.11.   The slicer circuit.

clamp diode.   Next, the emitter current is picked to provide the desired amplitude of output; this current in turn determines the emitter resistor and its return voltage.   Finally the supply voltage of the left section is picked so that it can supply the current required by the emitter resistor when the input signal is at its most positive value.

So long as the peak-to-peak amplitude of the input signal exceeds twice the cutoff voltage of the active element, the effect of this circuit is to take a voltage slice through the input signal and to amplify the slice.   Thus, the slicer circuit is useful for shaping a signal, or rejecting noise components which are outside the sliced region.   The rate of change of voltage at the output can exceed the rate of change at the input, but the actual time to rise at the output cannot exceed the time of the input to rise through the sliced interval.

The asymmetrical toggle (page 8.77) has the same property as the slicer circuit.   For signals of one polarity at the left control, it will flip one way, but for signals of the opposite polarity, it will flip the other way.   Hence, for a sufficiently large signal fluctuating in both directions around a nominal level, the asymmetrical toggle will flip back and forth in response to the signal.   However, its slicing interval is smaller because of the loop gain in the circuit.   For example, consider the transition from current in the left side to current in the right side. In the slicer proper, the left control must move from cutoff above the fixed potential of the right control to cutoff below it.   In the asymmetrical toggle, as the left control moves downward, the right control moves upward to meet it, and hence the voltage difference to accomplish the transition is smaller.

The design problem for the asymmetrical toggle is a little different when it is used as a signal shaper. Because of the load in the right collector, there is enhancement of the collector-control capacitance in the right side and, therefore, some effect on the speed of the circuit.

ENCODERS AND DECODERS

Because of the resemblance of the circuit diagram and sometimes also the resemblance of the actual physical configuration to a rectangular array, a particular arrangement of diode gates is often called a *matrix* (8). A *decoding matrix* usually accepts groups of input digits and maps them onto 1-of-n outputs, whereas an *encoding matrix* maps the n inputs onto groups of output digits.

EXAMPLES

1. A particular matrix decoder is to accept two binary digits as input and is to output a signal on 1-of-4 wires. The inputs are the four possible binary 2-tuples (00, 01, 10, 11), and each of the four output wires can be considered as described by a Boolean variable which is in the true state one out of four times. Hence the truth table which describes the complete matrix will contain two variables, and there will be four different output functions of these variables.

A	B	OUTPUT 1	OUTPUT 2	OUTPUT 3	OUTPUT 4
0	0	1	0	0	0
0	1	0	1	0	0
1	0	0	0	1	0
1	1	0	0	0	1

Four algebraic functions will be required to describe this composite table.

$$\text{Output 1} = \bar{A} \cdot \bar{B}$$

$$\text{Output 2} = \bar{A} \cdot B$$

$$\text{Output 3} = A \cdot \bar{B}$$

$$\text{Output 4} = A \cdot B$$

Thus, the decoder will consist of four 2-input AND gates. Moreover, since the variables appear not only as themselves but also complemented, there must either be four input terminals (two with variables and two with complemented variables), or there must be two input terminals followed by two NOT circuits.

Assuming that the variables and their complements are available, the four AND circuits are shown in Figure 10.12 in a matrix arrangement. Each input line connects to two diodes, and each output line is fed from two diodes. The Input A is at $+10$ volts when variable $A = 1$. When $A = 1$, $\bar{A} = 0$ by definition, and therefore if Input A is at $+10$ volts, Input $\bar{A}$ must be at -10 volts, and vice versa. The four outputs in this example in effect respond to the four minterms of two Boolean variables.

The current demand on the gate drivers is a little different. Only one of the AND gates can be true at a time; therefore, the gate current of the true one will be shared by the two inputs which make it true. The gate currents of the three false gates must be shared by the two remaining inputs. In Figure 10.12, if, say, output 4 is true, inputs A and B share its gate current. Output 3 is held false by $\bar{B}$, output 2 by $\bar{A}$, and output 1 by $\bar{A}$ and $\bar{B}$ together. Hence, the $\bar{A}$ and $\bar{B}$ drivers must handle one-and-a-half times the current of one gate. On the other hand, the A and B drivers must accommodate the capacitance load and the back current of two additional diodes, one to output 3 and one to output 2. The back current of this pair turn up as an additional burden on the $\bar{A}$ and $\bar{B}$ drivers. In this example, therefore, each driver must accommodate on a steady-state basis half again as much gate current as in a single AND, plus the back current of two additional diodes.

2. The inputs to Figure 10.13 are 1-of-8 possible signals; one and only one of the eight inputs can be true at a time. The outputs are the direct (A, B, C) and complemented $(\bar{A}, \bar{B}, \bar{C})$ variables of the triads which correspond to the octal digits. This is an octal-binary *conversion matrix*. There are eight input var-

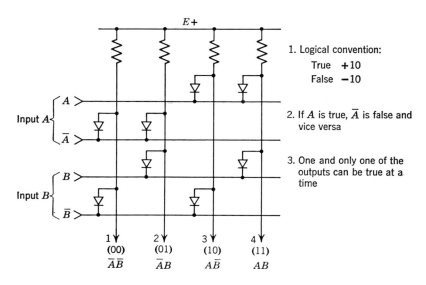

Figure 10.12. A diode decoder.

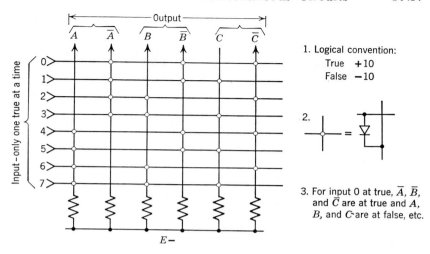

1. Logical convention:
   True $+10$
   False -10

2.

3. For input 0 at true, $\overline{A}$, $\overline{B}$, and $\overline{C}$ are at true and A, B, and C are at false, etc.

Figure 10.13. An octal-binary conversion matrix.

iables for this matrix, and there are six output functions of these variables. The truth table is as follows:

INPUTS								OUTPUTS					
I_0	I_1	I_2	I_3	I_4	I_5	I_6	I_7	A	$\overline{A}$	B	$\overline{B}$	C	$\overline{C}$
1	0	0	0	0	0	0	0	0	1	0	1	0	1
0	1	0	0	0	0	0	0	0	1	0	1	1	0
0	0	1	0	0	0	0	0	0	1	1	0	0	1
0	0	0	1	0	0	0	0	0	1	1	0	1	0
0	0	0	0	1	0	0	0	1	0	0	1	0	1
0	0	0	0	0	1	0	0	1	0	0	1	1	0
0	0	0	0	0	0	1	0	1	0	1	0	0	1
0	0	0	0	0	0	0	1	1	0	1	0	1	0

This table is to be interpreted as follows. For I_0 true, the octal input digit to the matrix is 0_8. The outputs $\overline{A}$, $\overline{B}$, and $\overline{C}$ are each 1 or the variables A, B, and C are each 0. The binary tetrad corresponding to 0_8 is 000. The complemented output terminals of the matrix will be used to set toggles to their 0-states, the direct output terminals, to set toggles to their 1-states. The algebraic expressions follow immediately; typical ones are:

$$A = I_4 + I_5 + I_6 + I_7$$

$$C = I_1 + I_3 + I_5 + I_7$$

$$\overline{B} = I_0 + I_1 + I_4 + I_5.$$

Normally each of the terms ORed together in the algebraic expressions would be an 8-way AND; one of the eight variables would be in direct form, and the other seven, complemented. However, only one of the inputs is true at a time, and so to speak, the lines of the table are mutually exclusive. In any vertical column, only one 1 appears and if, say, I_0 is true, all other inputs are a priori guaranteed to be false. A full table of eight variables would have 2^8 entries; we have only eight entries. Hence we expect that a straightforward use of the Boolean expansion theorem will lead to logical expressions which contain possibilities that cannot occur because of other constraints of the situation. In this particular instance, we can (by inspection) deduce the simpler logical expressions.

The complete truth table requires six 4-input OR circuits to realize. Figure 10.13 shows these OR circuits in a matrix configuration. Because one and only one of the input variables can be true at a time, one and only one input to each OR gate is true at a time. This simplifies the design problem of the OR gate somewhat; in particular, it abolishes the source of logical noise. However, each input driver must handle the current of three OR gates, and must, therefore, be designed for a heavier current than usual.

In general, both a binary variable and its complement appear at either the input or output terminals of a matrix. Moreover, the truth table need not be exhaustive. For example, although all four minterms in the first example were of interest, and all 2^2 combinations of the variables appeared, in the second example only eight of the 2^8 combinations of the variables were of concern. Except for the new aspects noted in the examples, the design techniques of Chapter 9 cover the situation.

Sometimes it is necessary to transliterate from one code to a second one, e.g., from one binary-decimal code to another one. This can be done by decoding from the input code to a 1-of-n representation, and then encoding the 1-of-n information into the desired output code. The translation will require two back-to-back matrix switches, and we see from our examples that the design job is essentially that of AND-OR gates. However, the important new aspect is that the AND gates of the decoder may have to drive several OR gates of the encoder. The techniques of Chapter 9 can be readily applied to this new circumstance.

EXAMPLE

Suppose that it is necessary to translate from an 8, 4, 2, 1 code to a 5, 4, 2, 1 code. We can decode the input groups to a 1-of-10 representation and then re-code the 1-of-10 information into the output code. The decoding truth table is as follows.

INPUT				OUTPUT									
A	B	C	D	0	1	2	3	4	5	6	7	8	9
0	0	0	0	1	0	0	0	0	0	0	0	0	0
0	0	0	1	0	1	0	0	0	0	0	0	0	0
0	0	1	0	0	0	1	0	0	0	0	0	0	0
0	0	1	1	0	0	0	1	0	0	0	0	0	0
0	1	0	0	0	0	0	0	1	0	0	0	0	0
0	1	0	1	0	0	0	0	0	1	0	0	0	0
0	1	1	0	0	0	0	0	0	0	1	0	0	0
0	1	1	1	0	0	0	0	0	0	0	1	0	0
1	0	0	0	0	0	0	0	0	0	0	0	1	0
1	0	0	1	0	0	0	0	0	0	0	0	0	1

The encoding truth table is as follows (W, X, Y, Z is the output tetrad):

INPUT										OUTPUT							
0	1	2	3	4	5	6	7	8	9	W	$\overline{W}$	X	$\overline{X}$	Y	$\overline{Y}$	Z	$\overline{Z}$
1	0	0	0	0	0	0	0	0	0	0	1	0	1	0	1	0	1
0	1	0	0	0	0	0	0	0	0	0	1	0	1	0	1	1	0
0	0	1	0	0	0	0	0	0	0	0	1	0	1	1	0	0	1
0	0	0	1	0	0	0	0	0	0	0	1	0	1	1	0	1	0
0	0	0	0	1	0	0	0	0	0	0	1	1	0	0	1	0	1
0	0	0	0	0	1	0	0	0	0	1	0	0	1	0	1	0	1
0	0	0	0	0	0	1	0	0	0	1	0	0	1	0	1	1	0
0	0	0	0	0	0	0	1	0	0	1	0	0	1	1	0	0	1
0	0	0	0	0	0	0	0	1	0	1	0	0	1	1	0	1	0
0	0	0	0	0	0	0	0	0	1	1	0	1	0	0	1	0	1

The decoding matrix consists of ten 4-input AND circuits, only one of which is true at a time. Probably both direct and complemented variables will be used as input information. The encoding matrix is eight OR circuits; one of these is an 8-way OR, two are 6-way, two are 5-way, two are 4-way and one is 2-way. The output of each AND gate must drive the inputs of four ORs. The decoding matrix accounts for forty diodes, and the encoding matrix, another forty. If only the direct variables must be produced for the output, the OR gates are a 5-way, two 4-way, and a 2-way for a total of fifteen diodes in the encoder.

Another way to regard this problem is to consider that the four (or eight) output functions depend directly on the four input variables. Such a truth table is as follows, for only the direct output variables:

INPUT				OUTPUT			
A	*B*	*C*	*D*	*W*	*X*	*Y*	*Z*
0	0	0	0	0	0	0	0
0	0	0	1	0	0	0	1
0	0	1	0	0	0	1	0
0	0	1	1	0	0	1	1
0	1	0	0	0	1	0	0
0	1	0	1	1	0	0	0
0	1	1	0	1	0	0	1
0	1	1	1	1	0	1	0
1	0	0	0	1	0	1	1
1	0	0	1	1	1	0	0

This truth table defines four functions (W, X, Y, Z) of the variables A, B, C, D. By a straightforward application of the expansion theorems, the four functions can be exhibited algebraically and implemented. There will result four gating networks, each producing one of the output variables and driven in parallel at the input. Each is either an AND of ORs or an OR of ANDS depending upon which expansion method has been used. In either case, no gate circuit will have to drive more than one other. Moreover, we observe that the first five code groups need no translation, and we expect that some simplification will be possible because of it.

COUNTERS

A counter is a device to record the number of times some event has happened. A convenient way to implement this requirement is to symbolize each occurence of the event by the digit 1, and to accumulate the number of 1's which appear. A counter, therefore, is a device which accepts an input of 1, and accumulates the quantity of 1's which come. The successive contents of a counter correspond to the successive entries in a counting table for some number system. We, therefore, expect that a counter will be concerned with representing information in a positional notation scheme, and probably will be concerned with addition.

Although a counter is in a sense a special kind of circuit, it is not a basic circuit in the sense that it is made of toggles and gates. Since we have not yet considered arithmetic circuits, it is appropriate to postpone the discussion of counters. Since a counter tends to be used most frequently in the control part of a machine, discussion of its principles of operation is given in Chapter 13.

COLLATERAL READING

1. Valley, G. and H. Wallman, *Vacuum tube amplifiers;* McGraw-Hill Book Co., New York, 1948.

   Millman, J. and H. Taub, *Pulse and digital circuits;* McGraw-Hill Book Co., New York, 1956; chapter 3.

   Hurley, R. B., *Junction transistor electronics,* John Wiley and Sons, New York, 1958; chapters 13, 14, 15.

   Arguimbau, L. B., *Vacuum tube circuits and amplifiers;* John Wiley and Sons, New York, 1956; chapters 3, 5, 6, 10.

   DeWitt, D. and A. L. Rossoff, *Transistor electronics;* McGraw-Hill Book Co., New York, 1957; chapters 8, 10.

2. Chance, B. *et al., Waveforms;* McGraw-Hill Book Co., New York, 1949; chapter 6.

   Millman, J. and H. Taub, *Pulse and digital circuits;* McGraw-Hill Book Co., New York, 1956; chapter 9.

   DeWitt, D. and A. L. Rossoff, *Transistorized electronics;* McGraw-Hill Book Co., New York, 1957; p. 301.

   Richards, R. K., *Digital computer components and circuits;* D. Van Nostrand Co., Princeton, N.J., 1957; pp. 121–125.

   Hurley, R. B., *Junction transistor electronics;* John Wiley and Sons, New York, 1958; pp. 416–420.

   Hamilton, D. J., A transistor pulse generator for digital systems; *IRE Transactions on Electronic Computers,* vol. EC-7, September, 1958; pp. 244–249.

3. Mills, B. Y., Transient response of cathode followers in video circuits; *Proceedings of the IRE,* vol. 37, June, 1949; pp. 631–633.

   Millman, J. and H. Taub, *Pulse and digital circuits;* McGraw-Hill Book Co., New York, 1956; pp. 85–89, 138–139.

4. Millman, J. and H. Taub, *Pulse and digital circuits;* McGraw-Hill Book Co., New York, 1956; chapter 6.

   DeWitt, D. and A. L. Rossoff, *Transistor electronics;* McGraw-Hill Book Co., New York, 1957; pp. 302–303.

   Pettit, J. M., *Electronic switching, timing, and pulse circuits;* McGraw-Hill Book Co., New York, 1959; pp. 131–163.

5. Pettit, J. M., *Electronic switching, timing, and pulse circuits;* McGraw-Hill Book Co., New York, 1959; pp. 199–204.

6. Smura, E. J., A binary weighted current decoder; *IBM Journal of Research and Development,* vol. 1, October, 1957; pp. 356–362.

7. Millman, J. and H. Taub, *Pulse and digital circuits;* McGraw-Hill Book Co., New York, 1956; pp. 117, 479–480.

8. Richards, R. K., *Digital computer components;* D. Van Nostrand Co., Princeton, N.J., 1957; pp. 56–60.

   Siegel, P., *Understanding digital computers;* John Wiley and Sons, New York, 1961; pp. 192–195.

   Flores, I., *Computer logic;* Prentice-Hall, Englewood Cliffs, N.J., 1960; pp. 189–196.

   Brown, D. R. and N. Rochester, Rectifier networks for multiposition switching; *Proceedings of the IRE,* vol. 37, February, 1949; pp. 139–147.

Smith, C. V. L., *Electronic digital computers;* McGraw-Hill Book Co., New York, 1959; pp. 164–167.

Murphy, J. S., *Basics of digital computers;* John F. Rider Publisher, New York, 1958; pp. 102–113.

EXERCISES

10.1. Perform the Laplace transient analysis referred to at the bottom of page 10.7. Hence verify Figure 10.5. Do the analysis first with only a resistive load, and secondly, with both a resistive and capacitive load.

10.2. Design a follower to drive a capacitance load of 2000 mmf. The signal levels are ±5 volts, and the transition from one level to the other occurs in 0.1 μsec. Specify the active element in terms of the collector current that it must be able to handle. Assume a 50% derating on the element.

10.3. The output to be driven by the follower of Figure 10.3 is as follows:

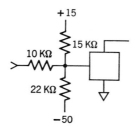

Redesign the follower to accommodate this load.

10.4. Consider a capacitance loaded follower driven from some source. The source cannot supply sufficient current to the control of the follower to permit its collector to furnish the current required by the capacitor for the given rate-of-change of voltage. How can the circuit adjust to these circumstances?

10.5. A follower has been designed to handle a mixed capacitance-resistance load. The input to the follower is a toggle in a register. At a later date, the same follower is used to connect the toggle to a part of the machine which is thirty-five feet distant. The behavior of the circuit is erratic; sometimes the toggle flips from one state to the other for no apparent reason. What might be happening? What might explain the spurious response of the toggle? How can the difficulty be fixed?

10.6. The follower of exercise 10.2 is driven from a source which can be represented as a voltage in series with a resistance of 500 Ω. Assume that the element is (as you wish) a 5844 tube or a 2N404 transistor. What is the maximum capacitance load that can be driven and still maintain the transition time of 0.1 μsec? (See pages 8.92–8.93 for characteristic curves.) Assume that the element has been derated 50% on power and current.

10.7. How should Figure 10.6 be designed (or used) to minimize the change in delay time as the operating environment changes? Suppose that it were necessary to provide maximum stability of the delay time. What additional components might be added to the circuit or what modifications might be made to achieve it?

10.8. How does the width of the trigger affect the output signal of Figures 10.6 and 10.8? Suppose that the width is

(a) just equal to the output signal;
(b) considerably wider than the output signal;
(c) much narrower than the output signal.

Sketch the relation between width of trigger and width of output.

10.9. Modify the toggle designed in exercise 8.8 to be the monostable multivibrator of Figure 10.6. The nominal delay time is to be 10 μsec. Calculate the maximum tolerance to be expected in this value as all parameters drift $\pm 5\%$.

10.10. Repeat exercise 10.9 for the toggle from exercise 8.35 and the circuit of Figure 10.8. Specify the trigger amplitude and calculate the change in output signal width as this amplitude varies $\pm 15\%$.

10.11. Perform a Laplace transient analysis of a parallel inductance-capacitance-resistance circuit driven by a current step of amplitude I. Verify the statements on page 10.12 concerning frequency of oscillation, amplitude of oscillation, and value of critical damping resistance.

10.12. In designing an L-C pulser to furnish an adjustable output width, would you make the inductance, the capacitance, or both variable? Why? How does the duty cycle change as the output width is changed?

10.13. Design a current switch to switch 10 ma to a constant voltage load. (Use the 5844 or 2N404 as you wish. See pages 8.92–8.93 for characteristic curves.) Specify the input signal and supply voltages.

10.14. The slicer (Figure 10.11) does not have hysteresis at the input terminal. The voltage at which it switches from state A to state B is the same as the voltage at which it switches from state B to state A. Does the asymmetrical toggle have the same property? Contrast the two circuits in this regard. Does the magnitude of the loop gain of the asymmetrical toggle have any influence on the situation?

10.15. Design a slicer (Figure 10.11) to square the output of an L-C pulser. Assume that the input is a half-sinusoid of amplitude 20 volts and 0.5 μsec wide at the base. The slicer must preserve the width of the signal within 5%, provide an output of 15 volts with transition no slower than 0.2 μsec across a 10 mmf capacitance load. (Use the 5844 or 2N404 as you wish. See pages 8.92 to 8.93 for characteristic curves.)

10.16. A second way of implementing a code-to-code conversion is suggested on page 10.20. Complete the implementation. Expand W, X, Y, and Z in terms of A, B, C, D; reduce the functions and determine the number of diodes in the resulting network. Discuss the burden on the drivers which supply current to the network.

10.17. Repeat the example on page 10.19 for the following situations:

(a) 8, 4, 2, 1 code to 2*, 4, 2, 1 code
(b) 2*, 4, 2, 1 code to 5, 4, 2, 1 code
(c) 7, 4, −2, −1 code to 5, 3, 1, 1 code
(d) 5, 3, 1, 1 code to 8, 4, 2, 1 code.

In each case specify the total number of each kind of gate, and identify any unusual design restrictions or current demands on gates or drivers.

PROBLEMS

10.1. Consider a follower driving a resistance-capacitance load. Let the output levels be e_u and e_l, the emitter resistor be R, I_{max} the maximum current allowed in the resistor at the upper level (e_u), E the voltage to which R is returned, and C the capacitance load.

    (a) In terms of these parameters, determine T_r, the fastest transition time which the resistance-capacitance network can achieve if E is very large compared to $e_u - e_l$.

    (b) Now determine the actual fall time (t) if E is a few times $e_u - e_l$, i.e., if the transition is exponential and not a straight line. Express t/T_r solely in terms of the several voltage parameters.

    (c) Determine the power (P) in the resistor when the output is at e_u. Define $P_0 = (e_u - e_l)I_{max}$ and express P/P_0 as a function of the several voltage parameters.

    (d) Identify the physical significance of P_0.

    (e) Plot t/T_r and P/P_0 as functions of E/e_l for various ratios of e_u/e_l.

    (f) Discuss the use of the graphs in part (e) for determining the compromise between rise time and power dissipated.

10.2. Consider the companion AND and OR diode configurations, i.e., ones which have the same logical convention. If a follower is designed to drive only AND gates, will it also be able to drive the same number of OR gates? If it was designed to drive some number of OR gates, will it be able to drive the same number of AND gates? By what factor must the equation for P/P_0 (problem 10.1(c)) be multiplied if the follower is driving only ANDs? Driving only ORs?

If the follower is designed to drive some number of one kind of gate, even though it may be able to swing the same number of other kind of gate, will it be able to provide the same transition time in each case?

10.3. Can the internal resistance of the conducting element be used as the damping resistance in an L-C pulser? Is this a good idea? Why? Might the L-C circuit be put in the emitter circuit?

10.4. Design an L-C pulse generator to provide an output of 10 volts with a width of 0.5 μsec. The driving current is 10 ma. The damping resistor must be chosen to maintain critical damping even though both L and C have drifted 10% in the worst direction. Under this circumstance, calculate the maximum duty cycle of the circuit when both L and C have drifted 10% in the opposite direction.

10.5. Discuss the practical problems governing the width of the slicing interval when the asymmetrical toggle is used as a slicer. Can it be made indefinitely small? Can the loop gain be made as large as desired?

10.6. Generalize the point made by the discussion on pages 10.19 and 10.20 and by exericse 10.16. Assume some arbitrary code to be converted to some other code, and give some guidelines to assist in selecting which of the two schemes to use for the conversion network.

Section *III*

eleven

Arithmetic Section

Except for some special techniques required in the store, we now have in hand all the basic circuits required to construct a digital computer. We also have the design techniques necessary to progress from a verbal description of desired machine operations to a Boolean description of these operations and finally to a circuit which realizes the operations. It remains only to study the internal organization of the major sections of a machine.*

For each major section of a machine, there is a tremendous number of choices available to the designer; they are often equally good alternatives. We cannot make an exhaustive survey of all possible internal machine organizations; we will discuss typical situations but include sufficient diversity to suggest the range of choices which are possible.

REVIEW

Remember that the principal function of the arithmetic section is to perform the arithmetic operations $(+, -, \times, \div)$ which are needed to manipulate information. Not all machines have all of the four basic arithmetic manipulations. The minimum is one—say, addition. By representing negative numbers in complement form, subtraction can be accomplished. Given shifting ability both to the right and to the left, multiplication (division) can be programmed from addition (sub-

---

* The reader may find it profitable to reread the first three pages of Chapter 8.

traction via complements), and from the shifting. As a matter of convenience to the programmer, most machines do incorporate all four basic arithmetic operations.

If a machine is intended for a class of problems which involves frequent arithmetic-like operations other than the basic four, additional capability may be incorporated into the arithmetic unit. Some machines, for instance, have the ability to extract the square root directly, rather than requiring it to be programmed. Occasionally, machines also have the ability to directly compute (say) the sine, cosine, inverse tangent, etc. When such operations do exist directly in a machine, the necessary extra equipment is usually charged to the arithmetic section, and the operations are spoken of as arithmetic operations, although they are in fact mathematical analytical functions which have been implemented from arithmetic processes.

We have seen (Chapter 6) that it is also convenient to be able to manipulate data in non-arithmetic fashion—the so-called *logical operations*. Therefore, the arithmetic section often contains additional equipment for such operations. In special cases, the functions of the arithmetic unit may be predominantly logical in nature and it perhaps ought to be called the *logical unit* or the *arithmetic-logical unit* (*ALU*) (1).

While the arithmetic unit is here being considered as the part of the machine which performs the bulk of the arithmetic required in the overall complete system, there may, in fact, be substantial amounts of arithmetic ability elsewhere. The input-output may, for instance, have enough arithmetic ability to do, say, binary-decimal and decimal-binary conversion. The control may have some arithmetic ability to assist in modification of instructions. The tendency in more recently designed machines is to provide arithmetic (and logical) ability wherever it is needed, rather than forcing the programmer to bring everything which he may need to manipulate arithmetically into the main arithmetic unit. The principles of organization which we will shortly develop will, however, be applicable wherever arithmetic operations must be implemented.

Finally, insofar as interaction is concerned, the control, the arithmetic unit, and the store have the most to do with each other, at least in a time sense. The control obtains instructions from the store, and the arithmetic unit transfers information back and forth to the store. This requires that the speed of operation of these three sections be compatible. A slow arithmetic unit and a fast store will not, in general, be an efficient design. Thus, of the many possible choices for this arithmetic unit, some will be unlikely in a given case because of inadequate speed capability.

Serial versus Parallel *

Arithmetic in a machine may be performed one column at a time (*serial*) or all columns at once (*parallel*). A person customarily performs addition serially, working with one column at a time from least toward most significant digit. We might organize a group of people to do parallel arithmetic. Each person would be assigned the job of adding just those digits in a given column of the operands; we will need as many people as there are columns in an operand. Obviously some sidewise communication between individuals is necessary to perform the carry function in addition, but we will consider that problem later. Parallel arithmetic tends to be faster than serial arithmetic because it performs operations in all columns at once, rather than in one column at a time. On the other hand, parallel arithmetic clearly requires more total equipment since independent adders must be provided for each column. Serial arithmetic requires less equipment, because it uses the same adder time sequentially for successive columns. This is one of many instances in which cost as represented by the total amount of equipment can be traded for time as represented by the rate of operation.

If the word length is n digits, equipment will have to be provided for each column in parallel arithmetic. In the serial situation, only one column of equipment is provided, and hence parallel arithmetic represents of the order of n times as much equipment as serial arithmetic. Moreover, all columns of parallel arithmetic are in operation at essentially the same time, and it is, therefore, tempting to conclude that it is n times as fast as serial arithmetic. However, at this juncture, we have not studied any details of adders, nor have we investigated the carry aspect of the addition process. We can return later for a sharper look at the speed differences between serial and parallel arithmetic.

Mixed systems are also possible. A binary-coded-decimal machine, for instance, may operate in parallel on the four bits of the tetrad which encodes a decimal digit but in series on successive decimal digits. In principle, *serial-serial, serial-parallel, parallel-serial,* and *parallel-parallel* machines are possible.

* See page 11.31 for some other implications of serial versus parallel.

Minimum Requirements

In order to perform any arithmetic, a machine must "know" the addition table of the base in which it works. One possibility is to store the addition table either in the main store of the machine or in a small supplementary store.* The two digits to be added are then used to enter the stored table to find the sum and carry. Our work in programming the interpreter indicated how (in that case) a numeric operation code was used to develop an address that led to the appropriate part of the store. In a similar way, we might program the process of addition after storing the necessary tables. We might even wire-in such a routine and, in effect, produce what might be called a *stored-table adder*. Its obvious difficulty is that it must consult the store for each pair of digits to be added, and for words of n columns, the addition time is of the order of n cycles of operation of the store. It is clearly serial arithmetic.

We already appreciate that a full word of information can be obtained from one consultation of the store, and hence a more usual arrangement is to embody the addition table in a special piece of hardware called an *adder*. In effect, the adder contains all the information necessary to produce any entry in the addition table, given two input digits. An explicit adder (with its cost) buys speed of operation by minimizing the number of consultations of the store. We appreciate that complement representation lets us merge the operations of addition and subtraction, and in principle a machine might have a subtractor rather than an adder.

Since arithmetic operations require two operands and produce a result, facilities for accommodating three factors (usually each a word) must exist. A storage device which holds an operand is called a *register*. It must be capable of being written into, and of being read from. It may also have other properties, such as shifting features.

In a machine which does parallel arithmetic all three registers are usually provided (Figure 11.1). It may be possible be introducing temporary storage in the form of a delay element to cause one register to double as two by time staggering its functions (Figure 11.2). In such an arrangement, the delay element must be long enough (measured in time) to permit the sum to be correctly formed before the sum replaces one of the operands.

In a machine which does serial arithmetic the successive digits of

---

* One model of the IBM 1620 performs its arithmetic by table lookup. Part of the main store is used for the tables.

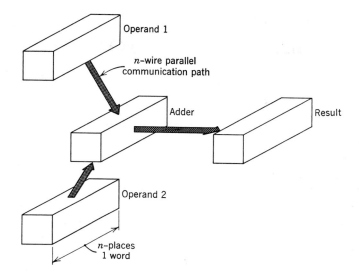

Figure 11.1. The arrangement for parallel arithmetic with three registers.

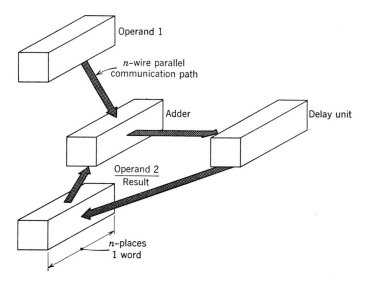

Figure 11.2. The arrangement for parallel arithmetic with two registers.

a word are required only one at a time. In principle, no registers are required if the store can simultaneously provide the digits of the two factors and accept the successive digits of the result—all time sequentially. On the other hand, three registers can be provided. Any arrangement in between is possible; often there are only two registers.

EXAMPLE

Suppose that one of the operands directed to a serial adder flows time sequentially from the store. Generally the least significant digit will appear first in time.

The second factor can flow time sequentially out the end of one register and the sum digits, as they are produced, can be lodged in a second register.

As each digit of the second factor flows from its register, so to speak, a digit is consumed and the register becomes partially empty at the other end. As this digit is consumed, however, a digit of the sum is produced and can be entered into the part of the register that has just been emptied. Partway through the addition, the single register will contain some yet unused digits of the second operand and the early digits of the sum.

Since multiplication (division) requires that the partial product (partial remainder) be shifted sidewise relative to the multiplicand (dividend), some of the registers will need to be able to displace their contents sidewise. Which registers need this property, and how many need it, will depend on the details of the multiplication and division process in a particular case. Generally, two registers are provided with shifting properties.

Minimum typical requirements for the arithmetic section are thus:

1. an adder,
2. two shifting registers,
3. a simple register,
4. the switching and communication network that links these parts.

As we have previously noted, less equipment may be possible in a serial (or partially serial) machine organization.

ADDERS

The One-Column Binary Adder

A base-b adder is one which implements the base-b addition table. An elementary one-column binary adder is, therefore, one which implements

DIGIT 1	DIGIT 2	SUM	CARRY
0	0	0	0
0	1	1	0
1	0	1	0
1	1	0	1

Figure 11.3. The truth table of 2-input binary addition.

the truth table of Figure 11.3; it can sum two binary digits and it produces a carry of 0 or 1. Consider, however, the addition process in the ith column of a word (Figure 11.4). As this figure indicates, there may be a carry (of 1) from the $(i-1)$st column, and the ith column will produce not only a sum digit but it also will produce a carry (0 or 1) to the $(i+1)$st column. A one-column *full adder*, is therefore a 3-input, 2-output device (2). The composite truth table of Figure 11.5 defines its characteristics. Any device which implements this truth table by means of gating networks is generally called a *logical adder*.

The truth table of Figure 11.5 defines two Boolean functions: carry-out and sum. According to the first expansion theorem of Boolean Algebra (page 4.15), the corresponding algebraic expressions are

$$\text{Sum} = \bar{A}\bar{B}C + \bar{A}B\bar{C} + A\bar{B}\bar{C} + ABC$$

and,
$$\text{Carry} = \bar{A}BC + A\bar{B}C + AB\bar{C} + ABC.$$

These may be put into various forms by manipulation; in particular, the carry proposition can be reduced to

$$\text{Carry} = AB + AC + BC.$$

This reduction clearly points out that the carry is 1 when any two of the three inputs are 1, i.e., when a majority of the inputs is 1. The case of all three inputs being 1 is included in the first three cases.

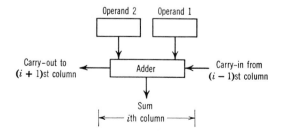

Figure 11.4. A typical column in an addition.

A DIGIT A	B DIGIT B	C CARRY-IN	SUM	CARRY-OUT
0	0	0	0	0
0	0	1	1	0
0	1	0	1	0
0	1	1	0	1
1	0	0	1	0
1	0	1	0	1
1	1	0	0	1
1	1	1	1	1

Figure 11.5.   The truth table of 3-input binary addition.

There are many forms of the Boolean expressions for sum and carry-out, and there are many circuit techniques for implementing the necessary gating operations.   In particular, any of the gating schemes of Chapter 9 can, in principle, be used.   In the design of an adder there is a great variety of choice just at this one place.

The Binary Half-Adder

A *half-adder* is a 2-input, 2-output adder (Figure 11.6) (3).   We recognize from its truth table that the sum proposition is the exclusive OR (f_6, Figure 4.5, page 4.19) and that the carry proposition is

DIGIT A	DIGIT B	SUM	CARRY-OUT
0	0	0	0
0	1	1	0
1	0	1	0
1	1	0	1

Figure 11.6.   The truth table of a binary half-adder.

the AND (f_1, Figure 4.5).   This device is called a half-adder because two of them plus an additional OR gate together constitute a full adder (Figure 11.7) (see exercise 11.5).

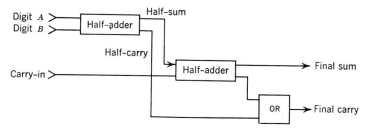

Figure 11.7. A full adder from half-adders.

The Serial Carry Problem

As a person performs addition, he either remembers that a carry has arisen in a particular column of addition, or he makes some specific mark as a reminder. In either case, he uses the carry generated in the ith column when dealing with the $(i + 1)$st column. In a serial arithmetic process, the successive digits of the two operands parade time sequentially through a full adder (or the half-adder equivalent) (4). This implies that the digits of each operand must be transmitted serially to the adder. Furthermore, the successive digits of the sum will be formed time sequentially, and transmitted serially from the adder to some other part of the machine. A carry produced when dealing with column i at time t_1 must be stored and used later when dealing with column $i + 1$ at time t_2. A typical

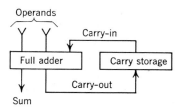

Figure 11.8. The arrangement for a serial adder.

serial adder is shown in Figure 11.8 and clearly produces the digits of the sum in time sequence.

The specific nature of the delay or storage element depends on the nature of the input streams. If the successive digits of the two input operands appear at regularly spaced intervals, the delay element can be, say, an electromagnetic delay line of fixed time delay. On the other hand, if the input streams contain irregular spacings between digits, the delay element needs a variable delay feature; this is most conveniently accomplished by using, say, a toggle as a storage device. The toggle is written into at time t_1 (column i) and read from at time t_2 (column $i + 1$). However, if the spacing between successive digits is irregular, the irregularity must be the same for both input streams. The ith digit in each input word must be present at the adder at the same time.

The need for a carry storage device arises from the intrinsic nature of the serial arithmetic process; it has nothing to do with the internal details of the adder. A common phrase is that "carry storage is logically required." Furthermore, so far as the adder is concerned, the ultimate rate at which it can operate depends only on the time delay through the adder. It can accept the next round of input information just as soon as it has produced the sum and carry from the last round.

The Parallel Carry Problem

As we have suggested, the human analog of a parallel adder is a group of people, each told to add the digits in the one column given to him. On signal, each person adds his column. This implies that in parallel arithmetic, all columns of both operands must be simultaneously available (5). We have gained speed by increasing the amount of equipment (people) used, but what about the carry? Any one person (or several) might have generated a carry in his column; this fact is of concern to at least the person on his left who handles the next more significant digit, and perhaps to all persons on his left. In the worst case for, say, binary addition, if the sum in every column but the least significant were a 1, and the least significant were to generate a carry, the effect of this carry will propagate sequentially through every column.

The ith individual will hear "carry" from the $(i - 1)$st. He injects this carry into his column of digits; this might make the sum in his column change and it, therefore, might give rise to a carry from his column. If so, he turns to the $(i + 1)$st individual and says "carry." In the extreme case, the recitation of the word "carry" will ripple down the line of people from the least to most significant columns. Notice what can happen. A carry can start at the least significant digit and go through the whole word (Figure 11.9-a); but it also can start anywhere within the word and go only a few columns (Figure 11.9-b). There can also be more than one carry within a word (Figure 11.9-c). This same behavior of the carry can also, of course, occur in serial arithmetic, but the rippling of the carry overlaps the time sequential appearance of the serially transmitted stream of input digits.

As the human analogy suggests, a parallel adder consists of many one-column adders, each linked to its neighbors to form the carry

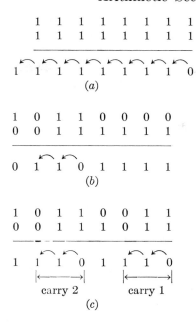

Figure 11.9. (a) *A full-length carry.* (b) *A short carry.* (c) *Two short carries.*

chain. The individual one-column adder can be the same one used in a serial adder. Terminology is loose; the term *adder* is often used without a descriptor to mean a one-column, a many-column, a parallel, or a serial adder.

The sum in any column can be wrong until sufficient time has elapsed for a possible carry from the least significant column to arrive. There may not be such a carry; but then again, there may be. Thus a characteristic of prime concern in a parallel adder is the *carry propagation time* (6). In a binary adder (Figure 11.5), if the two digits into a stage are each 1, a *local carry* will originate in the stage and be propagated to more significant columns; the sum digit will be 0. An additional incoming carry can only change the sum digit from 0 to 1. However, if the two digits into a stage are unlike, no carry can originate within the stage, and the sum digit will be 1. An incoming carry will not only change the sum digit but it will also cause the stage to produce a *propagated carry*. Generally, the time delay from the receipt of the carry-in to the emergence of the carry-out limits the maximum speed of a parallel adder, and an otherwise straightforward adder design will often be deliberately modified in

(a)

01010 ... 01 ← Operand 1
00101 ... 10 ← Operand 2
─────────────
01111 ... 11 ← Sum from adder

(b)

01010 ... 01 ← Operand 1
00101 ... 11 ← Operand 2
─────────────
10000 ... 00 ← Sum from adder

Figure 11.10. Carry propagation and carry collapse.

order to favor preferentially the reaction time of the carry process. For example, the gating circuits which handle the carry can be significantly faster than those which produce the sum digit. The faster carry circuit might imply faster components, which in turn can imply more expensive components.

There are really two kinds of carry in a parallel adder. If the adder initially is forming the sum shown in Figure 11.10-a, and the situation changes to that of Figure 11.10-b, a carry will propagate all the way and change the string of 1's to a string of 0's. It might have been that the situation of Figure 11.10 represented a trial operation; e.g., in restoring division a trial subtraction can be implemented by adding a complement. If the divisor does not go, the trial sum from the adder will not be written into a register but will be discarded. Therefore, the possibility exists that the situation could progress from Figure 11.10-b to Figure 11.10-a; a carry will then unpropagate all the way. The former is sometimes called *carry propagate* and the latter, *carry collapse*. It can happen that the two occur at different speeds, depending on specific details of the design. This amounts to the observation that the true-to-false and the false-to-true transitions in a circuit need not occur at the same rate. We must be alert to this situation because both cases can occur.

In the worst case, the time for a parallel adder to form the correct sum is the carry propagation time plus the time to form the sum digit in one stage (the most significant place). A fast carry circuit is, therefore, very desirable.

Ripple and Bypass Carry

One way to deal with the carry in a parallel adder is to build the adder as a direct-coupled network. Carry effects propagate in either direction at a rate determined by inherent time constants, and after sufficient time, the adder becomes quiescent. Such a scheme is often called a *ripple carry*.

A way to deal with the "carry-in produces a carry-out" problem is the *carry bypass* scheme. If the digit inputs are unlike (which will permit this possibility), supplementary gate circuits are enabled which route any incoming carry around the stage directly to the carry output terminal and on to the next stage.

Carry Storage

Sometimes additional storage elements are provided which accept the carry produced by each stage. At a special time, the stored carries are discharged into the following stages. It can happen that this gives rise to new carries which are again stored. In the case of an n-place word, as many as $n - 1$ additional specific operations might have to be scheduled to propagate a carry completely.

However, it can be shown that for certain situations such as the intermediate steps of a multiplication (7), it is unnecessary to propagate the carry completely. The carry is allowed to propagate one stage only (*partial carry*), and any carries resulting from this are stored for the following step. Only on the last step of the multiplication is a fully propagated carry necessary.

EXAMPLE

The multiplication $(11011) \cdot (1111)$ is carried out below in two ways. First, it is done as a normal multiplication, and the carries are allowed to propagate fully at each step. Secondly, it is done as a partial carry multiplication; any carry which arises is allowed to propagate only one place leftward.

1.

11011		Multiplicand
1111		Multiplier
11011	①	First partial product
11011		
1010001	②	Second partial product
11011		
10111101	③	Third partial product
11011		
110010101	④	Final product

2.

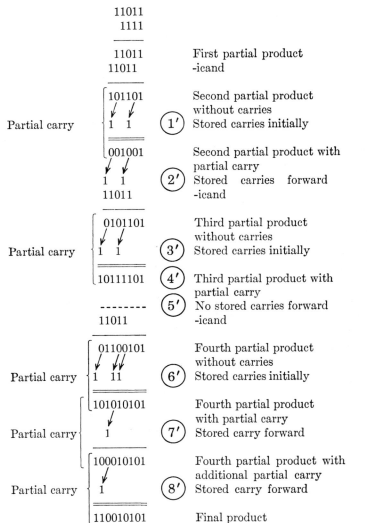

11011
1111

11011   First partial product
11011   -icand

Partial carry

101101   Second partial product
              without carries
1 1 (1′) Stored carries initially

001001   Second partial product with
              partial carry
1 1 (2′) Stored   carries   forward
11011   -icand

Partial carry

0101101   Third partial product
              without carries
1 1 (3′) Stored carries initially

10111101 (4′) Third partial product with
                  partial carry
-------- (5′) No stored carries forward
11011   -icand

Partial carry

01100101   Fourth partial product
              without carries
1 11 (6′) Stored carries initially

Partial carry

101010101 Fourth partial product
              with partial carry
1   (7′) Stored carry forward

Partial carry

100010101 Fourth partial product with
              additional partial carry
1   (8′) Stored carry forward

110010101 Final product

Several points: Had the carries at 1′ been allowed to propagate completely rather than being stalled at 2′ and carried forward, the partial product at 2 would have been obtained. At 1′ the assimilation of stored carries gave rise to new carries which are carried forward at 2′. At 3′, the assimilation of the stored carries produced no new carries; therefore, there are no carries forward at 5′ and the partial product at 4′ agrees with the partial product at 3. At 6′ the assimilation of the partial carries gave rise to new carries (at 7′) whose assimilation gave rise to yet new carries (at 8′). In this example three successive partial carries (6', 7', 8') were necessary to complete the final step of the multiplication.

One possibility of avoiding the $n - 1$ extra cycles at the end is to switch the adder to ripple-carry during the last step. Another possibility is to sense the carry storage devices and only execute partial carry cycles until all storage devices are empty of carries. Which of these alternatives is more desirable depends on the average length of the expected carry, and the cost of implementing each of the several schemes.

Carry Sensing

The designer does not know and cannot control which particular numbers a user will put into the adder on a given occasion. The problem therefore arises: How much time shall be allowed for the adder to propagate (or collapse) a carry? This problem, while present in a parallel adder, does not arise in a serial adder, because the time to perform the addition is determined by the rate at which the input digits are serially presented to the adder. The carry time of the serial adder need only be less than the time spacing between successive input digits.

One choice is always to allow sufficient time for the longest carry. After the operands are presented to the adder, a waiting interval equal to the carry time along the whole adder is allowed before the sum from the adder can be used. Obviously, however, this situation will not occur every time, and we expect that much of the time the carry will be less than a full word long. Experiments have suggested that on the average, the longest carry in binary addition is of the order of one-eighth the word length (8), which means that if a scheme can be found for detecting when all carries are completed, roughly an eight-fold increase in the average speed of the parallel adder can be realized.

It is possible to incorporate additional gating circuits into each stage of the parallel adder to detect the cessation of carry effects (8). Such additional logical complexity is one way that a designer can realize greater average speed from an adder; he incorporates more of the same kind of circuits rather than searching for new kinds of faster circuits. He improves the logical or organizational sophistication of the device (9).

Which Is Really Faster?

It is worth noting the following point for perspective. Consider two adders—one serial and the other parallel but without carry sensing. If the time between consecutive digits into the serial adder is just equal to the carry delay through one stage of the parallel adder, the two adders are equally fast and produce the sum in the same time. Hence it is possible under appropriate circumstances to substitute a fast serial adder for a slow parallel adder or vice versa. However, there are other aspects of the problem to be considered.

As a ground rule for this discussion, we must assume that equally fast circuit technology is used for either the parallel or serial adder. Hence, the speed of a circuit can be estimated in terms of the time delay (Δt) through a logical decision (a level or layer of logic as the term was used in the discussions of Chapter 9). The sum and carry logic can always be implemented in two levels of logic, and hence one stage of a parallel adder and the serial adder are basically equally fast. The reaction time of either is $2\Delta t$. For a word length of n places, the carry process in the parallel adder may propagate through $2n$ logical elements, and experience $2n\Delta t$ of delay.

We also need a definition. A serial adder requires the digits to be presented time sequentially at its input. The time interval between adjacent digits is called the *digit time*, and the time required to present one word's worth of digits is called the *word time*. For a word length of n places, the word time is n digit times. The serial adder always requires one word time to complete an addition. Whether a carry propagates through each place in the addition or not, there is always enough time for such a full-length, one-word carry to occur. Hence any parallel adder which, in some way such as carry sensing, waits only long enough for the actual carries to occur and does not wait every time for a full length carry, will be guaranteed to be faster.

How about the serial adder versus the full adder when the latter always waits for a full length carry? In this case, we must look outside the adder to resolve the question. Since the least time delay through any one-column adder is $2\Delta t$, the digit time must be at least $2\Delta t$, and for n digits, the least addition time and hence word time is $2n\Delta t$ units of delay. As we observed above, this is the same as the parallel adder. In the optimum serial case, there is no carry storage (Figure 11.8), and the emergence of the carry from the adder is just in time for the next input digit. Therefore, the intrinsic reaction time of the adder will establish the time scale for the serial transmission of information between the adder and, say, the store or a register. The inference is that all other parts of the machine must be locked in step to the adder. Now what happens if component parameter drifts in the adder change its response time? Unless the digit spacing changes accordingly, malfunction is certain. In the practical case, the tolerance problem denies a digit spacing equal to the adder reaction time. There must be some external carry storage, and the serial addition process becomes slower.

There is another related practical problem. The serial adder fits naturally with a machine which within itself transmits information serially. For example, suppose the store were to produce information in parallel. It would have to be converted to serial form for the adder, and extra equipment will be required. As we will see in Chapter 12, some stores naturally deal with information serially, and of course part of the argument here is: can we find a store which traffics information whose digit spacing is $2\Delta t$? If we cannot, we will have to provide parallel-serial conversion equipment, and we might as well consider the parallel adder in the first place. But even suppose that we do find a suitable store. How closely can we maintain the spacing between adjacent digits during serial transmission? How much jitter is there in the time position of the signals?

To function properly the adder requires that the corresponding digits of the two operands and the carry from the previous step be present concurrently. If the delay time through the adder is $2\Delta t$, this implies that the signals must be simultaneously present for the same order of magnitude of time. If there is any jitter whatsoever, the signals must be wider than $2\Delta t$, and the maximum rate of the serial adder diminishes. The jitter problem of course increases as the overall speed scale rises. For signals which are, say, a few milliseconds wide, the jitter problem is inconsequential; but for signals which are, say, a few millimicroseconds in width, the jitter problem is severe. The practical resolution of this is to design for signals which are wider than the time delay through the adder, which in turn implies external carry storage and a slower operating rate. In order to accommodate tolerances in the serial adder speed, the signal which determines the spacing of the input digit streams must also be used to read the external carry storage and hence used to inject the carry input at the proper time (Figure 11.11).

The jitter problem, of course, also troubles the parallel adder—but in a different way. As information propagates in parallel along a multiwire transmission path, it will not do so in a perfectly straight company-front line. The input to the parallel adder will, therefore, not be quite simultaneous in all columns, but whatever jitter is expected adds just once to the overall carry time. In the serial adder, it adds to each digit time, and therefore it adds n-fold to the word time.

There is yet another practical aspect of the situation. In the serial adder, the pulse signals which represent digital information can be no wider than the digit time. Unless the pulse widths are suitably short, the process of addition will not be completed properly. As the digit time becomes shorter, the pulse widths become narrower, and the difficulty of handling them increases. In the parallel adder there is no such restriction, especially in the case of a direct-coupled ripple adder. The input signals can be much wider than the overall carry time, and the carry will still propagate at its high rate, and the sum will be available rapidly. The width of the input signal is determined more by the rate at which successive additions are to be done, than by the internal detail of doing one addition (Figure 11.12).

When all is said and done, the serial adder tends to be appropriate for the slower machine in which timing difficulties are not severe, and the parallel adder tends to be appropriate for the fast machine in which timing problems can be very severe. This very point of timing difficulty will appear again in our discussion of the control (Chapter 14). There is an interesting hybrid possibility that might be useful in some circumstances. Consider a 40-bit fast parallel machine. We might build a 40-column parallel adder, or we might build, say, a 10-place parallel adder and sequence four passes through it to handle successively the four 10-place parts of the overall addition.

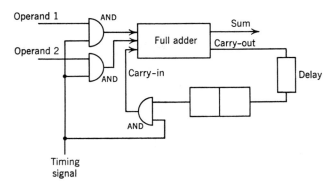

Figure 11.11. Timing details in a serial adder.

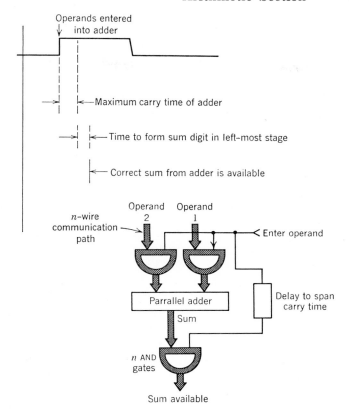

Figure 11.12. Timing details in the parallel adder.

By properly choosing the length of the parallel adder and, therefore, the number of successive passes per addition, we hopefully would not lose too much speed compared to the parallel case, but will nonetheless save considerable equipment.   On the other hand, we must be careful that the amount of equipment committed to timing and sequencing the successive passes does not equal or exceed the part of the parallel adder that we do not have to build.

The Many-Column Adder

So far, we have considered only the one-column adder, which implements the addition table for the base in question.   In a serial version, one such adder is used time sequentially, whereas in the parallel version, many such adders are deployed spatially and linked via the carry process (10).

In the parallel case, the carry formation results from a sequential decision-making process. The sum digit in any given column depends on all of the events in the columns to its right. Moreover, the correct effect of these columns to the right can only be known by sequentially dealing with them—from least toward most significant. The carry process is intrinsically sequential in nature, and the time to complete the carry aspect of an addition can never be collapsed to zero.

There is a scheme which appears to violate this statement but really does not. In principle, the logical relation between each sum digit and all of the input digits on which it depends can be stated, and this logic can be realized. There are two points. First, we are no longer dealing with a single-column basic adder, but rather with an n-column basic adder. Instead of the binary adder, we are now considering an adder for the base-2^n system and are dealing with few (or perhaps even just one) column numerical expressions in a very large base. Secondly, although the logical nature of the carry process may have been sidestepped by sticking to one-column numbers in a large base, time delay is still present. Quite aside from the staggering amount of equipment that such an n-column adder would consume, there must be a minimum of two logical decisions (an AND-OR, or an OR-AND) to implement the proposition for each sum digit (see problem 11.1). Thus at least two units of time delay are unavoidable.

EXAMPLE

Consider building a base-4 adder. The symbols in the number system will be 00, 01, 10, 11, and the addition table will be as follows:

	00	01	10	11
00	00	01	10	11
01	01	10	11	(1)00
10	10	11	(1)00	(1)01
11	11	(1)00	(1)01	(1)10

Call one input digit A_1A_2, the other one B_1B_2, the sum S_1S_2, and the carry C. The addition table can be rewritten as the following truth table:

A_1 A_2	B_1 B_2	S_1	S_2	C
0 0	0 0	0	0	0
	0 1	0	1	0
	1 0	1	0	0
	1 1	1	1	0
0 1	0 0	0	1	0
	0 1	1	0	0
	1 0	1	1	0
	1 1	0	0	1
1 0	0 0	1	0	0
	0 1	1	1	0
	1 0	0	0	1
	1 1	0	1	1
1 1	0 0	1	1	0
	0 1	0	0	1
	1 0	0	1	1
	1 1	1	0	1

From this table, the corresponding algebraic expressions can be stated, and the gating networks designed. For instance,

$$C = \bar{A}_1 A_2 B_1 B_2 + A_1 \bar{A}_2 (B_1 \bar{B}_2 + B_1 B_2) + A_1 A_2 (\bar{B}_1 B_2 + B_1 \bar{B}_2 + B_1 B_2).$$

As this expression is written, it will require an AND-OR-AND-OR configuration for implementation. After expanding the parentheses, an AND-OR configuration is sufficient.

If the base-4 adder had been implemented as two binary adders linked by a carry chain (as it could have been), there would have been two layers of logic involved in the carry at each stage. Hence the final carry output would have depended on a 4-layer logical network.

This is another example of the exchange of equipment for time. The adder which spatially deploys many one-column elementary adders will form the carry by a sequential decision-making chain of gates. At the cost of extra equipment, the single-column large-base adder forms all sum digits by a multiplicity of simultaneous decision-making chains, each of which can have as few as two cascaded decision elements.

If logical connectives other than the AND, OR, and NOT can be implemented directly in hardware, the previous statements about minimum time delay may not be true (see exercise 11.30).

The Decimal Adder

As we have previously seen (Chapter 3), a binary adder under appropriate circumstances can be made to do decimal addition. To a basic four-column binary adder, we must append some sort of detector to determine when a corrective action is necessary, and we must add a mechanism for inserting the appropriate corrective term. The precise nature of the detector and the magnitude of the corrective factor will depend on the code used to represent the decimal digits. Generally, the detector will consist of a gating circuit which responds to certain combinations of digits or to certain carry conditions in the preliminary sum (11).

There are several possibilities for dealing with the corrective term. One is to cascade two adders (Figure 11.13). The second adder inserts the corrective term or it inserts zero, depending upon the output of the detector. An obvious alternate is to reuse the first adder; i.e., time sequence two passes through one adder instead of cascading two adders. Some temporary storage will be necessary for the intermediate preliminary sum. In this case, the adder might be operated at double time rate in order not to penalize the rest of the machine.

Another possibility is the four-input adder (Figure 11.14). After the corrective term (or terms) necessary for a given code have been determined, the logic required in the adder can be determined, and the resulting gating networks designed (see problem 11.6).

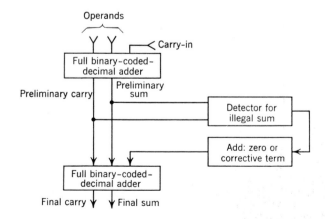

Figure 11.13. A decimal adder using cascaded binary-coded-decimal adders.

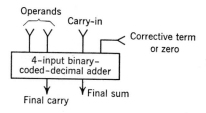

Figure 11.14. A 4-input decimal adder arrangement.

The four-column adder can be either serial or parallel; the addition of adjacent decimal digits can be either serial or parallel. Hence decimal addition of n-column words can consist of $4n$ passes through a one-column binary adder equipped with proper control and carry storage features (*serial-serial addition*), but it can also be n passes through a four-column parallel binary adder, again with proper control and carry storage (*serial-parallel addition*). For enough equipment, clearly *parallel-parallel addition* can be implemented.

The Decimal Matrix Adder

A completely different approach to the decimal adder is to implement the decimal addition table using, however, the symbols of a binary code. This is very much like the stored-table adder except that the table has been wired in place. Figure 11.15 is part of the decimal addition table written in the symbols of the 8, 4, 2, 1 code. An adder which implements this table will have nine bits of input (a tetrad for each of the two-decimal digits and one bit for the carry) and will produce five bits of output (one tetrad for the decimal sum digit and one bit of carry). This adder will, therefore, be defined by five propositions, the truth table for each of which will contain two hundred entries— each decimal digit paired with every other decimal digit, with and without a carry-in. Figure 11.16 shows a portion of the composite truth table.

The matrix adder requires a lot of equipment, but it offers some advantages. There is no concern about corrective procedures. The code need exhibit no regularity in behavior; any arbitrary code can be used. The codes of the two input digits need not be alike, and each could differ from the output code. Alternatively, a translation of code could be effected in an adder of this kind by using one code for

	0 0000	1 0001	2 0010	3 0011	4 0100	5 0101	· · ·
0 0000	0 0000	1 0001	2 0010	3 0011	4 0100	5 0101	· · ·
1 0001	1 0001	2 0010	3 0011	4 0100	5 0101	·	· · ·
2 0010	2 0010	3 0011	4 0100	5 0101	6 0110	·	· · ·
3 0011	3 0011	4 0100	5 0101	6 0110	7 0111	·	· · ·
4 0100	4 0100	5 0101	6 0110	7 0111	8 1000	·	· · ·
5 0101	5 0101	6 0110	7 0111	8 1000	9 1001	·	· · ·
·	·	·	·	·	·	·	· · ·
·							
·							

Figure 11.15.   A decimal addition table in binary symbolism.

DIGIT A $A_1A_2A_3A_4$	DIGIT B $B_1B_2B_3B_4$	CARRY- IN	SUM $\Sigma_1\Sigma_2\Sigma_3\Sigma_4$	CARRY- OUT
0000	0000	0	0000	0
0000	0001	0	0001	0
·	·	·	·	·
0000	0001	1	0010	0
·	·	·	·	·
0010	0111	0	1001	0
·	·	·	·	·
0010	0111	1	0000	1
·	·	·	·	·
0101	0110	0	0001	1
·	·	·	·	·
0101	0110	1	0010	1
·	·	·	·	·
·	·	·	·	·
·	·	·	·	·

Figure 11.16.   A part of the truth table of a matrix adder.

the two input digits but a second code for the output digit. A parallel decimal matrix adder represents very much equipment but, of course, can be as fast as a parallel binary adder.

The Subtractor

In light of the previous discussion of adders, the design of a *subtractor* is straightforward (12). Write down the subtraction table in the base of interest and implement this table. In the binary number system, the addition and subtraction tables are very similar; Figure 11.17 is the binary subtraction table, and we see that the only difference is the borrow column.

DIGIT A	DIGIT B	DIFFER- ENCE $(A - B)$	BORROW
0	0	0	0
0	1	1	1
1	0	1	0
1	1	0	0

Figure 11.17. The 2-input binary subtraction truth table.

Since a subtractor implements the subtraction table, if a larger number is subtracted from a smaller one, the device will borrow to the maximum of its ability in order to try to complete the subtraction. This is another way of pointing out that in such a case a subtractor will produce a complement representation of the negative answer. A desk calculator also will give a complemented answer in the same situation. The example of Figure 11.18 shows that the subtractor has not produced -2 but rather 30 which is the complement of -2 with respect to 32. The complement is with respect to 32, because the example happens to use 5-bit numbers.

$$A: \quad 00100 \rightarrow \quad 4$$
$$B: \quad -00110 \rightarrow \quad -6$$
$$\overline{\qquad\qquad\qquad\qquad}$$
$$11110 \neq -2$$

Figure 11.18. A complement result from a subtractor.

The Adder-Subtractor

In the binary system, an adder plus a borrow circuit will implement an *adder-subtractor*. Whether it is an adder or a subtractor depends on whether at a given moment the carry circuit or the borrow circuit is operative. In the subtract mode, it is possible to obtain a complement result, even though the device implements the subtraction table and is, therefore, a subtractor. We may have to do something about complementing the result.

Subtraction and Complementing *

As we saw in the discussion of complements, the sign digits in a complement scheme behave arithmetically just like any other column of the numbers being added. If a machine represents negative numbers in complement form, the problem of subtraction is straightforward. The sign position of the parallel adder, or the corresponding step in serial addition, is just like all other columns. However, since the instruction to be executed may have been Subtract, there must be a way to complement numbers en route to the adder. Hence a negative number from the store to be subtracted in the adder is complemented prior to presentation to the adder, and actually enters the adder as a positive number; i.e., $-(-A) = +A$.

In the binary system, the true complement is formed in part by swapping 1's and 0's. This means either: insert a negation between the adder and the source of the incoming information; or, if each binary digit as well as its 1's complement is available (as would be the case for digits stored in toggles), select the complemented rather than normal form of the digit; e.g., use the output from the other side of the toggle. The rest of the complementing process requires that a 1 be inserted into the least significant place. It must be done in the adder because a carry may result and must be propagated. If the least significant column of the adder is like all other columns, it will have a carry-in terminal, but it will be unused. This is a convenient place into which to insert the additional 1, which is sometimes referred to as an *artificial carry*.

It is also possible to represent a negative number as a (radix − 1)

---

* See page 2.23 of volume I of this book for a discussion of complements and examples of complement arithmetic.

complement, e.g., a 1's or 9's complement.   In this circumstance, it turns out to be necessary to couple the carry-output terminal of the most significant stage of the adder to the carry-input terminal of the least significant stage of the adder.   The *end-around carry* in a sense plays the role of the extra 1 inserted into the rightmost place during the formation of a true complement (13).   Since each (radix − 1) complement is too small in the rightmost place by 1, the addition of two such complements will be too small in the rightmost place by 2. However, it can be shown that in this circumstance, an end-around carry of 1 will always occur and cancel one of the 1's, leaving the result too small by 1.   This is just how it should be for the result to be a (radix − 1) complement.   If the addition process involves only one complement (the other operand being a positive number), the result will be small by 1 in the right place, as it should be.   In this case, the end-around carry will be a 0, leaving the result deficient by 1 in the rightmost place as it should be (see exercise 11.8).

If a machine represents numbers in sign-and-magnitude form, the situation is a little more complicated.   First of all, the signs must be dealt with separately; no longer does the sign position behave arithmetically like all other steps of the addition (see exercise 11.15). If an adder-subtractor has been used, it may give a complement result if a large number is subtracted from a smaller one.   There are two ways out: decomplement the result or make a second pass through the adder-subtractor with the operands reversed.   Either of these requires extra time to complete the operation.   Alternatively, two adder-subtractors can be provided; one will do $A - B$ and the other $B - A$.   Whichever result is not in complement form is retained. This solution increases the amount of equipment to at least double.

This whole situation is mildly embarrassing because part of the point of sign-magnitude representation is to avoid complements and complementing.   Nonetheless, a frequent choice in sign-magnitude machines is to flank the adder on both input and output sides with a complementing device.   So far as the adder is concerned, negative numbers appear as complements, but elsewhere in the machine, sign-magnitude representation is used (14).

EXAMPLES

1. Consider a machine operating in sign-magnitude representation, and assume that complements are formed temporarily for implementing subtraction. The incoming number must be complemented if it is negative, or if a

subtract operation is to be performed, but not both. If a negative number is to be subtracted, it enters as a positive number.

2. The complementer which stands between the adder and other parts of the machine will be controlled by the sign position of the adder. If the adder happens to produce a complement result, the sign digit will indicate this. Hence the output of the adder must be complemented before it is delivered to any other part of the machine.

Binary complementing is simple. A negation converts 1's to 0's and vice versa for a 1's complement. The true complement can be completed by an artificial carry into the least significant place of an adder.

In the decimal system, complementing can be easy if the code is a self-complementing one (Chapter 3). If it is not, sufficient logic must be provided to form the 9's complement of the incoming digit. The final 1 into the low-order place can be dealt with as for the binary case; i.e., inject an artificial carry into the least significant position.

The Analog Adder

The logical adder does not sum the input voltages (or currents) in a literal sense. It produces an output voltage (or current) which is the representation of the digit which is the arithmetic sum of the digits represented by the input voltages (or currents); it sums the input states. It is possible to build an *analog adder* which truly sums input voltages or currents. An obvious example is an analog summing amplifier (Figure 11.19). If each input is either 0 or E volts, the output sum of this adder is 0, E, $2E$ or $3E$ volts. As Figure 11.19 shows, these four levels must be mapped back onto the two levels of 0 and E to regain the digital representation. Some form of *analog-digital converter* is needed.

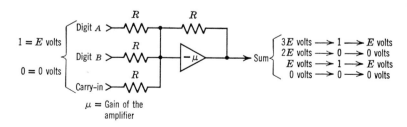

Figure 11.19. An analog adder.

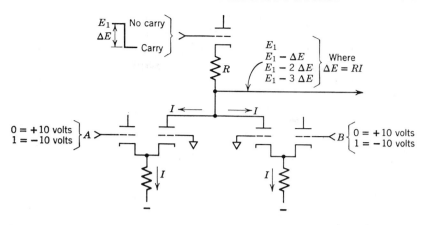

Figure 11.20. The Kirchhoff adder.

The so-called *Kirchhoff Adder* is another variant of an analog adder (15). It was used in some of the early Princeton-class * machines and represents an input digit as a unit of current. These currents are then summed. As a practical matter, the carry was inserted as a voltage step at the top of the summing resistor R (Figure 11.20) rather than as a current step like the other two inputs. Since the currents are added in a resistor, the sum output is again one of four levels of voltage and must be restored to a digital representation. In the case of the Princeton machine this was done by offering the sum output to a group of current switches, each of which could override the previous one. Collectively they acted as a form of analog-digital converter (15).

It is clear that in an analog adder the minimum spacing between adjacent output levels is largely determined by the precision with which the analog-digital converter can distinguish voltage levels. The output levels obviously depend also on tolerances of components and power supplies. The combination of these two effects generally requires that adjacent voltage levels be reasonably far apart. Typically, the differential between adjacent output levels is at least of the same order of magnitude as the input signals and may be larger. In a logical adder, there is no need for an output voltage swing which is larger than the input signal, and therefore some capacitance in the analog adder will have to be driven through a voltage swing at

* A family of machines all based on the work of the von Neumann group at the Institute for Advanced Study, Princeton, N.J.

least three times as large as any voltage swing required in the logical adder. For similar current magnitudes, the analog adder, therefore, tends to be significantly slower than a logical adder.

Occasionally, the analog adder is useful for non-arithmetic operations. Suppose we want to know how many 1's there are in a word; the positional significance of each digit is to be ignored. An analog adder with a multiplicity of inputs can produce an output which is proportional to the number of 1's present. If only an estimate of the quantity of 1's is desired, a low-precision analog circuit can be used. The logical circuit required to implement such a count of digits will contain a large amount of equipment.

An Adder Is Not an Adder

Most machines contain logical instructions which perform columnwise logical combinations on two words. Often additional equipment is appended to the adder to do such extra operations, and sometimes parts of the adder can be directly used. For instance, suppose that the carry chain is disrupted and that a carry of 0 is forced into each column. Figure 11.21 shows that the sum output is the exclusive OR of the inputs, and that the carry output is the AND of the inputs. On

A	B	CARRY-IN	SUM	CARRY-OUT
0	0	0	0	0
0	1	0	1	0
1	0	0	1	0
1	1	0	0	1

Figure 11.21.   The adder as an exclusive OR and AND.

A	B	CARRY-IN	SUM	CARRY-OUT
0	0	1	1	0
0	1	1	0	1
1	0	1	0	1
1	1	1	1	1

Figure 11.22.   The adder as the exclusive OR-NOT and OR.

the other hand, if a carry of 1 is forced into each column (Figure 11.22), the carry-output is the OR of the inputs; and the sum output, the exclusive OR-NOT. Depending upon the internal details of the adder, other possibilities may exist.

REGISTERS

A simple *register* consists of storage for as many digits as there may be in the word concerned, plus means for writing into the register and means for reading from it. Writing into the register, of course, destroys the prior contents, but reading is usually arranged to be non-destructive. The contents of the register are in effect copied into the destination.

Registers can be *serial* or *parallel*. In this connotation, the distinction has to do with how information is transmitted rather than how arithmetic is done. Information which parades time sequentially down one communication path is being transmitted serially; if the information proceeds in broadside along many communication paths, it is being transmitted in parallel. Mixed systems are obviously possible; an alphanumeric machine might transmit the 6-bits of a character in parallel but the successive characters in series.

A register might receive information in one fashion but transmit it in the other. In particular, a register which receives information serially but makes it available broadside (in parallel) is sometimes called a *staticizer*. Obviously such a register must have shifting properties, because the information appears time sequentially at the input terminal and must be passed along from stage to stage (16).

The Parallel Register

Figure 11.23 shows a typical parallel register. There will be as many columns as there are places in the word although sometimes registers are of special length, e.g., half-word, double word. In each column there is a storage element which might be any of the toggles discussed earlier, a write-in input gate, and an output buffer amplifier. Sometimes there may be a multiplicity of input gates in order to accept information from many sources. The output buffer amplifier is frequently a current amplifier and protects the storage element from the current demands of low impedance loads. Sometimes there are

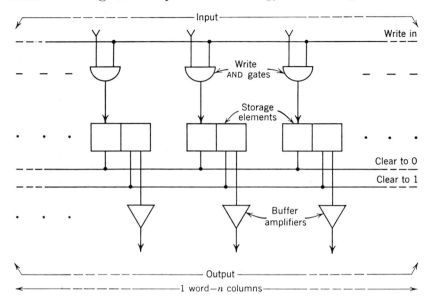

Figure 11.23. A typical arrangement for a parallel register.

also output gates, and there may be special control lines for setting the register to a prescribed configuration, e.g., all 0's, all 1's, an arbitrary pattern.

The Serial Register

In a machine which performs arithmetic serially and, therefore, usually also transmits information serially, there is no need to have all digits of a word available simultaneously. It is sufficient to parade the digits time sequentially past any point. Some economy of equipment can be realized by capitalizing on this observation.

It is clear that a parallel register which has sidewise shifting properties can serve as a serial register. The stream of input information is passed along the chain of storage devices one place each time the next input digit appears. In Figure 11.24, the first digit to appear will eventually arrive in the right-most column. Unless we desire to obtain the word last digit first (*reversed order*), the output terminal must be at the right end of the register. Each time the register shifts one place to the right, it emits one digit of its contents to the output

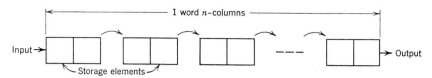

Figure 11.24. A static serial register.

terminal. If the word is n digits long, it takes n shifts to fill the register and n shifts to empty it. It is clear that the shifting signals have to be synchronized with the incoming information and with the desired output rate. If the digit time is Δt seconds, $n\Delta t$ seconds is the word time and the interval required to register the word or to transmit it—or for that matter, to pass it through an adder.

A serial register of the kind just described is sometimes referred to as a *static register* because the information, once written into the register, can remain quiescently in place until it is needed.

The Dynamic Serial Register

The central element of the *dynamic serial register* is a delay device which is one word time long (17). In principal, by connecting the tail of such a delay device to its mouth, information can be trapped and will continue to circulate around the closed loop. Periodically the information parades past the end of the delay element in the right order, and with the first digit in first position. In practice, perfect delay elements do not exist and auxiliary equipment must be provided to overcome their phase and amplitude distortions (Figure 11.25). In the dynamic register, the information never stands still; it is always on the move. Hence the name—*dynamic,* or sometimes, *revolving* or *circulating registers.* The only right time to accept information from this register is just as the first digit is emerging. At any other time, the digits of the word can still be obtained but cyclically permuted.

A static serial register is cheaper (but slower) than the parallel register because there need be only one input and one output terminal instead of n of each. (The tradeoff between time and money again.) The dynamic serial register is cheaper yet because the delay element utilizes either electromagnetic or acoustic propagation effects or the motion of a physical medium. Such phenomena are significantly

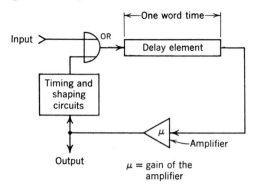

Figure 11.25. The arrangement for a dynamic register.

cheaper per bit than an electronic version of a delay device, e.g., a shift register.

Specific ways to provide the delay and the details of writing and reading the dynamic register are quite the same as one kind of store (Chapter 12); the detailed discussion will be found there. Do not miss the similarity to the dynamic toggle (page 8.80) which can be regarded as a one-column dynamic register.

Propagation rates are not readily changeable; hence dynamic registers are quite tightly tied to an absolute time scale and are most suited for a type of machine organization which we will later call *synchronous* (Chapter 13). In a synchronous machine, all events are very carefully scheduled to occur at precise time intervals. Among other things, the word in a dynamic register will circulate completely every word time. It will require one word time to register incoming information, and one word time to transmit outgoing information.

The Shift Register

Insofar as its internal communication is concerned, a machine can be thought of as largely a column-organized structure. The ith digit of a word coming from the adder goes to the ith column of a register and eventually resides in the ith column of a selected storage cell. The first and last digits of the machine word can be thought of as defining the geometrical edges of the machine. Shifting is a sidewise motion of information with respect to these edges. Unless a suitable arrangement is made in a shift operation, data can pass beyond the edge of

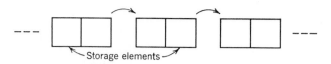

Figure 11.26. The logical paradox in shifting.

the machine, to be lost. One arrangement which can be made is to provide a special register longer than one word, e.g., a *double-length* or two-word register. Alternatively, for the needs of some instructions, an end of one register can be connected to an end of a second register, and thereby provide a temporary structure of extra length.

Consider an internal stage of a *shift register* (Figure 11.26); it finds itself in a logical paradox. It is required to transmit information to one neighbor but to simultaneously accept information from the other neighbor. Suppose that the central stage contains a 0 and its left neighbor, a 1. On the command to shift right, the stage in question must retain its 0-state long enough for the right neighbor to respond; but it is also concurrently being offered the 1 from the left neighbor, and must accept it. There is an obvious requirement for temporary storage between the stages of a shift register (Figure 11.27). Such interstage storage must retain the information until all transients incident to getting the information into temporary storage have died away, and the permanent storage units of the register are ready to receive new information.

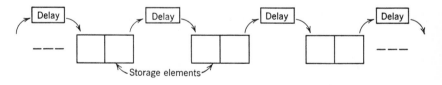

Figure 11.27. Interstage storage of information during shifting.

The Parallel Shift Register

Shifting in a parallel register is much like the sidewise motion of the carriage in a desk calculator except that there is no physical motion of the register itself; the information moves within the register. The interstage storage can be provided by electromagnetic delay lines (18)

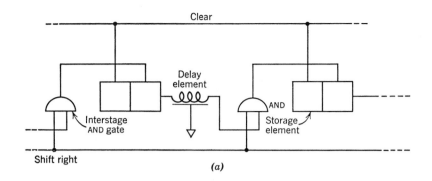

(a)

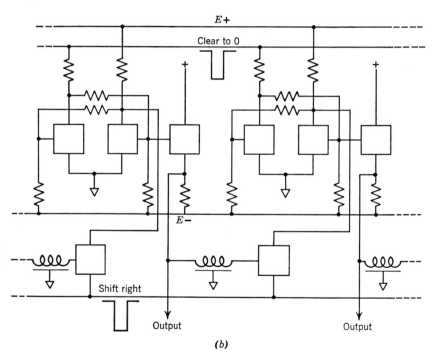

(b)

Figure 11.28.   Representative arrangements for a parallel shift register.   (a) The logical arrangement.   (b) Use of degenerate triode gates between stages.

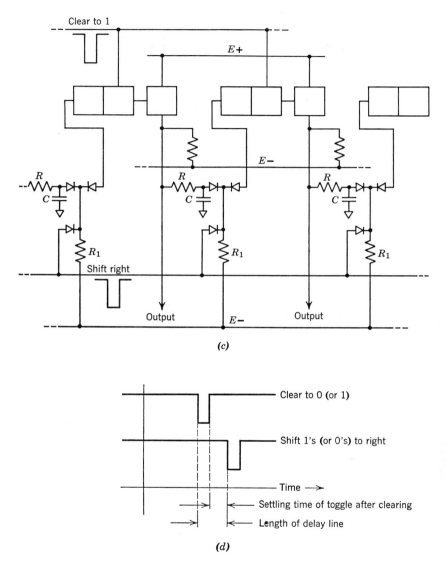

Figure 11.28 (Continued). (c) *Use of diode gates between stages.* (d) *The operating cycle.*

or by the delay which occurs in the voltage response of resistance-capacitance circuit. In either case, the amount of time that information can be held in limbo is set by the characteristics of the particular delay device; therefore, shifting must occur on schedule or information will be lost. A common way of causing the permanent storage elements to emit their information into temporary storage is by clearing the register to some state—say, to all 0's. All toggles which initially contain a 0 will transmit nothing to the neighbor, which will have already received a 0 through clearing. Any toggle which initially contains a 1 will, in changing to 0, enter a signal into the delay element. The interstage element must hold the signal in transit until the transients of clearing have subsided; finally the signal emerges from the delay and sets the neighbor to 1. If the delay is too short (perhaps, because of parameters which drift with time), the information can arrive too early and the neighbor toggle may not yet have recovered composure. If the delay happens to become too long, the gating signal may be missed.

It is clear that we have tolerance problems here which must be considered. Furthermore, the shift register which uses temporary storage of a transient nature is best suited to the tightly scheduled synchronous machine. Representative circuits are shown in Figure 11.28.

The Double-Ranked Shift Register

The interstage storage can also be provided by elements of unlimited storage time, e.g., toggles (19). Consider the circuit of Figure 11.29. The upper rank of toggles is the normal group which is required for an n-column register. The lower rank is solely for the purpose of providing temporary storage. In a shift sequence, information flows as follows: information in the permanent rank is transmitted to the temporary rank; after all transients have disappeared and the information is safely entered into the temporary rank, the contents of the temporary rank is transmitted diagonally back to the permanent rank —right or left as the case may be. Shifting in such a *positive acting register* is in the nature of a sawtooth—straight down and diagonally back.

The *double-ranked* or *ratchet register* offers considerable freedom from timing restraints. The return diagonal transfer can be done at any arbitrary time after the vertical transfer is finished. Moreover,

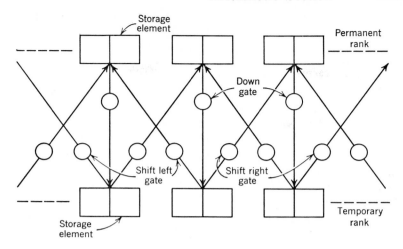

Figure 11.29. The double-ranked register.

if the gating circuits are direct coupled, considerable freedom from waveshape degradation is also available. The disadvantage of such a register is the cost of extra equipment; it is to be measured against the freedom from timing and waveshape which it offers. The double-ranked register also has a more complex operating cycle than a simple shift-register using time-limited temporary storage, and hence needs some additional controlling signals. For a given toggle and gate technology, the double-ranked register can operate roughly half as fast as the single-ranked register.

EXAMPLE

Suppose that a single-ranked register is to be operated in a *clear-and-gate* mode. This implies that the whole row of toggles will first be cleared to, say, 0, and then after the transients of clearing have settled, the 1's which have been held in temporary storage will be gated into the receiving stages. The operating cycle of the register is of the order of two toggle transition times—one to clear to 0, and one to receive the 1. In any given case, many toggles may not receive 1's, but the time must be allowed in the operating cycle because the designer has no control over the information which will be inserted into the register during its operating life.

   In the double-ranked register, four transition times are involved: clear the temporary rank, transmit information from permanent to temporary, clear the permanent rank, transmit information from temporary to permanent.

While a little overlapping of these operations may be possible, the speed of operation has been degraded to about one-half.

For extra equipment (and cost), the speed of operation can be restored. Suppose that the gating between permanent and temporary ranks is *symmetrical*. There will be a gate to transmit a 1 from one toggle to the other, and also a gate to transmit the 0; there will be a gate from each side of the transmitting toggle to the corresponding side of the receiving toggle. The operating cycle now requires only two toggle-transition times, but with symmetrical gating, the single-rank register will operate in one transition time.

End Affairs

As a parallel register is shifted right or left, end stages become vacant. Whether 0's or 1's are inserted into these places depends upon the particular shift being implemented. In left shifting of a single register, 0's are generally brought into the vacated spot at the right end. What happens at the left end on a right shift depends upon the kind of shift.

EXAMPLES

1. A *logical shift* usually includes the sign position as a column of the register and shifts through it right or left accordingly. If the shift is *cyclic*, there is an end-to-end connection, and the information inserted into the left end of the register (its sign position) is the digit emitted from the right end of the register.

2. There may also be a cyclic shift which excludes the sign position. The left end of the register is considered to be the position just to the right of the sign position.

3. A *power shift* amounts to a multiplication or a division by a power of the base. On a right power shift in a sign-magnitude machine, the digit 0 is inserted into the position just to the right of the sign position. On the right power shift in a complement machine, the sign digit does not participate, but the sign digit is copied into the position just to its right (see exercise 11.24).

Just as one register can be coupled by an end-to-end connection, so two registers can be coupled by an *end-around* path. Such a connection is likely to be physically long and, therefore, have additional capacitance loading. Current amplification in the end-around links may be necessary. Such links do not operate at all times, and hence may also contain additional logical elements to establish them when needed. A variety of end-around connections is possible.

1. In one scheme of implementing multiplication, the right end of the Accumulator is coupled to the left end of the MQ in order to provide a double-length register for the product. In this scheme, the sign digits of the two halves of the product are made alike, and hence the "left end of the MQ" is really the place just to the right of its sign position. The place just to the right of the Accumulator sign position receives a 0 or a copy of the sign digit according to whether the machine is a sign-magnitude machine or a complement machine.

2. With an end connection from the right end of the Accumulator to the left end of the MQ and another one from the right end of MQ to the left end of the Accumulator, we can have a cyclic shift of both registers. What is meant by "left end" depends on the kind of cyclic shift desired; i.e., are the sign digits included or not?

Other Shift Details

It is obvious that shifting in a binary machine means that each place in the register communicates with its immediate neighbor, immediate at least in the sense that the binary digits of a word are considered to stand adjacent. Shifting in a decimal or an alphanumeric machine means something else. In, say, a decimal machine a decimal digit is to be transferred to the adjacent decimal digit which implies that corresponding positions of the binary tetrads must communicate. The individual binary positions are not available in the sense that a binary position cannot be shifted into the adjacent binary position. Such binary shifting is often very useful, and a decimal machine may be provided with both binary and decimal shift features. By the same token, an end connection in a decimal machine is not one wire, but four.

For extra equipment, unusual internal shift features can be provided. For example, a set of gates and connections from each stage to the second one away yields a single step shift equivalent to scaling (in a binary machine) by 4 or $\frac{1}{4}$. The even stages of a register might be arranged to shift to each other independently of the odd stages, which might shift to each other. Any such special arrangements can be provided in the parallel shift register at the cost of more gates and connections.

The Serial Shift Register

In parallel representation of information, columnar position within a word corresponds to position in space; each stage of a parallel register corresponds to some particular position in space. In serial representation of information, columnar position corresponds to position in time; each stage of a serial register corresponds to some particular time slot, and eventually all digits of a word will parade past the same space position. Therefore, while shifting in the parallel register is a sidewise displacement in space, shifting in the serial register must be a displacement in time. Since time flows only in one direction, we anticipate that whichever direction of shifting amounts to advancing forward in time will have to be accomplished by really sliding backward, but less than one word time. In a dynamic serial register, it is tempting to suggest that shifting can be done by reading the register earlier or later than normal. To do this, however, requires that some part or all of the whole machine somehow skip or pickup a digit interval in time; this is not easily done.

Consider the four place register of Figure 11.30-a; this is a snapshot in time just as the word time interval is beginning. The digit A occurs in the first time slot t_1. After shifting left one place, the

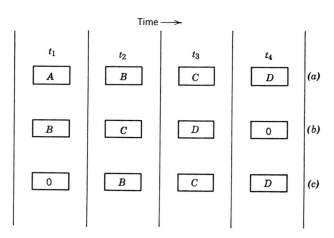

Figure 11.30. Left-shifting in serial representation.

situation must be that of Figure 11.30-b; digit B must occur in time slot t_1. The situation of Figure 11.30-c is not acceptable because digit B has not moved from its original time position.

EXAMPLE

Assume that there are two words whose first few digits are A_1, B_1, C_1, . . . , and A_2, B_2, C_2, ... If these two words were to be added as is, digits A_1 and A_2 would each occupy the first time slot, and the first sum digit would be formed in the first time slot. Digits B_1 and B_2 and the second sum digit would all be in the second time slot, and so on. In a parallel machine, the corresponding statement would be that digits A_1, A_2, and the first sum digit must all occupy the first column, and so on.

Assume that it is necessary for some reason to shift the second word two places to the left and then add it to the first word. Therefore, digits A_1 and C_2 must occupy the first time slot in their respective words. Digit C_2 must somehow move from the third time slot up into the first one. In the parallel machine, the digit C_2 would have originally been in the third column, but would have moved spatially sidewise into the first column.

It takes a little bit of chicanery to do serial shifting (20). The logical arrangement is shown in Figure 11.31. The total delay around the loop can be made $n - 1$, n, or $n + 1$ time units. Consider the specific four-place register of Figure 11.32. Three places are in the delay element, and two, outside. For normal storage, one external unit is in the loop. Figure 11.32 details the position of information for four successive time intervals; the word returns to home position every fourth time interval.

For left shifting, both external units are used; the extra one initially

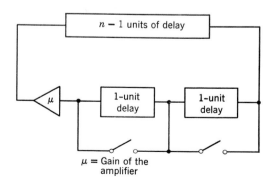

Figure 11.31. The logical arrangement for serial shifting.

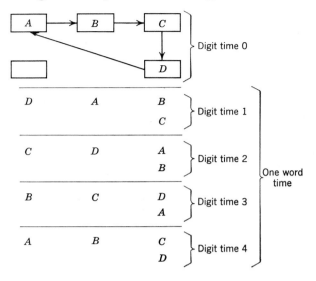

Figure 11.32. Normal circulation in a serial register.

contains a 0 (Figure 11.33). After four digit intervals, the fifth place contains the shifted-off digit. If the normal recirculation loop of n-time units is reestablished, the shifted word recirculates and the extra digit in the fifth place is discarded. Each place of shifting requires one word time.

For right shifting, the loop is $n - 1$ units long for $n - 1$ pulse digit times, and then $n + 1$ for the last (or first) digit time (Figure 11.34). The fifth place contains the 0 digit to be shifted into the left end. After n digit times, or one word time, the word is shifted right one place, and the additional external place contains the discarded digit.

Whatever the main delay medium may be, the external unit delays are frequently toggles which are written into at one digit time and read from the next digit time. These toggles, themselves, require temporary storage in order not to be in the same logical paradox as the internal stage of a parallel shift register.

Eventually (Chapter 13) we will have to investigate the control as the source of timing signals which cause events to occur elsewhere in the machine. It is appropriate to point out here how the details of the arithmetic processes interact with the control. For example, in the case of serial shifting, a special signal is required at the end of either the first or $(n-1)$st digit time in order to change the length of the recirculating loop.

As we see, shifting in a serial dynamic register requires one word time per place to be shifted. Compared to a parallel register, shifting is very inefficient of time. On the other hand, static registers in a serial machine are in effect a parallel register and shift equally rapidly. Therefore, money invested in static registers in a serial machine leads to faster shift instructions. However, divide time is the same in either case because a subtraction must be performed at each stage of division, and the shift in the dynamic register can be combined with the subtraction in one word time. The multiply time may or may not change. If the multiply is implemented as a sequence of add-and-shifts where either the multiplicand or zero is added to the partial product as determined by the multiplier digit, then the multiply time is the same for dynamic or static registers—for the same reason as in division. Conversely, a serial machine with dynamic registers gains nothing by implementing multiplication in a different way. However, the serial machine with static registers can improve its multiply time by omitting

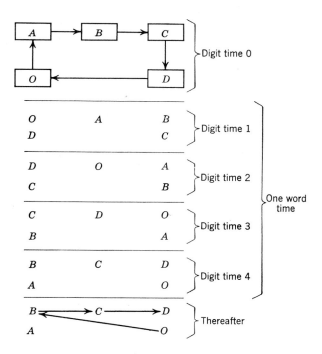

Figure 11.33. Left shifting in a serial register.

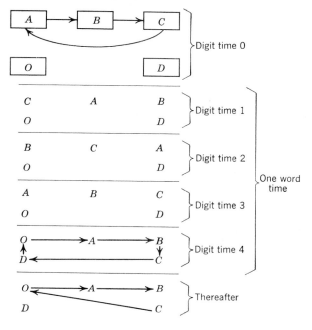

Figure 11.34. Right shifting in a serial register.

the add part of the add-shift whenever the multiplier digit is zero. Not only does the faster shifting of the static register pay off, but the word time needed to pass through a serial adder is avoided.

Hence, when all is said and done, it is not necessarily true that the cost efficiency of the dynamic register is a blessing. It may be worth the extra money of the static registers to buy faster machine operation.

ALL ELSE

The Accumulator

Usually one of the shift registers is permanently associated with and connected to the adder; together they are called the *accumulator* (21). This device has the property that it adds incoming information to its previous contents and replaces the former contents with the new sum —just like the dials in the carriage of a desk calculator. As we see in Figure 11.35, here is another merry-go-round problem. The adder

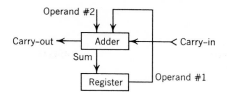

Figure 11.35. The logical merry-go-round in the accumulator.

combines the contents of the register part of the accumulator with the
incoming operand, but at the same time the new sum attempts to enter
the register whose contents is helping to determine the sum.   Same
story: some kind of temporary storage—either short term or long
term—must be put into the loop some place.

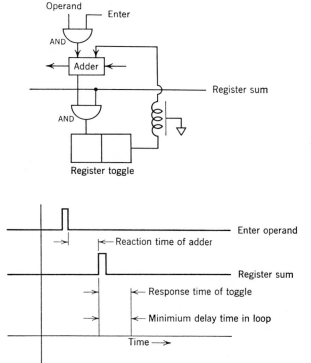

Figure 11.36. Loop delay in the parallel accumulator stage.

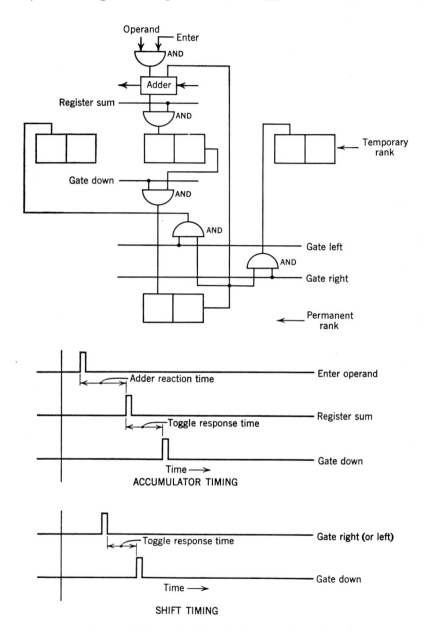

Figure 11.37. A double-ranked accumulator stage.

The storage can be provided by a delay line or by resistance-capacitance networks, but timing must be watched carefully. Figure 11.36 shows a typical configuration for the internal stages of a parallel accumulator. Alternatively, the register can be double ranked and the second rank made to serve not only for the accumulator's purpose but also for shifting (Figure 11.37). In the serial accumulator, the delay of the circulating loop itself avoids the problem (Figure 11.38).

Because the accumulator participates in multiplication and division, it must shift partial products or partial remainders sidewise. Hence the register portion of the accumulator is always a shifting register. Moreover, since the accumulator usually participates in several kinds of shifts, it will have special arrangements at its end stages to accommodate end-around connections to the MQ, or to copy the sign digit into the adjacent stage. The adder portion may also have a facility for the insertion of an artificial carry.

Often the adder will be supplemented with such extra equipment as may be needed to carry out the machine's logical instructions. Depending upon the details of the logical instructions, this may only mean the ability to interfere with the carry circuit of the adder, or it may mean a substantial amount of extra gating networks in the adder stage. In a logical instruction, typically the present contents of the

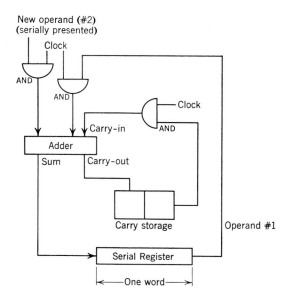

Figure 11.38. The serial accumulator.

accumulator is columnwise logically combined with a word from storage, and the result becomes the new contents of the accumulator.

In a serial machine it is very simple to interfere with the carry process and to force a carry of 0 or 1 into each column. Moreover, relative to a parallel adder, it is cheap to build a complex one-column device for addition and logical operations.

Other Arithmetic Processes

Our discussion has dealt extensively with addition and subtraction. From these plus shifting, multiplication and division can be performed. Hence in addition to the Accumulator, the MQ which is a shift register, and the non-shifting Number Register (which may not exist in a serial machine), the arithmetic unit contains several extra items relevant to multiplication and division. The shift equipment we have already considered, including the end-coupled registers. There must be a gate network which inspects the current digit of the multiplier and directs the current step of the multiplication to either add in the multiplicand and then shift the partial product, or to just shift the partial product. In a sign-magnitude machine, there must be a circuit to sense the sign digits of the multiplier and the multiplicand, and to determine the sign of the product. The signs of the two halves of the product must also be set equal. In a complement machine, other than making the signs of the halves of the product the same, no special action is necessary with respect to the signs. However, certain corrective actions are necessary to bring the final result into correct form (22) (see problem 11.18). Such equipment is usually part of the arithmetic section. In division, there must be a circuit which senses the sign of the trial difference and (in restoring division) either accepts the difference, inserts a 1 into the quotient and shifts the dividend and partial remainder; or rejects the remainder, inserts a 0 in the quotient and shifts (23). In non-restoring division, there are certain corrective steps which must be taken to bring the quotient into proper form; this equipment is generally considered part of the arithmetic section (24). Some rounding operation is usually performed on the final digit of the quotient, and there may be a Multiplication-with-Round-off instruction. Special action necessary for rounding is also the responsibility of the arithmetic section.

We have discussed some ways of doing multiplication and division in Chapter 5 (25). The precise details of these processes, the way in which negative numbers are represented, and the arithmetic instructions in the machine repertoire combine to determine the fine structure of the arithmetic section. We have discussed in detail only the major parts of the arithmetic section—the adder and the registers. The details of the other parts can be straightforwardly determined: from the details of the process, specify the logical decisions which must be made; construct the appropriate truth table; and finally design the circuit from gate and toggle technology.

Special Features

The arithmetic section may contain other equipment of many kinds. It is present perhaps to provide programming convenience, or to implement particular instructions. There may be an *overflow detector,* for instance. Its details will depend on how negative numbers are represented; the principles have already been given (page 2.27). There may be special arrangements for speeding up multiplication; a binary machine might be arranged to multiply in base 4 or in base 8 (26). The number of steps in the multiplication will be decreased accordingly, but the adder has to be a many-column adder (see page 11.19). In a decimal machine, there may be equipment for first generating and storing all multiples of the multiplicand in order to facilitate multiplication (see page 5.37) (27). There may be special division processes (28).

There may be error-detecting or error-correcting equipment which is concerned with the arithmetic process. For instance, there may be means for predicting how a parity digit should behave through arithmetic or * logical processes and † for conducting appropriate parity checks. The arithmetic section may generate a parity-check digit for all information which it transmits elsewhere. It may also verify parity checks on incoming words. There may be supplementary equipment for conducting a casting-out or *residue* check of the arithmetic processes (29). ‡ The arithmetic unit may have to cope with words which contain error-correcting codes.

There is usually some sequencing circuits and pulse generators concerned only with the arithmetic unit. Such equipment will normally be regarded as part of the arithmetic section (*arithmetic local control*) rather than part of the main control section. For instance, the circuits for sequencing a multiplication or a division might reasonably be

---

* The inclusive OR.

† Really equivalent to the inclusive OR.

‡ See Chapter 7, Volume I, page 7.4 for an example. See also exercise 11.29.

charged to the arithmetic section. Finally, there conceivably might be enough local control to execute very complicated instructions, e.g., sine, arc tangent, check sum, square root.

Floating Point

If the arithmetic section is required to do instructed (rather than programmed) floating-point operations, substantial additional equipment is needed. The mantissa and the exponent parts of a floating-point number are dealt with quite differently; the arithmetic unit must fracture a word into the two appropriate parts. There may be special counters for tallying the shift operations required in floating-point work; there may be a small supplementary adder (or accumulator) for dealing with exponents; there can also be a great deal of local control to sequence the floating-point operations. There may also be both an overflow and an *underflow detector*. The latter recognizes when a number grows smaller than the smallest non-zero number which can be represented in the machine. Overflow, as in fixed point is the situation of a number which would like to be bigger than the largest number which can be represented in the machine.

As an example of the extra equipment involved in floating point, consider the sequence of operations involved in a floating-point addition (or subtraction). Each operand comes to the arithmetic unit as a mantissa plus an exponent. For convenience, the two parts of each operand will probably be separated in the arithmetic section.

1. The exponents must be compared for size, to determine which is larger, and by how much. This implies that the exponents are subtracted, perhaps in a supplementary adder whose length is that of an exponent. If, say, exponent number 2 is subtracted from exponent number 1, and the difference is positive, exponent 2 is smaller and the difference tells by how much. If the difference is negative, exponent 1 is smaller, and the difference tells by how much. But, how was the subtraction done? In all likelihood, the negative difference is in complement form and may have to be converted to sign-magnitude form.

2. The operand with the smaller exponent must shift its mantissa to the right as many places as its exponent is small. Hence the sign of the difference of the exponents tells which mantissa to shift, and the magnitude of the difference indicates the number of places. Conceivably, the adder which differenced the exponents can be used to tally the number of shifts, by subtracting 1 from it for each shift. When it

becomes 0, shifting is complete (see exercise 11.27). If it happens that the difference of the exponents is greater than the number of places in the mantissa, the operand with the smaller mantissa can be made zero, and no shifting takes place. Otherwise, a great deal of useless shifting will waste machine time and slow its operating rate.

3. A fixed-point addition (or subtraction) of the mantissa is now made. If there is no overflow, all is fine and normalization can proceed. If there is an overflow at this point, the sum must be shifted right one place, the lost 1 inserted into the left-most place of the accumulator, and the exponent increased by 1. The accumulator may have an extra place to accommodate possible overflows. It may be that the exponent is already as large as it can be. If so, an overflow of interest to the programmer has occurred. A toggle will be set and there will likely be an appropriate Branch instruction which tests the toggle.

4. If necessary the sum of the mantissas is shifted to the left until there are no lead 0's (i.e., *normalized*), and a tally of the number of shifts is kept.

5. The exponent (the larger of the two initial ones) is decreased by the number of shifts made during normalization; and the exponent is combined with the mantissa to complete the result. It may be that the exponent is already as small as it can get, and an underflow of interest to the programmer has occurred. A toggle will probably be set to record this fact, and the machine may proceed on its own to convert the result to the smallest number it can represent—a zero mantissa and a maximum negative exponent. The programmer can test the underflow detector with an appropriate Branch instruction.

GENERAL COMMENTS

A rock-bottom arithmetic unit is an accumulator, plus one or two other registers plus some control and sequencing equipment. In a spartan situation division and perhaps also multiplication will be accomplished by the programmer with subroutines. A somewhat more elaborate arithmetic section will contain multiply and divide as wired-in operations. A yet more elaborate arithmetic section may have floating-point operations, or detectors for certain unusual situations (30). Where do we draw the line? How much of an arithmetic unit do we provide?

In this chapter, we have begun to see the interaction between the amount of hardware (and, therefore, equipment cost) and program-ming convenience. Desirable operations such as floating point imply substantial amounts of additional equipment, and the cost of such features is an important consideration in determining the overall structure of a machine and its repertoire. The nature of the problem enters into the system consideration also. For example, a machine in-tended for a single, well-understood problem—say air navigation—in which the behavior of all numerical values is well known, may be perfectly adequate and well balanced for its application with a minimal arithmetic unit. It may be possible to program the problem without division per se; or perhaps it may be possible to incorporate some sort of table-lookup scheme for assisting with multiplication. If so, the arithmetic section is correspondingly simplified.

The general purpose machines—especially the "big boys"—are the ones in which the arithmetic unit tends to become elaborate. Essen-tially nothing is known at design time about the details of the routines for which they will be used. The almost overwhelming factor is simply equipment cost versus programming convenience. Sometimes cost even takes a secondary role if a very elaborate equipment configuration is necessary to get some job done in a reasonable time, on time, or even at all. An elaborate arithmetic unit may be reflected in an extensive set of instructions in the repertoire, or it may not. An extensively self-checked arithmetic unit with special provisions for high-speed multiplication may account for very much equipment but be repre-sented in the repertoire by only a few simple arithmetic instructions.

We have also begun to see the large number of choices open to the designer. His choices come at several levels of detail. For example, consider addition. Is it binary or decimal? Is it parallel or serial? Are negative numbers represented as complements or not? If addition is parallel, how is the carry to be handled? Finally, what are the de-tails of the adder; is it many one-column adders, or a many-column adder—or if decimal, a matrix adder? What gating technology is to be used? What particular circuits are appropriate? What are the details of the registers? How is a register associated with the adder to form the accumulator? The inputs to these decisions are such things as the machine repertoire and the gross characteristics of the machine. Each decision reflects the ultimate use of the machine, the implications of the decision on the programmer's use of the machine, the cost of the equipment, the general speed range of the machine, the need to economize the amount of equipment perhaps even at extra cost, and the overall reliability expected of the machine. Often a decision cannot be a nice clean one, in the sense that convenience in one place crops out as a nuisance elsewhere. For example, sign-magnitude representation while convenient to the user creates extra problems in implementing subtraction; on the other hand, complement representation creates difficulties during multiplication or division. Moreover, it raises the problem of how negative numbers are to be inputted to the machine. Must they be complements or will the loading routine accept sign-magnitude representation and automatically form the complements? As an example of a decision which interacts with the programmer, consider a sign-magnitude machine whose accumulator contains an adder-subtractor. Suppose that equal numbers are added, but of opposite sign. Unless special care is taken with the handling of the signs, the resulting sum of 0 can carry the sign of the first number which entered the accumulator. Such a machine can represent 0 with either algebraic sign, and consequently create some nasty problems for the user.

In a large machine system, it is easy enough for situations awkward to the user to arise accidentally. Sometimes, cost restrictions or particular choices by the hardware designer can also lead to similar unfortunate results. Close interaction between programmers and engineers during the design phase can do much to minimize the risk of inconvenient organizational arrangements, or behavioral idiosyncrasies whose only value is nuisance.

COLLATERAL READING

1. Siegel, P., *Understanding digital computers;* John Wiley and Sons, New York, 1961; chapter 14.

   Flores, I., *Computer logic;* Prentice-Hall, Englewood Cliffs, N.J., 1960; pp. 145–189, chapter 12.

   Ledley, R. S., *Digital computer and control engineering;* McGraw-Hill Book Co., New York, 1960; chapter 11.

   Bartee, T. C. *Digital computer fundamentals;* McGraw-Hill Book Co., New York, 1960; chapter 6.

   Grabbe, E. M. *et al., Handbook of automation, computation, and control;* John Wiley and Sons, New York, 1959; vol. 2, chapter 18.

   Smith, C. V. L., *Electronic digital computers;* McGraw-Hill Book Co., New York, 1959; chapter 10.

   McCormick, E. H., *Digital computer primer;* McGraw-Hill Book Co., New York, 1959; chapter 7.

2. Smith, C. V. L., *Electronic digital computers;* McGraw-Hill Book Co., New York, 1959; pp. 222–225.

   Murphy, J. S., *Basics of digital computers;* John F. Rider Publisher, New York, 1958; vol. 3, pp. 128–129.

   Scott, N. R., *Analog and digital computer technology;* McGraw-Hill Book Co., New York, 1960; pp. 317–322.

3. Smith, C. V. L., *Electronic digital computers;* McGraw-Hill Book Co., New York, 1959; pp. 220–222.

   Murphy, J. S., *Basics of digital computers;* John F. Rider Publisher, New York, 1958; vol. 3, pp. 124–127.

   Scott, N. R., *Analog and digital computer technology;* McGraw-Hill Book Co.. New York, 1960; pp. 323–325.

4. Ledley, R. S., *Digital computer and control engineering;* McGraw-Hill Book Co., New York, 1960; chapter 15.

5. Ledley, R. S., *Digital computer and control engineering;* McGraw-Hill Book Co., New York, 1960; chapter 16.

6. Scott, N. R., *Analog and digital computer technology;* McGraw-Hill Book Co., New York, 1960; pp. 326–329.

   Bedrij, O. J., Carry-select adder; *IRE Transactions on Electronic Computers,* vol. EC-11, February, 1962; pp. 340–346.

7. Smith, C. V. L., *Electronic digital computers;* McGraw-Hill Book Co., New York, 1959; pp. 19–20.

8. Gilchrist, B. *et. al.,* Fast carry logic for digital computers; *IRE Transactions on Electronic Computers,* vol. EC-4, December, 1955; pp. 133–136.

   Reitwiesner, G. W., The determination of carry propagation length for binary arithmetic; *IRE Transactions on Electronic Computers,* vol. EC-9, March, 1960; pp. 35–38.

   Hendrickson, H. C., Fast high accuracy binary parallel addition; *IRE Transactions on Electronic Computers,* vol. EC-9, December, 1960; pp. 465–469.

   Smith, C. V. L., *Electronic digital computers;* McGraw-Hill Book Co., New York, 1959; pp. 239–242.

9. Sklansky, J., An evaluation of several two-summand binary adders; *IRE Transactions on Electronic Computers,* vol. EC-9, June, 1960; pp. 213–231.

   Lehman, M. and N. Burla, Skip techniques for high speed carry propagation in binary arithmetic units; *IRE Transactions on Electronic Computers,* vol. EC-10, December, 1961; pp. 691–698.

   Smith, C. V. L., *Electronic digital computers;* McGraw-Hill Book Co., New York, 1959; pp. 227–229, 242–244.

10. Richards, R. K., *Arithmetic operations in digital computers;* D. Van Nostrand Co., Princeton, N.J., 1955; chapters 4, 5.

    Salter, F., High Speed transistorized adder for a digital computer; *IRE Transactions on Electronic Computers,* vol. EC-9, December, 1960; pp. 461–464.

    Chew, M., A magnetic core parallel adder; *IRE Transactions on Electronic Computers,* vol. EC-7, December, 1958; pp. 262–264.

    Weinberger, A. and J. L. Smith, The logical design of a one microsecond parallel adder using 1 MC. circuitry; *Proceedings of the 1956 Western Joint Computer Conference,* San Francisco, 7–9 February, 1956; pp. 103–108.

11. Richards, R. K., *Arithmetic operations in digital computers;* D. Van Nostrand Co., Princeton, N.J., 1955; chapter 8, 9.

12. Scott, N. R., *Analog and digital computer technology;* McGraw-Hill Book Co., New York, 1960; pp. 330–333.

13. Scott, N. R., *Analog and digital computer technology;* McGraw-Hill Book Co., New York, 1960; pp. 334–337.

14. Scott, N. R., *Analog and digital computer technology;* McGraw-Hill Book Co., New York, 1960; pp. 337–341.

15. Smith, C. V. L., *Electronic digital computers;* McGraw-Hill Book Co., New York, 1959; pp. 234–239.

16. Smith, C. V. L., *Electronic digital computers;* McGraw-Hill Book Co. New York, 1959; chapter 8.

    Scott, N. R., *Analog and digital computer technology;* McGraw-Hill Book Co., New York, 1960; pp. 341–344.

    Baker, R. H. *et al.,* Transistor shift registers; *Proceedings of the IRE,* vol. 42, July, 1954; pp. 1152–1159.

    Anderson, J. R., A new type of ferroelectric shift register; *IRE Transactions on Electronic Computers,* vol. EC-5, December, 1956; pp. 184–191.

    Broadbent, K. D., A thin magnetic film shift register; *IRE Transactions on Electronic Computers,* vol. EC-9, September, 1960; pp. 321–323.

17. Smith, C. V. L., *Electronic digital computers;* McGraw-Hill Book Co., New York, 1959; pp. 190–191.

    Hargrave, L. E., Jr., A magnetostrictive delay line shift register; *IRE Transactions on Electronic Computers,* vol. EC-10, December, 1961; pp. 702–708.

18. Millman, J. and H. Taub, *Pulse and digital circuits;* McGraw-Hill Book Co., New York, 1956; chapter 10.

    Smith, C. V. L., *Electronic digital computers;* McGraw-Hill Book Co., New York, 1959; pp. 143–145.

    Scott, N. R., *Analog and digital computer technology;* McGraw-Hill Book Co., New York, 1960; pp. 403–407.

19. Smith, C. V. L., *Electronic digital computers;* McGraw-Hill Book Co., New York, 1959; pp. 180–182.

20. Murphy, J. S., *Basics of digital computers;* John F. Rider Publisher, New York, 1958; vol. 3, pp. 59–63.

21. Smith, C. V. L., *Electronic digital computers;* McGraw-Hill Book Co., New York, 1959; chapter 10, especially pp. 225–233.

22. Smith, C. V. L., *Electronic digital computers;* McGraw-Hill Book Co., New York, 1959; pp. 16–18.

    Scott, N. R., *Analog and digital computer technology;* McGraw-Hill Book Co., New York, 1960; pp. 353–357.

    Robertson, J. E., Two's complement multiplication in binary parallel digital computers; *IRE Transactions on Electronic Computers,* vol. EC-4, September, 1955; pp. 118–119.

23. Scott, N. R., *Analog and digital computer technology;* McGraw-Hill Book Co., New York, 1959; pp. 357–358.

24. Smith, C. V. L., *Electronic digital computers;* McGraw-Hill Book Co., New York, 1959; pp. 26–28.

25. Scott, N. R., *Analog and digital computer technology;* McGraw-Hill Book Co., New York, 1960; pp. 348–362.

26. Smith, C. V. L., *Electronic digital computers;* McGraw-Hill Book Co., New York, 1959; pp. 19–23.

    Lehman, M., High speed digital multiplication; *IRE Transactions on Electronic Computers,* vol. EC-6, September, 1957; pp. 204–205.

27. Eckert, W. J. and R. Jones, *Faster, faster;* McGraw-Hill Book Co., New York, 1955; chapter 2.

28. Robertson, J. E., A new class of division methods; *IRE Transactions on Electronic Computers,* vol. EC-7, September, 1958; pp. 218–222.

    Saltman, R. G., Reducing computing time for synchronous binary division; *IRE Transactions on Electronic Computers,* vol. EC-10, June, 1961; pp. 168–174.

    Wilson, J. B. and R. S. Ledley, An algorithm for rapid binary division; *IRE Transactions on Electronic Computers,* vol. EC-10, December, 1961; pp. 662–670.

29. Eckert, W. J. and R. Jones, *Faster, faster;* McGraw-Hill Book Co., New York, 1955; chapter 8.

30. Ross, H. D., Arithmetic element of the IBM 701; *Proceedings of the IRE,* vol. 10, October, 1953; pp. 1287–1294.

    MacSorley, O. L., High speed arithmetic in binary computers; *Proceedings of the IRE,* vol. 49, January, 1961; pp. 67–91.

    Ashenhurst, R. L., The MANIAC III Arithmetic system; *Proceedings of the 1962 Spring Joint Computer Conference,* San Francisco, 1–3 May, 1962; pp. 195–202.

    Buchholz, W., *Planning a computer;* McGraw-Hill Book Co., New York, 1962; chapters 7, 8, 14.

    Beard, A. D. *et al.,* Logic design of the RCA BIZMAC computer; *IRE Convention Record,* pt. 4, 1956; pp. 81–87.

    Hamilton, F. E. and E. C. Kubie, The IBM magnetic drum calculator type 650; *Journal of the Association for Computing Machinery,* vol. 1, January, 1954; pp. 13–20.

    Lourie, N. *et al.,* Arithmetic and control techniques in a multiprogram computer; *Proceedings of the 1959 Eastern Joint Computer Conference,* Boston, 1–3 December, 1959; pp. 75–81.

EXERCISES

11.1. In a serial read-out from some storage device (e.g., a register), when might it be convenient to have the most significant digit come first?

11.2. Throw the sum proposition of a one-column adder into various forms and sketch corresponding gating networks. Use diode gates, NOR gates, pentode gates.

11.3. Verify by constructing a truth table that Figure 11.7 does do binary addition properly.

11.4. Draw a timing diagram for Figure 11.8 and show that it does addition properly.

11.5. Demonstrate by means of appropriate truth tables that two half-adders plus an OR gate is required to make a full adder.

11.6. Show how one half-adder can be used time sequentially to implement a full adder. Is an extra OR gate necessary? What other extra equipment is necessary?

11.7. Develop the 3-input subtraction table.

11.8. Show that the end-around carry scheme works properly when negative binary numbers are represented as 1's complements. Work out the details of an end-around carry scheme when negative decimal numbers are represented as 9's complements.

11.9. How long can a carry be in an end-around carry situation? Can a carry ever propagate endlessly along the word?

11.10. In a machine which does arithmetic serially, would it be a wise choice to represent negative numbers in a (radix − 1) scheme and hence be required to perform an end-around carry? Why?

11.11. Consider a machine which performs arithmetic serially, and which represents numbers in sign magnitude form. What difficulty might arise if the sign digit is placed at the left end of the word? What can be done to alleviate the difficulty?

11.12. In a machine which performs arithmetic serially, would it be a wise choice to represent negative numbers in complement form? Is the situation any different for parallel arithmetic? (*Hint:* consider this question: Would an extra word time be required to complement the incoming information, or might the complementing operation be somehow overlapped with the addition process?)

11.13. Would you expect a serial machine to perform division by a non-restoring method? Estimate the number of word times required to complete a division with non-restoring and restoring methods.

11.14. Suppose that subtraction were to be implemented in a sign-magnitude machine by using an adder-subtractor; if a complement answer is produced, the subtraction will be repeated with the factors in reverse sequence. What extra hardware, if any, is required? Why? Might this scheme not work properly in all circumstances? Sketch the block diagram with all information flow paths and gates of such an add-subtract scheme.

11.15. Assume that numbers are represented in sign-magnitude and that the arithmetic unit contains an adder-subtractor. Describe in detail the sequence of operations necessary to perform both addition and subtraction for all combinations of signs of the two operands. Is there more than one way to arrange things? Indicate any extra equipment required in the arithmetic unit. Draw a block diagram of the arrangement including all information flow paths and gates.

Repeat the above for the situation in which the arithmetic unit has two adder-subtractors.

11.16. Construct the truth table which defines the logic necessary to do carry-sensing.

11.17. In a binary-coded-decimal adder, there is both a binary carry across the four bits of a tetrad and a decimal carry between adjacent tetrads. Discuss how these two kinds of carries can be handled in a serial-by-decimal-digit parallel-by-binary-digit adder. Draw information flow diagrams with all necessary gates. Does your answer depend on the code used?

11.18. Complete Figures 11.15 and 11.16.

11.19. Draw the complete block diagram of the equipment (registers, adders, and gates) necessary to carry out binary multiplication. Repeat but for binary division, both restoring and non-restoring.

11.20. Repeat exercise 11.19 except for decimal processes.

11.21. Describe in detail the end-to-end register connections in the divide process. What stage of each register communicates to what stage of the other register? Does your answer depend on the method of representing negative numbers?

11.22. The arrangement of gates in Figure 11.37 is obviously convenient for addition. Is it also a good arrangement so far as multiplication and division is concerned? Why?

11.23. Redraw Figure 11.36 to utilize a double-ranked register. Use (a) clear-gate transfer of information and (b) symmetrical gating for transfer of information. In each case, sketch the detailed timing of the sequence of events and indicate what interval of time is required for each.

11.24. Consider a binary machine which represents negative numbers in complement form. In the right shift, why is the sign digit copied into the place just to its right? Give some examples to support your answers.

11.25. Consider the shift register. If the right-most stage were shifted right first, then the second from the right shifted into the right-most, then the third from the right shifted into the second from the right, etc., it appears that the requirement for interstage delay is circumvented. Discuss this proposal; is it a wise suggestion; is it a practical idea; etc.?

11.26. Why does a human being not obtain a complement result when subtracting a large number from a smaller one? Compare your finding with the discussion of algebraic addition (page 11.27).

11.27. In the left shift required to normalize a floating-point number, how is the situation that there are no lead 0's detected? Sketch a block diagram showing how such a detector controls shifting and tallying of the counter; include all information flow paths and gates.

11.28. Work out the details of an overflow detector for a floating-point arithmetic unit. What information must be observed, and how is it combined to indicate overflow?

Consider the possibility that the magnitude part of the floating-point expression can be either in complement representation or in sign-magnitude representation.

11.29. The analog of a casting-out 9's process in binary is casting out factors of $2^n - 1$. For a binary word of given length describe how to form the residue of this word, modulo 31; i.e., cast out 31's and find the remainder.

Draw the block diagram of a scheme to implement such a process; include all information flow paths and gates.

11.30. Consider a majority element for four inputs. Write down the truth table and the algebraic description. Reduce the Boolean expressions, and sketch the block diagram of the device. Does it remind you of any other functional device, especially one for three inputs? Would it be useful in the design of any part of the arithmetic unit?

11.31. Describe the extra equipment that must be added to each stage of a parallel adder in order that it can also perform

(a) a columnwise AND,
(b) a columnwise exclusive OR,
(c) a columnwise inclusive OR.

Sketch one stage of such an augmented adder indicating all the control signal inputs.

11.32. Suppose that two operands are to be compared for equality by subtracting them and testing the difference to determine if it is zero. In problem 9.4, comparison was done by a gating network. Discuss the relative merits of the two schemes from the point of view of amount of equipment and speed of the machine.

11.33. Draw the circuit diagram of a 3-input, 2-output adder using relays.

11.34. Draw the circuit diagram of a shift register using relays. Indicate what temporary storage, if any, is provided. Repeat but for a double-rank shift register.

PROBLEMS

11.1. Estimate the amount of equipment (i.e., diodes) required to implement an adder for base 4 (i.e., for 2-column binary expressions); for base 16; for base 64. Extend your estimate to an adder operating in a base of 2^n.

11.2. A base-3 single-column full adder is to be designed. Each base-3 digit is encoded in a 2-bit character, the weights of the columns of which are 2, 1.

    (a) Write down the representation of the base-3 digits in the code.

    (b) Specify the truth table for the adder.

    (c) Implement the truth table straightforwardly as AND-OR functions, and also OR-AND functions.

    (d) Implement the adder as a base-3 matrix adder.

    (e) Deduce the corrective procedure necessary to make a 2-column binary adder operating in the given code perform correctly as a base-3 adder.

    (f) Comment on the relative amount of equipment and the speed of operation for parts (c), (d), (e).

11.3. Sketch the block diagram of a full adder which incorporates a carry-bypass scheme. Is it faster than a ripple-carry adder? Why? When, if ever?

11.4. Construct the truth table of a three-input binary adder-subtractor. Sketch the logical block diagram including the control inputs which determine whether the device is to add or subtract. Draw the circuit diagram using diode logic, NOR logic, NAND logic.

11.5. Construct the truth table which defines the operation of a matrix adder for decimal information encoded in

    (a) the 8, 4, 2, 1 code for input and output,

    (b) the 8, 4, 2, 1 code for input but the 2*, 4, 2, 1 code for output,

    (c) the 5, 4, 2, 1 code for input but the 7, 4, 2, 1 code for output.

Sketch the diode network for each case.

11.6. Construct the truth tables for one column of a 4-input adder. Such an adder might be used in a binary-coded-decimal machine where the fourth input is from the corrective quantity. Derive algebraic expressions, reduce them, and sketch the necessary networks using

    (a) diode logic,

    (b) NOR logic,

    (c) a logic utilizing only a 3-input majority element.

11.7. Deduce what corrective steps are necessary to make a 4-column binary adder perform decimal addition in the

    (a) 8, 4, 2, 1 code,

    (b) 5, 4, 2, 1 code,

    (c) 2*, 4, 2, 1 code,

    (d) 7, 4, −2, −1 code.

In each case draw the block diagram, including information flow paths, gates, and control inputs for implementing decimal addition using

    (a) a 3-input binary adder,

    (b) a 4-input binary adder.

11.8. Contrast the amount of equipment required to implement a decimal matrix adder in the 5, 3, 1, 1 code with that required to augment a straightforward 4-column binary adder which detects incorrect sums and takes appropriate corrective action. Repeat for the

    (a) $8, 4, 2, 1$ code,

    (b) $5, 2, 1, 1$ code,

    (c) $7, 4, -2, -1$ code.

11.9. How is overflow detected in an end-around carry scheme?

11.10. In view of exercises 11.10, 11.11, and 11.12, what would be your choice of how to represent negative numbers in a serial machine, and of how to implement the addition process? Defend your answer.

11.11. Indicate what extra equipment is required in the arithmetic unit of a sign-magnitude machine (such as HYPAC-I) if a result of -0 is not allowed to arise.

11.12. In problem 9.4, the comparator was implemented as a gating network. Describe how comparison can be accomplished using only a simple arithmetic unit such as HYPAC-I has. Program the scheme for HYPAC-I, and then describe the sequence of operations that would have to be performed in the arithmetic unit if HYPAC-I were to be given a Compare instruction. For what purpose would the address part of such an instruction be used? How would the result of such an instruction be indicated? Would a Compare-and-Branch instruction make sense? If so, how would the operands be located, and how would the location of the next instruction be specified?

11.13. Work out the details of an underflow detector for a floating-point arithmetic unit. What information must be monitored and how is it combined to indicate underflow? Consider the possibility that the magnitude part of the floating-point expression can be either in complement representation or in sign-magnitude representation.

11.14. Suppose that an overflow has occurred during the addition (or subtraction) of the magnitude parts of two floating-point numbers. The exponents are still within the range which the machine can accommodate. Is this situation an overflow that must be reported to the programmer? How can the situation be remedied? What extra steps are required in the addition (or subtraction) so that the final result is correct and has the maximum significance that the machine can represent?

11.15. Describe the detailed sequence of operations which must be performed to implement floating-point addition and subtraction. All overflows and underflows are to be handled properly, and maximum significance is to be retained in the final result. Draw the block diagram of the arrangement, and include all information flow paths and gates.

Do the above for each of four situations:

    (a) magnitude and exponent each represented as true complements,

    (b) magnitude and exponent each represented in sign-magnitude,

    (c) magnitude represented as a true complement with the exponent in sign-magnitude,

(d) magnitude represented in sign-magnitude but the exponent as a true complement.

Repeat the above but substitute (radix − 1) complements for true complements.

11.16. Lay out the details of the equipment required to give the HYPAC-I arithmetic unit floating-point addition (see problem 6.16(a) and problem 11.15). Draw the block diagram including information flow paths and gates.

11.17. Draw the complete block diagram of a multiplier (registers, adder, gates, and control inputs) for the base-4 system. Each base-4 digit is to be represented as a doublet of binary digits. For equivalent word lengths, estimate how much faster than a binary multiplier it will be, taking into account the more complex adder.

11.18. Consider a binary machine which represents negative numbers as 2's complements. Show that during a multiplication in which one or both factors are negative, the usual procedures for machine multiplication lead to an incorrect answer, insofar as the machine is concerned.

Deduce the corrective steps which are necessary to obtain the proper result. Indicate how these additional operations can be fitted into the normal procedure for multiplication. Sketch a diagram of the additional gates, toggles, information flow paths, etc. which are necessary to implement such corrective steps.

Repeat the above for division.

Repeat the previous parts for 1's complement representation of negative numbers.

11.19. Construct the truth table which describes the state of the parity check digit attached to a 4-bit group. Reduce the algebraic expressions, and sketch the resultant block diagram. Consider the possibility that a half-adder might be useful in implementing a parity checker. Sketch the block diagram, and decide whether or not the half-adder version is more economical of equipment.

11.20. With two operands, each having an odd parity digit, deduce the scheme for predicting the parity digit of the sum before it is actually formed. Indicate the equipment necessary to implement this scheme in a serial, and in a parallel machine.

11.21. Use two operands, each having an odd parity digit, and deduce a scheme for predicting the parity digit of the result formed by combining the operands

       (a) according to a columnwise exclusive OR,

       (b) according to a columnwise AND,

       (c) according to a columnwise inclusive OR.

11.22. Detail a casting-out-31 check for binary multiplication. Describe the complete process in detail, and draw a block diagram of the implementation.

11.23. For a casting-out-9's check on decimal information describe the class of errors which such a check will not detect. Now consider a check which casts out 99's. Describe the class of errors which such a check will not detect.

Consider checks which cast out 1's, 3's, 15's and 31's from binary information. In each instance, describe the class of errors which are not detected. Hence deduce the desirability of casting out the largest expression of the form $2^n - 1$. Estimate the relative amounts of equipment for implementing a casting out of 1's, 3's, 15's, and 31's. Hence discuss the tradeoff of the cost of equipment versus protection against a larger class of errors.

11.24. Design a parallel shift register. Select some toggle configuration, and a gating arrangement appropriate to it. Decide how the interstage delay problem is to be handled and specify the sequence of driving signals to cause the register to shift right, shift left, read-in, read-out. Draw the block diagram and detailed circuit diagram.

11.25. Consider a double-ranked shift register whose operating cycle is a sequence of two clear-and-gate operations. Consider the possibility that the clear operation and the gate operation start simultaneously, and that the gate signal outlasts the clear signal. Investigate this possibility in detail. What elements in the toggle move or do not move? Must the gate signal survive the clear signal by a time interval equal to the width of the gate signal were it to follow time sequentially the clear signal? Make a qualitative estimate of the difference in operating speed between the clear-followed-by-gate and clear-overlapping-gate modes. Does your answer depend on how the gating is done?

11.26. Is a 1's complement scheme faster overall than a 2's complement scheme for performing subtraction? (Consider the total length of carry that can arise in each situation, including those required to form complements.)

11.27. Draw a block diagram of an arithmetic unit which can be that of HYPAC-I. Include all information flow paths and all gates. For each gate, show all inputs, including those that must come from the control section. Assume that subtraction is handled by flanking the Accumulator with complementers on each side.

11.28. Continue problem 11.27. Select a toggle circuit and an appropriate gating scheme. Draw the detailed circuit diagram of the arithmetic registers and the adder part of the Accumulator. Draw the circuit diagram of the complementers. Insert followers wherever appropriate and sketch their circuits.

11.29. Continue problem 11.28. Carry through the detailed circuit design of the various toggles and gates. Use either vacuum tube or transistor technology as you wish. (See pages 8.92–8.93, 9.68–9.69 for suitable characteristic curves.) Design the circuits to tolerate $\pm 5\%$ variation in resistors, $\pm 2\%$ variation in supply voltages, and $\pm 25\%$ variation in the current capability of whichever active element you select.

twelve

The Store

GENERAL CONSIDERATIONS

Review

The store is that part of the machine into which is written preliminary data, intermediate results, final results and one or more routines to be executed (1). To maximize the amount of storage for a given cost, the store while functionally considered as one unit, physically is usually a hierarchal organization. Each level in the hierarchy is larger, and probably slower, and therefore less expensive than the preceding level. Each level of the store consists of a number of cells; each cell is capable of storing one information unit which is usually a word, although sometimes it is a character, digit, or bit. The primary level of storage is in the most intimate contact with the arithmetic and control units, and its speed of operation must be consistent with the other two. For the primary level, and possibly also for some of the higher levels, each cell is locatable by an individual address which is a reference tag used by the rest of the machine to specify a desired cell.

Normally each cell of the store can be written into or read from.* The writing operation destroys previously written information, and the read operation, so far as the rest of the machine is concerned, is generally but not always non-destructive. Such an arrangement permits the programmer to use the contents of one cell repeatedly without special attention.

Generally, the control and arithmetic sections communicate directly only with the primary level of storage because communication to

---

* We will later see an exception to this statement. See page **12.74**.

higher levels requires a relatively longer time. However, other levels of storage in communicating with each other often use the primary store or even the arithmetic unit as the route for interlevel transfers. In this sense, all levels of storage * communicate with the rest of the machine. Direct interlevel communication not involving the primary level, can, of course, be arranged.

There are two distinct aspects of a store from an equipment point of view. First, some physical phenomenon such as the distribution of electric charge or the state of magnetic flux is used to store information. Secondly, a second physical process is used to select the desired one of all the storage entities provided. These two properties may be commingled in one device but not necessarily. Many promising techniques for storing information have remained promising because the selection problem could not be solved economically or at all. For example, it is intriguing to consider a crystalline lattice as a store; each molecular element is a potential binary storage element, perhaps in terms of its magnetic moment. However, a selection scheme is needed which can single out one and just one of all lattice points.

Serial versus Parallel

The store may receive (and give) information time sequentially (*serially*), or it may traffic information essentially simultaneously in all columns of a word (*parallel*). The possibility of a hybrid scheme also exists, e.g., serial by decimal digit but parallel by the bits of the tetrad. So far as the store is concerned, serial versus parallel is concerned with the mode of transmission of information into or from the store.

Access Time

Given an address and asked to read or write, a store requires a certain amount of time in which to locate the desired cell and give or receive information. This time is called the *access time* and is a measure of the time that the rest of the machine must wait for the requested information. However, the term is imprecise. Usually access time

---

* There are no standard names for the levels in the store hierarchy. Primary, secondary, tertiary, etc., are as good as any. Often a level takes its name from the technique which is used to implement it, e.g., core or core store, drum or drum store.

specifies the time interval for a store to locate a given cell and to read its contents, but does not include any additional time required to complete the cycle of operation. Sometimes it is necessary to distinguish *reading access time* from *writing access time* because they may be different. Sometimes it is also necessary to distinguish each of these from the *cycle time,* which is the time required to complete one cycle of consultation. Sometimes a store has a short recovery period between successive cycles; if so, the cycle time plus recovery time is sometimes called *consultation time.* Occasionally access time is used as a synonym for cycle time, and sometimes access includes only the time to locate a cell and excludes any time to read or write it.

EXAMPLES

1. A given store has a total cycle time of 10 μsec, and it requires 2 μsec between cycles. Information is available 3 μsec after the cycle starts, but it requires a full cycle to complete a write. The reading access time is 3 μsec; the writing access time and cycle times are each 10 μsec. Finally, the consultation time is 12 μsec or the consultation rate, 88,000 per second.

2. Another store has a variable access time; the time to locate a cell can be as short as 1 μsec or as long as 19 μsec. This particular store, after it locates the desired cell, requires 1 μsec to read, but 5 μsec to write. Therefore, reading access time varies between 2 and 20 μsec, and writing between 6 and 24 μsec. Often the *average access time* is defined to be the average of the longest and shortest intervals. In this case, the average reading access time is 11 μsec, the average writing access time, 15 μsec.

If the store is such that the selection mechanism must in some sense scan through the cells until it reaches the desired one, the store is said to have *serial* or *sequential access.* The access time is very apt to be variable, and such a store is sometimes called a *variable-access store.* On the other hand, if the selection mechanism can proceed in essentially the same time to any desired cell, the store is said to have *random access.* Serial access must be distinguished from serial as it applies to the nature of transmission to or from the store. A serial or parallel store may be either sequential access or random access. Under a special circumstance, a variable-access store is sometimes called random access. If, on a particular problem, the time between consultations of the store by the routine is long compared to the longest access time, the variability of the access time does not limit the performance of the machine. For the particular problem, the store in effect displays random access. Under this definition, a store might be called random access for a sufficiently slow machine or on a given problem, but be called sequential access on a different problem or for a fast machine.

If information in a store is lost if the electrical or mechanical power to it is interrupted, the store is said to be *volatile*.

THE DELAY-LINE STORE

The delay-line store is both serial and serial access in nature and is really an extension of the notion of the dynamic toggle (see page 8.80) and the dynamic serial register (see page 11.33). It consists fundamentally of a delay medium, means for coupling signals to the medium, and means for recirculating information through the medium (Figure 12.1) (2). It is generally volatile. Checking, if it exists, is often

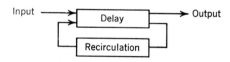

Figure 12.1. The basic elements of a delay-line store.

only a parity check although a more sophisticated error detecting-correcting code might be used. A few practical accessories are required.

No delay element is ideal. Due to phase and amplitude distortion, the output signal is both attenuated and distorted. Unless external amplification and reshaping is provided, the signals will completely dissipate after a few round trips. Moreover, if there is more than one such store, somehow all have to keep in step with each other or communication problems within the machine will be severe. This implies that the time at which information is reinserted must be carefully controlled. Figure 12.2 shows a typical arrangement. The signal called *clock* for the moment can be considered to be a master timing signal common to the whole machine. The output signals are synchronous with the clock, and the recirculated signal is also timed by the clock.* Binary information might be represented by presence or absence of signal, or by signals of opposite polarity.

* See page 9.11. The AND gates are satisfied only when all inputs are simultaneously present. Hence, if the recirculated signal is broad, the output of the

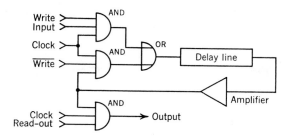

Figure 12.2. The details of a delay-line store.

The delay-line store intrinsically has a non-destructive read-out, but if writing is to occur, the recirculate loop must be opened. This store is useful principally for a machine in which both transmission and arithmetic are serial, and because of the delay medium, it is closely tied to an absolute time scale. It is, therefore, found in machines with a central source of timing signals.

The length of the delay element may be such as to accommodate one word or part of a word, in which case it is effectively a register; or it may be sufficiently long (in time) to accommodate many words. In a binary machine, there might be some 8-word units, some 64-word units, and perhaps even some 256-word units. In this case even the primary level of storage is itself hierarchal, although there might be communication from every delay unit directly to the arithmetic and control units.

Selection in a given unit of the delay store consists of waiting for the right time interval to come by. Some time interval will be defined as a reference or *origin time* for each delay element and at this time, all information will be considered to be in home position. In a multiword delay-line device, one word is immediately available; one word time later, a second is available and so on. Any delay-line store is obviously cyclic, and each word position will be accessible at regular intervals. As with any serial transmission, a word time is required for information to be read or written. Addressing in such a store consists partly of specifying the desired delay-line unit and partly of specifying the desired time position in the given unit.

gate will have the width of the clock signal and occur essentially coincident with it. In order to guarantee that the recirculate signal always arrives prior to the clock signal, the delay element must be slightly shortened; otherwise, the recirculated signal might arrive later than the clock, and therefore the time of reinsertion will no longer be established by the clock.

EXAMPLE

Suppose that a binary machine has a total of 512 words in its delay-line store; the address field is, therefore, nine bits long. If there is one 256-word unit, six 64-word units and sixteen 8-word units, addresses 0_{10} through 7_{10} specify the first 8-word unit; 8_{10} through 15_{10} (10_8 through 17_8), the second 8-word unit, and so on. Therefore, a 1 in the fourth binary place (from the right), but having all 0's on its left, indicates that the second 8-word unit is desired, and the bits in the first three places specify which of the eight word positions is desired. Similarly, a 1 in the fifth place (with 0's to its left) indicates the third unit; 1's in the fourth and fifth places specify the fourth unit, etc. Finally, 1's in places four through seven specify the sixteenth 8-word unit. Incidentally, if the word length is 30 bits, each 8-word unit is 240 bits long.

The sixteen 8-word units account for the first 128 words (addresses 0_{10} through 127_{10}). Address 128_{10} specifies a location in the first 64-word unit, and this is the first time a 1 appears in the eighth binary place of the address field. The six low-order bits specify which of the 64 positions is desired. Addresses 128_{10} through 191_{10} are in this unit. Addresses 192_{10} through 255_{10} are in the second 64-word unit; this is indicated by the presence of 1's in the seventh and eighth positions. Notice that the seventh position is now to be interpreted differently. Previously it helped to determine which 8-word unit was to be addressed; now it helps to determine which 64-word unit. The interpretation of the digit in the seventh place depends on what digits lie to its left.

It is the designer's problem to see that the digits of the address field are properly interpreted. The user will not be saddled with such details.

Sometimes the desired word will be just entering the delay line, but sometimes it will be just leaving it. On the average, the access time is half the length of the delay element, measured in time units. Hence there is a case from the user's point of view for a multiplicity of short delay stores; the machine will be faster. On the other hand, the per unit cost of storage goes down rapidly with long delay elements, and there must be some compromise between economic constraints and the user's wishes. A hierarchy of short, medium, and long delay elements is usually what evolves. Generally, the programmer must be responsible for moving information from one delay device to another.

The Electromagnetic Delay-Line Store

The high relative cost of electromagnetic delay lines and the high attenuation per unit length tend to make them suitable only for very small stores, or for the short units in larger stores (3). Sometimes electromagnetic delay lines are used to absorb tolerances in acoustic delay lines.

The Acoustic Delay-Line Store

Historically, the first acoustic store used the propagation of acoustic waves through a mercury tank as the delay (4). Piezo-electric crystals are used to couple to the mercury pool. Although the attenuation in the mercury itself is small, the attenuation through the crystal transducer is large. In order to solve the bandwidth problem at the crystal-mercury interface, a carrier technique is generally used. A carrier frequency from 5 to 30 Mcps is common.

The propagation time through a tank of mercury is a function of temperature. Therefore, mercury tank stores must incorporate very close temperature control. Parallel paths in one large tank provide a number of effective tanks in the same mercury pool. Temperature differences in one large pool are less likely than in several separated pools, but internal baffles may be required in the large tank to minimize crosstalk between adjacent paths. Frequently, all tanks of the store system are immersed in a huge mass of metal in order to maintain an equithermal condition.

Since each tank must contain an integral number of words, which in turn implies an integral number of digit signals, it is customary to compare the length of some path in a tank with a fixed number of the timing clock signals. Any difference is used to adjust the temperature; or alternatively, to adjust the time spacing between digits. This is another way in which tolerance problems appear. Finally, we must take care to minimize the energy reflected at the receiving end; multiple round trips cause trouble.

Typically, a mercury tank store operates with a carrier of 15–20 Mcps, and with a digit rate of a few megacycles. The propagation rate in such lines is about 0.06 inch per μsec, or the delay time, about 17.5 μsec per inch.

More recently developed acoustic delay lines propagate acoustic energy through metal castings or through quartz rods (5). Sometimes internal reflections can be used to increase the path length, e.g., a many-sided quartz polygon (Figure 12.3), or to deform the delay element to a more convenient or compact form.

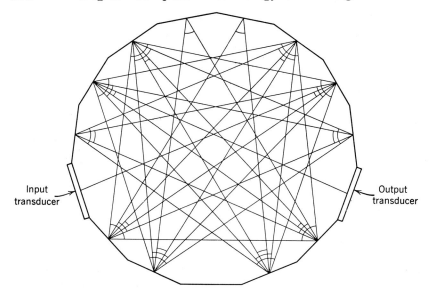

Input transducer

Output transducer

Figure 12.3. A multiple-reflection quartz delay line. (By permission of the Laboratory for Electronics, Inc.)

The Magnetostriction Delay-Line Store

It is possible to propagate magnetostrictive waves along a nickel strip; such lines have the distinct advantage of being easily adjustable in length since the coupling to the propagating strip is magnetic and involves no mechanical contact (6). The propagation rate in such lines is 0.1–0.3 inch per μsec, and the digit rate in the low megacycle range.

Addressing the Delay Store

Keeping track of the word positions in a given unit of a delay store is essentially a job of counting. Starting from origin time as the zero position, a counter which is advanced by 1 each word time will reflect the instantaneous position of information in the delay element. The appropriate part of the address which is offered to the store can be matched against the count in such a counter; a match indicates that the desired location is on deck, or perhaps, will be on deck at the

beginning of the next word time. The rest of the address will have
been used to select the desired one of the many units in the hierarchy.

THE ELECTROSTATIC STORE

The electrostatic stores depend on secondary emission phenomena to
produce charge distributions on insulating surfaces. Such a store can
be organized either as a serial or a parallel store, is generally random
access, and also volatile. Commonly, the electrostatic store uses only
a parity check, if there is any checking.

The Williams Store

The Williams store uses the electron beam of a conventional cathode-
ray tube to deposit charge on the phosphor of the tube (7). An external conducting screen, capacitively coupled to the phosphor through
the glass envelope is the output terminal. The selection process in
this store consists of directing the electron beam to a desired spot on
the phosphor; it is, therefore, clear that the beam can be directed to
any desired position in essentially the same time. Selection consists
of applying suitable voltages to the X and Y deflection plates of the
tube; the magnitude of each deflection voltage is determined by the
appropriate part of an address. Typically, a square array of points
on the phosphor is selected for storage positions. A serial store will
then be arranged as in Figure 12.4; a parallel store, as in Figure 12.5.
If the first word is read in the serial store, the four digits of the word
appear time sequentially on the output terminal of the left-most tube

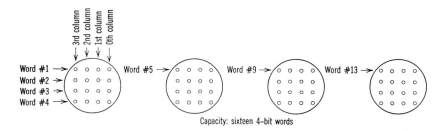

Capacity: sixteen 4-bit words

Figure 12.4. The arrangement of information in a serial electrostatic store.

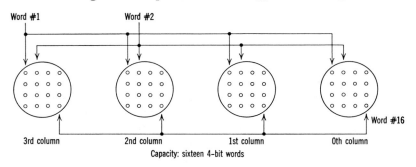

Figure 12.5. The arrangement of information in a parallel electrostatic store.

(Figure 12.4); if the thirteenth word is read, the four digits appear time sequentially on the output terminal of the right-most tube. It is clear that since only one tube of the four produces information for a given address, the output terminals of the four tubes can be connected together—effectively an ORing. If the first word is read in the parallel store (Figure 12.5), the left-most digit of that word appears on the output terminal of the left-most tube, etc. One digit of the selected word appears on each output terminal. Hence the output points of the four tubes must be kept separate and represent the multi-wire path for the parallel transmission of information from the store.

Binary information is represented by the presence or absence of charge. If a beam of sufficient energy is turned on at an uncharged spot of a phosphor, more secondary electrons will leave than primaries arrive, since the secondary emission ratio of the phosphor will exceed unity for a sufficiently energetic beam. Thus an area of positive potential will develop under the beam, creating a potential well by excavation. If the beam is moved to a nearby area and the process repeated, the secondaries from the second excavation will be attracted to the positive region of the first position and will refill the potential well which was created there. There is thus a mechanism for depositing or removing charge at selected points on the phosphor. There are other ways of handling the refilling problem (8).

Reading of the store is destructive. It consists of selecting a spot and turning the beam on. If a potential well already exists, nothing happens other than a slight reexcavation which may occur because charge has leaked away. If there is no well, one will be dug and the resulting flow of charge will develop an output signal on the external screen. Therefore, for either initial case, the final condition of the chosen spot is with a potential well. External equipment (Figure 12.6) is provided to rewrite at the same spot, the information which is destroyed during reading. Therefore, to the rest of the machine, the store appears to have the desired non-destructive read. It is clear that the rewriting time does not affect the read access time, but it does affect the cycle time. A complete cycle consists of a read part followed by a rewrite part. Writing, when it occurs, replaces the rewrite part and is preceded by a spurious read part. Hence it follows that the read access time is shorter than the write access time.

Since the phosphor surface has finite resistivity, the charge distribution tends to dissipate with time. Therefore, it is necessary to sweep periodically through all storage spots on the phosphor and to *regenerate* each one by reading it and rewriting it. Consultations of the store from the rest of the machine are sandwiched in between regeneration cycles. The ordinary cathode-ray tubes which are intended for display purposes often prove to have phosphors with imperfections which fail to store. To avoid this trouble, special tubes have been developed which have exceptionally clean phosphors and clean interiors (9).

Since regeneration sweeps cyclically over the face of the tube, it is possible for one region of the face to be consulted many times between regenerations. Each reading produces some spurious secondary electrons which are collected by those storage spots which are neighbors of the one which has been read. Thus potential wells in a region which has gone too long without regeneration can be filled accidentally, and

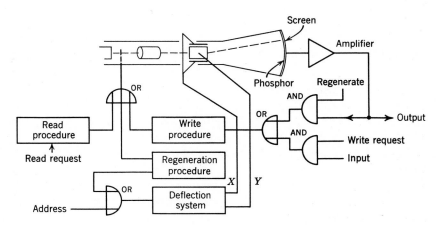

Figure 12.6. The essential features of an electrostatic store.

hence information will be lost. This so-called *read-around* problem can impose a limitation on the programmer by forcing him to avoid consulting a restricted region of the store at too high a rate.

The Williams store poses many difficult design problems. Since the refilling technique requires placing the beam on two spots separated about 1½-beam diameters, and since adjacent storage spots must remain separated several beam diameters, a very precise and stable deflection system is required. The read signal is a few tens of millivolts. Thus a stable and noise-free output video amplifier is required for each output terminal of the store. The cathode-ray tube itself must be shielded against spurious magnetic fields to avoid unwanted deflection of the beam. Finally, the whole system is very sensitive to electrical noise and must be carefully shielded and isolated electrically.

The density of storage spots depends on the fineness of the beam, its uniformity of focus over the face of the tube, and on the mutual interference between adjacent spots. Typically, one or two thousand spots can be stored on a 3-inch or 5-inch tube. The output voltage is likely to be 10–20 millivolts, and the cycle time of a Williams store will be in the range of 6–12 μsec. This implies that voltage changes in the deflection system must occur and be substantially quiescent in a few microseconds.

The Barrier-Grid Electrostatic Store

This is very similar to the Williams store except that a special barrier-grid storage tube is used instead of an ordinary cathode-ray tube (10). Such a tube has additional electrodes near the secondary emitting surface for better collection of secondary electrons; this results in a higher density of storage positions and an improved read-around situation.

The general characteristics of the barrier-grid store are similar to those of the Williams store except that possibly ten or twenty thousand spots can be placed on a 5-inch tube.

The RCA Selective Electrostatic Storage Tube

This specially designed storage tube (Figure 12.7) is in many respects a discrete storage element version of the Williams store (11). As Figure 12.7 shows, there is an electron optical system of vertical and horizontal bars which permits selective opening of windows to the

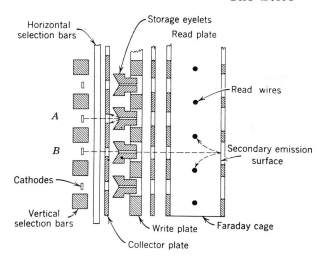

Figure 12.7. Cross section of the RCA selective electrostatic storage tube. (After Rajchman, RCA Review, March 1951, pp. 59, 60, 63.)

beam. Addressing this store consists of selecting the bars which are appropriate to opening a desired window. The storage elements are secondary emitting discrete eyelets mounted in an insulating plate; the collector plate accepts the secondary electrons emitted from the front faces of the eyelets. Because of the capacitance coupling between the write plate and the storage elements, the whole group of eyelets (with the beam off) can be manipulated up and down in voltage. Proper sequencing of the signals on the write plate and control of the beam through one window permits a selected eyelet to be placed either at cathode potential or at collector potential. By virtue of the secondary emission from the front face, each position is one of stable equilibrium, and represents one of the two values of a binary digit. Reading of the store is non-destructive. Beam electrons will be attracted toward and flow through the center hole of a selected eyelet if it is at collector potential (point *B*, Figure 12.7). Otherwise, the electrons will be repelled if the eyelet is at cathode potential (point *A*, Figure 12.7). The output terminal of the tube (read wires) is, therefore, a current source. The Faraday electrostatic shield surrounding the read wires is necessary to isolate them capacitively from the large voltage excursions of the other elements in the tube.

   This special tube can be randomly accessed and, like the Williams store, can be organized into either a serial or parallel form of store.

There are some leakage paths to the eyelets, and it is necessary, therefore, to periodically regenerate all eyelets. This is conveniently done by opening all windows and flooding the faces of the eyelets with electrons. The tube stores 256 bits and has one particular advantage. Since the output terminal is a current source, the output voltage can be small or large, depending on how long the designer can afford to have the machine wait during reading, and on how low he can maintain the capacitance at the output terminal.

Time (cycle time of the store) can be exchanged for gain in the reading amplifier; output signals can be as high as a few volts or as low as fractions of a volt. The various electrodes of the selective electrostatic storage tube present principally capacitance loads, and therefore the overall time scale of such a store depends on the amount of current drive that can be provided. A typical cycle time falls in the 5–20 μsec range.

THE MAGNETIC DRUM STORE

There is a group of storage devices which use the same physical phenomenon—the ability to create two different states of flux in a magnetic material. Because flux remains in existence after the current which created it has disappeared, magnetic storage exists which, in principle, can be non-volatile. In practice, it may be difficult to provide this feature because spurious writing signals may occur during power-on or power-off operations. The geometry of the magnetic material, the method of selection, the addressing, and the access time are all quite different from one to the next of the magnetic stores. The first one for discussion is the *magnetic drum store* (12).

A magnetic drum (Figure 12.8) is a right circular cylinder which rotates on its axis of symmetry and whose surface—perhaps even the ends—is covered with a material which can be locally magnetized. This material is typically a nickel alloy which has been electroplated onto the drum, or a dispersion of iron oxide in a plastic binder which has been sprayed onto the drum. Drum sizes vary from a few inches in either dimension to a few feet; rotation rates can be many 10,000's of revolutions per minute for a small drum or a few hundred revolutions per minute for a large one. Surface speeds are generally from 1500 to 3000 inches per second.

A read-write communication station called a *magnetic head* (Fig-

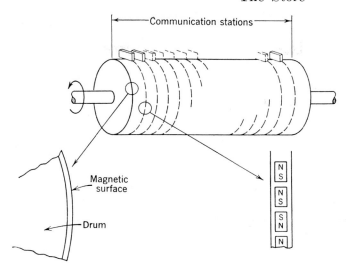

Figure 12.8. The major features of a magnetic drum store. (*Adapted from* Automation in Business and Industry, *edited by Eugene M. Grabbe, John Wiley and Sons, New York.*)

ure 12.9) is placed in close proximity to the drum surface (13). Current in the head will cause leakage flux to form at the air gap of the head. The flux then penetrates the magnetic surface of the drum reorienting or creating elementary units of magnetization in the surface. This operation is the write operation. Conversely, as the drum rotates,

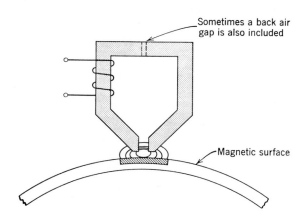

Figure 12.9. A magnetic head.

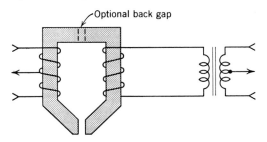

Figure 12.10.   Two arrangements for the write winding.

the leakage flux of the elementary magnets on the drum is coupled through the head.   Hence, the magnetic state of the drum surface can be read as an induced voltage in a winding on the head.   Reading, therefore, is non-destructive.   Many geometrical structures for the head, as well as a variety of coil configurations, exist.   Both magnetic metals and magnetic ceramics are used for heads.

In the surface of the drum, if, say, a North-South elementary magnet represents binary 0, then a South-North magnet represents binary 1. In order to establish either polarity of flux in the surface, it must be possible to establish flux in the head in either sense.   Typically, a center-tapped write winding, or an arrangement to drive current in either direction through a single winding is provided (Figure 12.10). Sometimes a separate winding is provided for the read output; some-times, the write winding is also used for reading (Figure 12.11).   Typi-cally, write currents are several tens to several hundreds of milli-amperes, depending on the number of turns on the windings; read

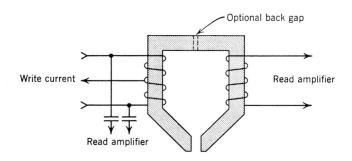

Figure 12.11.   Possible arrangements for the read winding.

voltages are from tens of millivolts to fractions of a volt. Writing time can be as low as a few microseconds; and head spacing is from a few milli-inches to 50 or 100 μin.

Drum Organization

The surface of the drum which sweeps by under one head is called a *track* or *channel*. For a serial machine, words are generally recorded circumferentially in one track. For a binary-coded-decimal machine, four tracks might be associated to form a *band* in which a decimal digit will be recorded axially, while successive digits of the word will be recorded circumferentially. For a parallel machine, a number of tracks equal to the word length might be associated together and the word written completely axially.

EXAMPLE

A drum contains 64 tracks and 1024 bits per track; it has a total storage capacity of 65,536 bits. It can be organized in at least the following three ways:

1. Sixty-four bands of one track each; there will be thirty-two 32-bit words in each track. In turn, each 32-bit word might be eight decimal characters of four bits each. The drum will have sequential access and transmission to or from it will be serial. In the case of the eight decimal digit word, transmission is serial-serial.
2. Sixteen bands of four tracks each; each band contains sixty-four 16-decimal digit words. Access is sequential; transmission is serial-parallel.
3. Two bands of thirty-two tracks each; each band contains 1024 32-bit words. Access is sequential; transmission is parallel.

If the drum rotates at a rate of, say, 32 msecs per revolution (approximately 1800 rpm), the transfer rate to or from the drum for each case will be:

a. $\qquad 32 \dfrac{\text{words}}{\text{revolution}} \times \dfrac{1}{32} \dfrac{\text{revolutions}}{\text{msec}} = 1000 \dfrac{\text{words}}{\text{second}}$

b. $\qquad 64 \dfrac{\text{words}}{\text{revolution}} \times \dfrac{1}{32} \dfrac{\text{revolutions}}{\text{msec}} = 2000 \dfrac{\text{words}}{\text{second}}$

c. $\qquad 1024 \dfrac{\text{words}}{\text{revolution}} \times \dfrac{1}{32} \dfrac{\text{revolutions}}{\text{msec}} = 32{,}000 \dfrac{\text{words}}{\text{second}}$

In each case, the bit rate through any head will be

$$1024 \frac{\text{bits}}{\text{revolution}} \times \frac{1}{32} \frac{\text{revolution}}{\text{msec}}$$

or
$$32,000 \frac{\text{bits}}{\text{second}} \approx \frac{30 \ \mu\text{sec}}{\text{bit}}.$$

Selection and Addressing

Selection of the desired cell in a drum store is simply the problem of getting the right part of the drum surface under the head. Addressing, therefore, consists partly of specifying the desired track(s) (or band), and partly of specifying the desired angular position of the drum. In a special set of tracks, there is often an origin position of the drum together with reference marks at the beginning of each word. The instantaneous angular position of the drum will be known by counting reference marks from the origin. At the desired position, the signals from the heads over the selected track(s) are gated through to the rest of the machine. Alternatively, the address of each angular position can be permanently recorded in a group of address tracks. For 1024 angular positions, this requires ten address tracks ($2^{10} = 1024$).

In case c of our previous example, it might happen that 32,000 words/sec is a faster rate than the other parts of the machine can tolerate. It is possible to *interlace* the cells of the drum so that consecutively numbered cells occur in, say, every fourth actual angular position. If the interlacing were, say, 4-to-1, the flow rate will be 8000 words/sec, and four revolutions of the drum will be required to completely transfer the 1024 words contained in one band. Starting from the origin, the first few actual addresses are: 0000, 0256, 0512, 0768; 0001, 0257, 0573, 0769; etc.

Access Time

It is clear that the drum is a serial access store. The access time depends not only on the rotation rate but also on the angular position of the drum relative to the address of the cell to be consulted, and on the logical organization, e.g., interlacing. If the method of addressing the drum is such that all cells of a band are scanned in one revolution, the access time can be essentially zero (if the desired cell happened to be right under the head), or it can be one revolution (if the desired cell happens to have just passed the head). Generally, the two situations are contracted to the single statement that the average access time is one-half revolution (16 msec for case *a* of the previous example). If the drum is interlaced or another method of determining angular position is used, the average access time can be longer. However, once the first word is located, successive words flow from the drum at a high rate. Hence both the initial access time and the *flow* or *transfer rate* are needed to characterize a drum store completely.

Drum Instructions

A magnetic drum is often the secondary level of storage to a faster store such as a magnetic core store. If so, extra instruction types are usually included within a machine's repertoire in order to facilitate communication between the drum and other levels of storage.

EXAMPLES

1. *Select Drum* can be used to establish a communication path between a drum and some other part of the machine. An associated address part can identify the desired one of many drums.

2. *Write Drum* transfers information from primary storage to the drum storage. If there is one address part in the instruction, it might identify the location of the first word in primary storage to be transferred. The programmer must have previously provided in some special place in the machine, information which indicates how many words are to be transferred, and where on the selected drum the information is to go.

3. *Read Drum* non-destructively reads information from the drum and writes it into some other level of storage, usually the primary level. If there are three address parts in the instruction, one can indicate the first location in primary storage to be filled; a second, the last location in primary storage to be filled; and the third, the location of the first word on the drum to be transferred. By differencing the first and second addresses, the control can deduce how many words are to be transferred. If the drum is larger than the primary store, the address part relating to it must also be larger, or the drum must be considered as containing blocks of information, the individual words of which are not addressable.

4. *Transfer Drum* might be arranged to transfer information either to or from a drum. Part of the address field might be used to identify the drum; and another part to indicate flow to or from the drum. If the particular machine happens to be arranged to transfer always in blocks of fixed

length, the only supplementary information needed will be the number of the block to be read (or written) on the drum, and the first location in primary storage to be written (or read).

Methods of Recording

There are a number of ways to record binary information on a magnetic surface. One is the notion of elementary units of magnetization of two polarities; this was used for an earlier illustration. Methods fall broadly into two classes: *return-to-zero* which more properly can be called *return-to-reference,* and *non-return-to-zero.* In the former, the flux in the surface always returns to a reference value (which may be zero) between bits of information; in the latter, the flux does not return to a reference value between digits. Since only two values of information are being recorded (0 and 1), it is customary to saturate the magnetic surface. From the designer's point of view, it is preferable to use magnetic materials which have a flat saturation characteristic. This means that the voltage recovered from the head is less sensitive to variations in write current.

The density with which information can be recorded on the surface depends partly on the magnetic behavior of the head-surface combination, and partly on the mechanical problem of mounting adjacent head structures close together while still maintaining electrical and magnetic isolation. Since recovered signal is proportional to the time rate-of-change of flux, a higher surface speed leads to more recovered signal; so does a wide track. However, the economic pressure for high storage density (low cost per bit) generally leads toward a narrow track. In addition, there is a guard region between adjacent bands to minimize crosstalk. Typical axial spacing of tracks is 10 to 100 per inch.

Circumferentially, the density of packing is related to the width of the tuft of flux which penetrates the surface. Thus very narrow head gaps and very close head-drum spacings contribute to a high circumferential density, which typically is from fifty to a few hundred bits per inch. The packing density also depends on the precise method of recording, as we will see later.

Generally, the surface speed of a drum is such that in-contact recording is difficult because of frictional heating problems. Mechanical tolerances and thermal expansion problems combine to determine the minimum practical head-drum spacing for heads which are in fixed radial position. With sufficiently low surface speeds (and, if necessary, appropriate lubrication), in-contact recording at 1000-and-up bits per inch is possible. With special heads which are not fixed radially but float on a cushion of air (14), a density of 1000 bits per inch also is possible.

Return-to-Zero Recording

True return-to-zero (RZ) recording uses a round-trip excursion from zero flux to one saturation level to represent binary 0 and a round-trip excursion to the other saturation level to represent binary 1 (15). The flux departs from the zero flux state and goes to saturation, and returns for each digit recorded (Figure 12.12). We see that there are two flux changes for each binary digit recorded—zero to saturation and saturation back to zero. Since flux is proportional to the current which establishes it, ideally the write current will have the same shape as the desired flux pattern. In a practical case, the flux will be a distortion of the write current due to such things as non-sharp edges of the flux tuft which penetrates the drum surface, interference between adjacent units of magnetization of the drum, or loss of high frequency components in the current-to-flux transformation by the head.

The recovered or read-back voltage is proportional to the time rate-of-change of flux; it is, therefore, proportional to the derivative of the flux (Figure 12.13). In RZ, we see that there is more information present than is really needed. The recorded pattern can be determined from an inspection of the information which is present at leading-edge time; or equally well, from the information at trailing-edge time. An obvious way to recover the flux pattern is to integrate the signal; unfortunately, integrators which respond fast enough and which have sufficiently small drift are very difficult to build.

As the signal comes from the drum, it is of the order of small fractions of a volt; it likely contains noise, and it is probably poorly shaped. Generally, the signal from the head is first amplified, then

Figure 12.12. RZ *recording.*

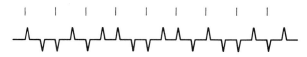

Figure 12.13. Read-back signal from an RZ *recording.*

clipped to remove noise, and perhaps also shaped. The resulting signal can then be time-sampled (*strobed*) at leading-edge time to determine whether it is positive or negative (Figure 12.14). Alternatively, the signal of one polarity (say negative) might be discarded. Therefore, the presence of a signal at strobe time will indicate one kind of binary digit; the absence of signal, the other kind of binary digit.

A recorded signal is erased by simply recording (i.e., writing) the new information over the old. In order to avoid spurious signals from repeated overwriting, the writing signals must be carefully and consistently timed with respect to drum angular position. This can be done conveniently by recording the necessary timing signals right on

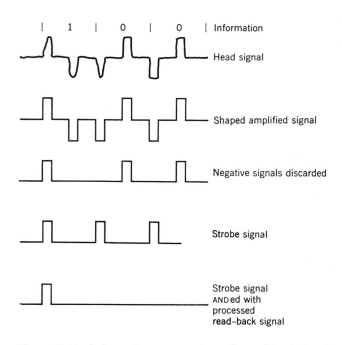

Figure 12.14. Information recovery from the read-back signal.

Figure 12.15.   Return-to-bias recording.

the drum in a special track. This arrangement has the further advantage that everything stays synchronized even though the drum rotation speed may fluctuate. We see here another reason for using materials which saturate well, and for writing always to saturation. Since the previous information is unknown, the writing signal must be sufficient to drive the magnetic material from one saturation state to the other. The programmer can perfectly well write a 1 over a 0, or vice versa. On the other hand, the new digit can be the same as the one already there. If the latter, we certainly do not want the flux level representing the digit to change appreciably; otherwise the amplitude of the recorded signal can depend on the digital history.

Return-to-bias is very similar to RZ except that the reference is one of the saturation levels (Figure 12.15). One binary digit is not recorded at all, and the other one is recorded by a pulse of flux to the opposite saturation state. An advantage of this scheme is that the recovered signal is roughly twice as much as for RZ, and the *read* (or *sense*) *amplifier* does not have to deal with bipolar signals. Information recovery is similar to that for RZ recording.

Non-return-to-Zero Recording

RZ recording identifies a digit with a flux excursion from a reference state to a saturation state and back. *Non-return-to-zero* (NRZ)* recording identifies a digit with a flux level, rather than with a change of flux (16). If flux at one saturation level represents 0, flux at the opposite saturation level then represents 1. If a string of digits of like kind is being recorded, the flux remains unchanged at the saturation level even between the digits. The flux changes only when successive digits are unlike (Figure 12.16).

We see that the maximum number of flux changes occurs when the digit pattern alternates 0's and 1's, and that even under this condi-

* This term is used to describe not only a generic set of recording techniques, but also the specific member of the set described here.

Figure 12.16. NRZ recording.

tion, the number of changes of flux is half what it would be in an RZ system (Figure 12.17). NRZ recording is, therefore, capable of twice the packing density of an RZ system.

Reading the recorded pattern consists of using the recovered signal to indicate when the digit changes state. There is clearly a problem of getting started, however. Until the first change occurs, there is no information for the reading system to work with. To provide a known digit in a known position, generally each word to be recorded in an NRZ scheme is prefaced by a supplementary reference digit, which by convention for a given machine is always, say, zero. The reference lead digit is not transferred elsewhere in the machine, and the drum system must append a lead digit to all incoming messages.

One way to read an NRZ-written drum is to separate the positive and negative signals and to recombine them, after having inverted the polarity of, say, the negative string (Figure 12.18). All signals, of course, will have been amplified, clipped, and shaped first. If the resulting combined sequence is applied to the complementing input of a toggle, it will cause the toggle to follow the flux pattern. Getting started consists of setting the toggle to the agreed-on reference state during the time that the reference digit position is under the head. Sampling the toggle at each digit time, therefore, identifies the state of the digit which has been recorded. Clearly the sampling or strobe signal must be carefully synchronized with the drum rotation rate.

In Figure 12.18 all flux transitions from the 0-to-1 state are negative while the transitions from 1-to-0 state are positive. If the positive and negative signals are separated from each other, they can be ap-

Figure 12.17. An alternating pattern recorded in NRZ.

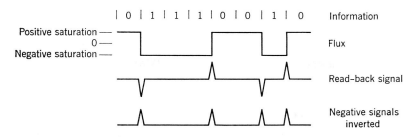

Figure 12.18. Information recovery from the NRZ *read-back signal.*

plied respectively to the set-to-0 and set-to-1 inputs of a toggle which will then reproduce the flux pattern. The toggle will be cleared to the agreed-on reference state during the reference digit position.

NRZI Recording

This is a form of recording which belongs to the generic class of NRZ-type techniques; the I means *invert* (17). It records only one kind of the binary digits (say, the 1's) as a single flux change (Figure 12.19). Sometimes a digit is indicated by a positive signal from the head, and sometimes by a negative signal from the head. As with the previous NRZ scheme, the number of changes of flux is half what it would have been in RZ.

Recovery of the information is rather obvious in the light of previous discussions (Figure 12.20). After amplification and cleaning up, all signals are made of one polarity and the resulting sequence strobed at each digit time. Presence of a signal indicates a 1; absence, a 0.

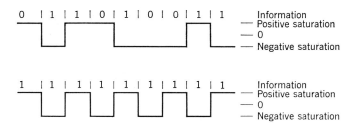

Figure 12.19. Two digit patterns in NRZI *recording.*

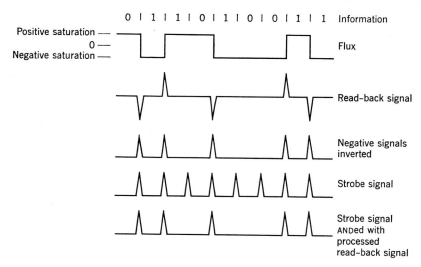

Figure 12.20. Recovery of information from the NRZI *read-back signal.*

Phase Recording

Phase (or *Ferranti* or *Manchester*) *recording* is again an NRZ-type system, in that the flux is always in one of the saturation states except during flux changes, but sometimes there are two changes of flux per digit (18). One digit (say, 1) is represented by positive flux

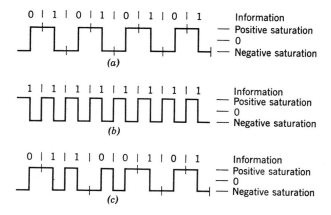

Figure 12.21. Three patterns in phase recording.

followed by negative and the other (0), by negative flux followed by positive (opposite phase). The important point is that the flux change which contains the information is in the center of the digit interval. It is clear that the lowest frequency of the flux pattern occurs for an alternating digit pattern and the highest frequency, for an unchanging digit pattern (Figure 12.21). One of these is twice the frequency of the other, and therefore the maximum and minimum frequency components which can occur in a system of this kind are readily determined. Such information can be of help in the design of the amplifiers and perhaps the head. Furthermore, there is no D-C component in the write current, and transformer-coupled write amplifiers can be used. In the usual NRZ scheme there can be substantial low-frequency components. For example, suppose the reference digit is 1. For a sequence of words, each containing all 1's, the current in the head stays quiescent at the 1 level.

Recovery of the information again is straightforward (Figure 12.22). The signal is strobed at the center of each digit interval; a positive signal indicates a 0; a negative signal, a 1. Alternatively, signals of one polarity can be discarded; presence of signal indicates one digit and absence, the other. Notice that the reading time is half a digit interval later than the writing time. This requires carefully controlled timing signals; or, if the drum speed is precise enough, a head with properly spaced reading and writing gaps.

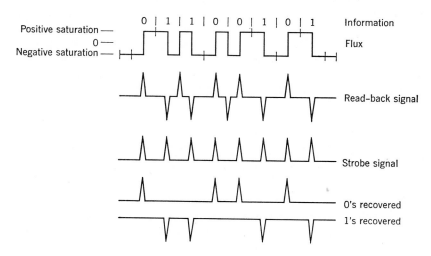

Figure 12.22. Information recovery from the phase-recorded read-back signal.

Writing

Writing for each of the schemes just discussed consists of generating a current in the write head of the same general shape as the desired flux pattern. Generally the information to be written on the drum is stored in one or more toggles; in a serial mode one toggle will hold the successive digits time sequentially. The output of the toggle is logically combined with suitable timing signals, and the resulting signal now contains not only digital information but whatever details of shape and timing which are appropriate to the recording signal. Usually a current amplifier is necessary to bring the current magnitude up to the level required by the head.

So far as writing is concerned, the maximum density is limited only by the rate at which current can be switched through the head, and the frequency pass band of the head structure, i.e., its ability to satisfactorily replicate a current pattern as a flux pattern at the gap. The frequency response of the head is related to the inductance of the winding, the capacitance of the winding, and such properties of the magnetic material as the switching time from one saturation state to the other, and resistivity which bears on the losses and the penetration of flux into the material. A head must clearly be operated on the low-frequency (inductive) side of resonance; otherwise the write current flows mostly through the shunt capacitance, and little flux results. Hence, high-frequency writing is largely a problem of head and write amplifier design. A high rate of writing does not necessarily imply a high density of information on the drum surface. For example, if the digital rate into a head is maintained, but the surface speed of a drum is doubled, the density of recording on the surface halves. The digital flow rate into or from the drum remains unchanged.

Reading

Typical reading schemes have been suggested under the discussion of each recording method. There are general comments which apply to each scheme. The signal recovered from the reading head depends quite sharply on the spacing of the head from the drum; small changes in head spacing reflect in relatively large changes in output signal (19). As it turns out, the ratio of head-surface spacing to the wave length of the information as it is recorded in the surface controls the

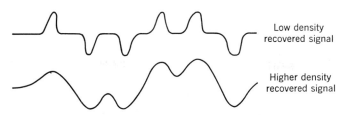

Low density
recovered signal

Higher density
recovered signal

Figure 12.23. The effect of recording density on read-back signal.

recovered signal. Furthermore, the output signal depends on the width of the air gap in the head relative to the recorded wave length; for some gap widths, there is no signal no matter how close the head may be. On writing, the gap width does not influence the width of the flux tuft too strongly, and hence the reading operation is the controlling parameter in designing the gap part of the head.

As information is packed more and more densely in the drum surface, either by increasing the digital input rate or by slowing the drum, the adjacent areas of magnetization begin to interfere and the recovered signal degrades (Figure 12.23) (20). In effect, the higher frequency components of information get lost, the fine structure of the signal disappears, and the reading system has a harder and harder time to distinguish 1's from 0's. As the density of packing increases, more and more sophisticated reading schemes are necessary to extract the information contained in the signal. For example, an obvious suggestion is to pass the signal through a high-pass filter—a differentiating network—in order to accentuate the high-frequency components. A double differentiation might do even more. Unfortunately, a high-pass filter also accentuates the high-frequency noise components, and may make the signal-to-noise ratio impossibly low. Another possibility is to search for more involved characteristics of the signal; e.g., a positive-going slope followed by a negative-going slope. The pressure for high-density recording is of course economic, a low cost per digit stored. On the other hand, the offsetting influence is the extra cost of the more complex equipment to do the reading.

Choice of the Recording Scheme

Any one of the NRZ schemes requires current in the head at all times; this means increased power in the head and in the write drivers relative to RZ. On the other hand, NRZ schemes can offer increased density.

Suppose that it is desired to selectively change one digit in a sequence. In an RZ scheme, this is easily done; find the interval in question, and write the desired new digit. There is a fair amount of leeway in timing because the interval in which the flux is zero is effectively a guard interval between adjacent digits. If the rewritten signal does not quite obliterate the old signal, there may be some spurious signal along the axis. Successive rewriting is one source of the noise that must be clipped off during reading.

In the NRZ schemes, selective rewriting often can still be done, but the timing must be carefully controlled. Consider Figure 12.24. Figure 12.24-a is the original recording; Figure 12.24-b is the desired new recording; Figure 12.24-c is what can happen if the rewriting is slightly behind schedule. Such spikes of signal can produce spurious information. In the phase system of recording, spikes such as these are not likely to cause trouble because reading occurs later in the digit interval.

Now consider NRZI. Figure 12.25-a is the original recording; Figure 12.25-b, the altered recording. We see that selective rewriting cannot be done without rewriting everything beyond the point of change.

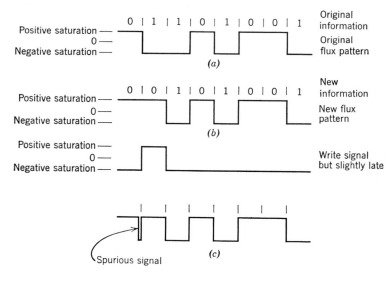

Figure 12.24. Selective rewriting in NRZ.

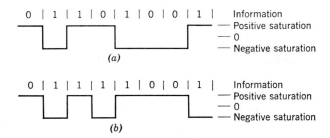

Figure 12.25. Attempted selective rewriting in NRZI.

In a drum which stores the digits of a word circumferentially, selective rewriting is not likely to be a problem since complete words will probably be changed and a guard interval between adjacent words can be established. However, some store instructions (for instance, the store address, page 5.41) insert only part of a word into the store. Such an instruction might be hard to implement with some kinds of recording.

In a fully parallel drum, successive circumferential positions contain information from a different word. It is practically guaranteed that the programmer will want to selectively change a word in a particular angular position; this must be considered in selecting the recording scheme. Alternatively, the designer can insist, if the drum is a secondary level of storage, that transfers to and from the drum occur only in blocks. He then has a freer hand in his choice of type of recording, since there can be a guard interval between adjacent blocks.

Timing Tracks

We have made several references to timing signals for writing or reading the drum. Usually, such timing signals are recorded in special tracks which are used for no other purpose. There might be one track with writing signals and a second one, with slightly delayed reading signals. There might be a timing track which marks only the beginning of each word and another one which marks the digit positions within the word; alternatively, the beginning of each word position can be deduced by counting the digit position marks. The timing tracks can be arranged to leave any guard intervals that may be required between words. Sometimes such special tracks instead of being magnetically recorded are mechanically engraved on the drum. A variable reluctance pickup reads the marks.

If a drum is the primary store of a machine, the timing signals on the drum may be used throughout the machine for synchronizing purposes. This has the advantage that the whole machine stays in synchronism even though the drum speed may change. Typically, one track has a signal at the beginning of each word; another has signals at each digit position; another marks selected positions within each word, and so on.* Signals within a given track need not be equally spaced but can be arranged to suit any special needs of the store or of other parts of the machine.

Mechanical Problems

A drum can be a difficult mechanical design problem. The machining must be done to very close tolerances, and bearings must be excellent in order to maintain the close head-drum spacing during rotation. Maintaining the small head-surface spacing can also be difficult under temperature variations; it is essentially the problem of trying to maintain a small difference between two large numbers—the distance from the drum axis to the head mount and the radius of the drum. Sometimes vibration problems can cause cyclical variation of head spacing which results in amplitude modulation of the head signals. Sometimes the drum distorts under rotational stresses, and so on, and so on, and so on.

Multiple Head Stations

It is tempting to consider more than one head per track (or band) in order to decrease access time, e.g., three heads per track displaced by 120°. This can be done, although difficulties may arise. The angular spacing must be exactly right or information written by one head may not be readable by another one. For example, suppose that a drum is written in RZ style. The information signal occupies only part of each digit interval, and the strobe reading signal will be adjusted to fall in the center of the interval. If information is written by one head but read by a second one, the strobe signal may fall

---

* Such special position marks are required to time the shifting process in the serial dynamic register.

near one edge of the recovered signal or even completely outside it, if the angular position of the second head is too far off. From this point of view, an NRZ scheme is less critical because the information signal occupies the whole width of the digit interval. On the other hand, phase recording will tend to be more critical. Furthermore, a considerable amount of extra equipment can be involved just to decide which head is closest (in an angular sense) to the requested cell. The cost of the extra heads and the equipment to switch among them is also not trivial. All in all, multiple stations can be an expensive way to decrease access time.

Moving Heads

The unit cost of storage on a drum can be further decreased at the expense of increased access time—that tradeoff between time and money again! It is possible to consider providing only one head which moves axially along the drum. The device which makes such a suggestion feasible is the *air-floated head* (21). By properly adjusting the flow of air between a head and the drum surface, it is possible to make the head float at a fixed and small distance from the surface; typically the distance is from a fraction of to a few tens of micro-inches. Imperfections in the drum surface are followed by the head, since its position relative to the surface is an equilibrium position. The air may be introduced from a pump through special openings in the head structure, or it may be windage air dragged along by the moving drum surface. A suitable mechanical indexing mechanism must be provided to position the head over a selected track. Access time to drums of this kind can be of the order of fractions of a second to a few seconds; a multiplicity of independently moving air-floated heads of course helps to decrease access time.

Revolvers

If a read head and a separate write head are angularly separated but positioned over the same track (Figure 12.26), the time for information to travel from one head to the other can serve as a delay time (22). Such an arrangement can, therefore, function as a delay line. By adding suitable gating circuits and spacing the read and write heads one word length apart, this arrangement can be made into a *revolving* or *circulating dynamic register*.

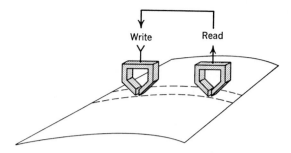

Figure 12.26.   The concept of a circulating storage loop.

Short Storage Loops

By lengthening the distance between heads, a *recirculating storage loop* several words long can be provided.   Several such short loops (and registers) can be accommodated at different angular positions of the same track.   Erase heads between adjacent segments will not be needed if recording happens to be any of the NRZ schemes.

The access time to such short loops is, of course, faster than to the drum at large.   If there are N words serially deployed around a drum, a short loop of n words has an access time (n/N)th of the access time to the drum proper.   In effect, the speed of the drum is N/n times faster in the short loop.   Sometimes several such short loops are really the primary storage of a machine, and the balance of the drum is a secondary store.   Since everything is physically part of one drum, synchronization between parts of the drum is no particular problem.

Drum Checking

Generally, drums are well enough behaved that no checking will be provided.   Each word on the drum may, of course, contain special information which is to be used for some check elsewhere in the machine.   If there is checking, usually it is only a simple parity check on each character, word, or group of words stored.   If it were necessary in special circumstances, other checks of drum performance could be done.   For instance, the drum might read out not only the contents of a cell, but also the address of the cell; the latter could be verified against the address originally given to the drum.   Another possibility would be to reread immediately every message written into the drum and compare it with the original. Such things, however, are not usually done for a drum store.

THE MAGNETIC-TAPE STORE

Most of the discussion and principles given for the drum store are applicable to the *magnetic-tape store* (23). In it, instead of recording on a rotating drum, recording is on a long ribbon of tape (Figure 12.27). The tape frequently is a dispersion of iron oxide in a binder which has been coated onto a flexible plastic base. Alternatively, the tape can be made from a nickel alloy, which doubles as a mechanical base and a magnetic medium. Tape widths vary from ¼ inch to several inches; and lengths, from a few hundred feet to a few thousand feet.

Typically the magnetic tape is contained on reels, although the shorter lengths are sometimes gravity dropped into a simple bin. The tape passes from one reel, through a feed loop and over idlers to drive rollers, over the head, perhaps over more idlers, through another feed loop to the take-up reel. Feed loops are generally necessary because the start-stop time of the tape over the head is fast compared to the rate at which the reels can change speed. The device for mechani-

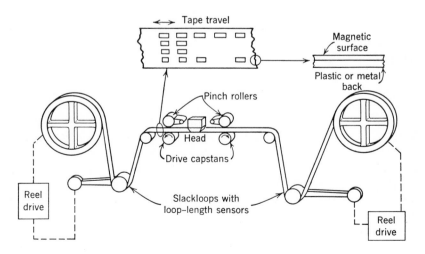

Figure 12.27. The essential features of a tape transport.

cally moving the tape is called a *tape transport,* and there may be a multiplicity of them in a tape storage system (24). The transport must be capable of starting and stopping the tape rapidly (of the order of a few milliseconds), because often only a few inches of a tape are used at a time, and therefore a slow start-stop time will waste tape length and also time. The transport must move the tape forward at an appropriate read-write speed, and sometimes also backward at read-write speed; it may have a fast-forward, -backward, or both search speed; and it will usually have a high-speed rewind.

Communication with the magnetic surface is through the read-write head which, however, is in contact with the tape. Reading is clearly non-destructive. The linear tape speed is commonly 50 to 150 inches per second and sometimes as high as several hundred inches per second. Transverse track density is 12–16 per inch but the longitudinal density can be several hundred bits per inch because of the contact between head and tape. The head is generally similar in principle to a drum head, although special precautions must be taken to insure that the contact surface is extremely smooth. Otherwise, dirt and magnetic dispersion from the tape collect on the rough areas and result in erratic behavior.

Selection, Addressing, and Tape Instructions

Selection of the desired information consists of getting the right area of magnetic tape to pass over the head. Addressing, therefore, consists partly of selecting the proper tape transport in a multiple-transport system and partly of specifying the right position along the tape. A machine will generally contain an instruction type for selecting the desired one of many tape units in the system; the address part of such an instruction will designate the unit. There will generally also be read-tape and write-tape types of instructions; the address part might specify the position of the cell in primary storage to be read or written. In this case, in some special place in the machine, the programmer must have prepositioned a word which specifies the number of words to be transferred. Alternatively, the tape system might require a special routine to handle each word and to, say, count words or perform error checks (25).

Linear position along the tape can be found by counting the words which have gone by since the beginning of the tape. Alternatively, special tracks can be used to block the tape into sections; counting of such *block markers* plus counting within a block can also locate position along the tape. Frequently, a group of words is considered to be associated together for storage purposes; such a group is sometimes called a *record*, or a *block*. A group of records is often called a *file*. The end of each record and of each file is indicated either by a mark in a special track, by a special symbol in the information tracks, or by short lengths of blank tape. In the latter case, record and file marks are read by noting the passage of certain time intervals without the appearance of signals. However, the programmer is still obliged to keep track of things by counting words, records, and files. Alternatively, a programmer might preface each record with an address; in reading each record the routine will consider the first word as the address of the block. Extra equipment and tracks can also be provided to do *block addressing*.

EXAMPLES

1. A given single-address binary machine has 8_{10} ($= 10_8$) tape units available to the primary store. There is a special tape register which contains the number of words to be transferred. A typical sequence of instructions for reading 127_8 words from tape unit 3_8 and writing them into the store from location 63_8 onward is:

A	Select 3
A + 1	Load tape register A + 3
A + 2	Jump A + 4
A + 3	+127
A + 4	Read tape 63
A + 5	Branch on tape register Y

The instruction in A + 4 is not completed until all words have been transferred. Therefore, between A + 4 and A + 5 there is a relatively long wait on the part of the control.

If a 1 is subtracted from the tape register for every word transferred, the register should contain zero at the completion of the instruction. The *Branch on Tape Register* instruction gives the programmer an opportunity to check that the proper number of words have been moved.

Address Y is the location to which the routine will branch if other than the 127 words have been transferred. In location Y and beyond, the programmer will insert his error-detecting or correcting procedure. One possibility he might elect is to try the tape operation three times; if it fails each time, the machine will be halted. If he has a reread option, obviously there must be a backspace operation.

2. In a three-address machine, a tape instruction might be:

Read tape	A	B	C

This could mean: read from the tape which is designated by address part A, a number of words specified by the address part B, and write them into the primary store starting at the cell specified by address C.

3. Other tape instruction types might be:
   a. *Skip Forward*. The address part gives the number of records to be passed over.
   b. *Skip Backward,* or *Backspace*.
   c. *Rewind*. The address part tells which tape unit to rewind.
   d. *Write Mark*. The mark could be an end-of-record or end-of-file mark and the address will specify the tape unit to be dealt with. Alternatively, if the machine has selected a tape unit at a previous instruction, the address part can specify the kind of mark to be written.

Access Time

It is clear that the tape store is a serial access store. The flow of information can be serial, full parallel, or hybrid. The initial access can be long (seconds or minutes) if the desired part of the tape is all the way down at its other end. However, once the initial access is made, the flow rate can be high. Usually this rate is measured as the number of transverse lines of recording transmitted per second, although sometimes it is given as words per second or bits per second.

EXAMPLE

A tape moves at 75 inches per second. Recording in each track is 200 bits per inch; therefore, the flow rate per track is 15,000 bits per second. If the tape has 36 channels to accommodate a 36-bit word in parallel, the information rate is 15,000 words per second or 540,000 bits per second. If the tape has only 6 channels, each 36-bit word will consist of 6 characters of 6 bits each. The character rate is, therefore, 15,000 characters per second, but the word rate, only 2500 words per second, and the bit rate, 90,000 per second for all six tracks.

Sometimes, in order to minimize waiting time, a tape-storage system is given sufficient autonomy in terms of local control, so that several tape units can be independently searching for desired locations. As soon as a transport finds the location asked of it, it stops and waits to read or write on a subsequent request.

Reading and Writing

The various methods of writing are the same as for the drum. Since magnetic tape itself occasionally has flaws in the dispersion, sometimes markers are put in a special track during a preliminary testing cycle to indicate which physical parts of the tape must not be used.

A frequent wish of programmers is to change one or a few words in a larger record. With some kinds of recording, he must rewrite the entire record. With other types of recording selective rewrite of part of the record is permitted, provided timing signals which are precise enough in time position have been provided. One possibility is a special track on the tape for timing signals which act effectively as a sprocket to index the position of the tape for writing or reading. If the timing signals come from a source external to the tape itself, or if the timing signals are somehow derived from the information on the tape, it is unlikely that selective rewriting of partial records can be done. Even when rewriting a complete record, tolerances including stretching of the tape can be a problem. Fluctuations in tape speed, in start-stop time, or in external timing signal frequency must be absorbed in a sufficiently long guard gap at the end of each record.

Reading is also much like the drum except for one or two new twists.

Skew, Reassembly, and Timing

Tape has a tendency to run across the head slightly skewed, in spite of good mechanical tape guides and careful design. Therefore, the exact angular position of a tape relative to the axis of the read-write head is likely to change from transport to transport, or even on a given transport as the tape starts and stops, and as parts wear. The effect of *skew* is to cause the signals from the several tracks across the tape to appear unevenly positioned in time. It may be necessary to resort to special gating schemes, or even to special assembly registers for each track in extreme cases (26). Skew, by the way, is one of the factors which makes interchangeability of tapes among transports difficult, and since its severity increases with linear tape speed and with high recording density, a high tape speed and a high recording density are mutually antagonistic.

Since a word is often read from the tape in pieces (e.g., six characters of 6-bits each), it first may have to be reassembled (for instance, by a shift register) before being used elsewhere in the machine.

Finally, what about timing tracks for reading, for example, the strobe signal? It may be possible to find a reading scheme which does not require them. Otherwise, if there is a special track for write timing signals, it can also furnish read timing signals. Sometimes, it is possible by picking the recording scheme and the word format properly, to find an arrangement in which there is a signal from some track every character time, no matter what the digit content of the word may be. By ORing together the information signals from all tracks, a timing signal can be derived. Alternatively, information can be derived which can be used to synchronize an external timing oscillator; the technique is similar to the phase-locked horizontal sweep circuit of a television receiver.

Sometimes a tape unit is provided with the ability to read even if the tape is in reverse motion. This causes extra complications in control and word reassembly, but has some programming usefulness. Reversing tape direction almost certainly changes the skew position of the tape—just another problem for the designer.

EXAMPLE

Consider a 7-channel tape which is recorded in NRZI. One channel is an odd parity check; six are for information.* Consider the all 1's character; the parity bit will also be a 1 (Figure 12.28). If in the following character, at least one track remains a 1, there will be a flux change in that track because of the NRZI recording. The only problem, therefore, is what happens when the all 0's character follows. In this case, the parity bit remains 1 and contributes a flux change. Thus a timing signal can be derived from 7-way ORing of all tracks.

Mechanical Problems

Many of the mechanical problems of the tape transport have already been suggested. There must be a mechanism for accelerating (and decelerating) the tape from standstill to full speed in a few milliseconds. There must also be a reel control arrangement which varies the average reel speed as the quantity of tape on the reel changes. Since

---

* This arrangement happens to be a standard IBM format.

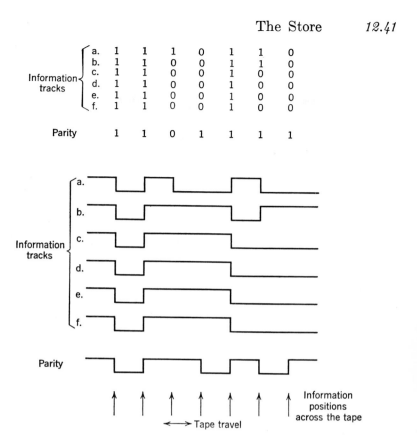

Figure 12.28. A particular tape format.

it is unlikely that the reels can accelerate as rapidly as the tape at the head, there are usually slack loops to provide (or accept) tape until the reels can move. There must be a means for guiding the tape across the head with precision and for maintaining head contact. Finally, there ought to be dirt control measures; dirt and dust on the tape can cause it to lose contact with the head and thereby produce erratic signals.

Checking

Since a magnetic tape store is prone to errors not only from dirt and dust, but also from flaws in the tape surface, it is customary to do

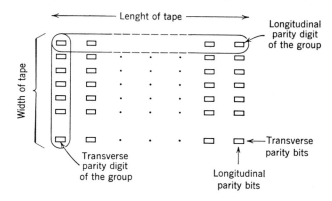

Figure 12.29. Longitudinal and transverse parity checks.

some kind of checking of tape information. There is almost always a transverse parity check per line of information, be it a character or a word. There may also be a longitudinal parity check along each track at the end of a record (Figure 12.29). Each tape transport mechanism will probably contain whatever equipment is necessary to generate parity digits during recording, and to perform the parity check during read.

Another possibility is a second read station adjacent to the write station. Freshly written information can be promptly reread and echoed back against the original information. In particular circumstances, more elaborate checking schemes can be devised if felt necessary, e.g., error-detecting and -correcting codes.

THE MAGNETIC CORE STORE

The *magnetic core store* is completely different from the previous magnetic stores (27). The drum and tape techniques use continuous magnetic surfaces which are in motion. The core technique utilizes a discrete element for each bit to be stored; generally, the unit storage element is an annulus of magnetic material. Such a core can be made of several wraps of a thin ribbon of metallic material, or it can be a powdered magnetic ferrite material which has been pressed into shape and fired. Metal cores are typically ¼ to 1 inch in diameter; ferrite cores, from approximately 0.030 to 0.100 inch in diameter.

In the geometry of an annulus, a flux can be established circumferentially in either sense (Figure 12.30). The two directions correspond to the two binary digits. It is a property of the magnetic materials selected for storage that the flux established in response to a current does not disappear when the current ceases, but instead remains at some remanence value (points A and B, Figure 12.31). Furthermore, the material does not respond in a simple linear fashion to the driving current, but exhibits the bivalued hysteresis loop behavior shown in the figure. If the material is at point A, a certain amount of current ($I_{\min}$) is required to drive it to the other saturation level (and eventually to B). Any current less than $I_{\min}$ will not get the core to B but to some intermediate position B'. It is convenient to select a material which exhibits a flat saturation characteristic in order to relieve the tolerance problem on the drive currents.

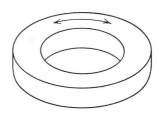

Figure 12.30. The geometry of a magnetic core.

The flux pattern can be established by suitable current linkages, which typically are generated by one or more windings on the core, or by one or more wires passing through the core (Figure 12.32). The winding technique has the advantage of a lower drive current,

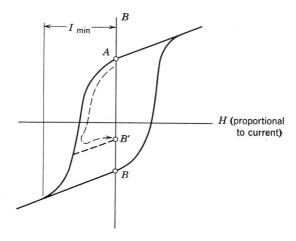

Figure 12.31. Magnetic storage of information.

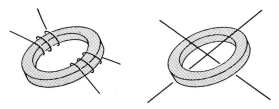

Figure 12.32.   Current linkages of a magnetic core.

but poses more tedious fabrication problems and increases the inductive back voltage; the wire technique—a higher drive current but easier fabrication, and low inductive reaction.

Switching Current

For the materials of interest in storage devices (28), there is a magnetic field and, therefore, a current below which switching from one state to the other will not occur. For the least current which will cause switching, there is a natural switching time (*turnover time*) which depends on the magnetic and structural properties of the material. Beyond this point, the switching time decreases with increasing drive in such a way that the reciprocal of switching time is a linear function of the field (and current) (29). Thus the designer has some control over the overall speed of his store by fixing the drive currents at certain magnitudes. However, as we will see later, not always can he invoke this privilege if he elects a certain kind of selection scheme.

Not only does increasing speed demand increasing current, but increasing core size also requires increasing current. With more material to be switched, more current must flow to provide the energy required for switching.

The internal behavior of magnetic materials during switching is very complicated and not fully understood. Some of the internal flux changes can be elastic or reversible in nature, so that the magnetic flux will spring back to its prior state when the perturbing field vanishes. Other kinds of internal changes are irreversible, and the flux state remains changed after the driving field ceases.

For driving fields which persist for at least one microsecond or so, the switching of the core from one remanence point to the other occurs by *domain wall motion.* This involves the propagation of a wall of magnetic effect through the material, and relatively large groups of internal magnetic structures act in unison. For larger driving fields which persist for only fractions of a microsecond, switching of the core occurs in a rotational mode which involves individual magnetic structures.

Reading

How can we detect the state of flux in a core? Typically, this is done by driving the core in some specified direction (say, toward the 1-state). If the core is already in the 1-state (Figure 12.33-a), there will be very little flux change and the material will make an excursion along the saturation (i.e., flat) part of the hysteresis loop. There will be little or no voltage induced in a *read wire* (or *read winding*). If, however, the core is initially in the 0-state, there will be a large flux change in the core and a large voltage in the read wire (Figure 12.33-b). When reading is complete, the core will be in the 1-state under any circumstance. Reading in this way is therefore destructive, and provision must be made in the store system for rewriting the destroyed information automatically—so that the store system will appear to have a non-destructive read so far as the rest of the machine is concerned.

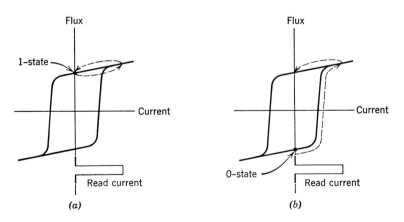

Figure 12.33. Reading the stored flux.

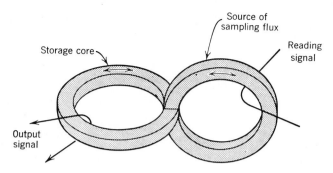

Figure 12.34. One kind of non-destructive reading.

Non-destructive Reading

We anticipate that a destructive read followed by automatic rewriting of the information will result in a longer cycle of store operation than if a non-destructive read cycle were used. Hence, from the point of view of conserving time (i.e., speeding the store process) and simplifying the store operating cycle, non-destructive read schemes are of considerable interest.

One possibility is the linked-core arrangement of Figure 12.34 (30). So to speak, the flux produced by the reading core samples the flux state of the storage core. Because the reading flux is perpendicular to the direction of the storage flux, the resultant magnetic vector swings in position to A'. It cannot change its length appreciably because the material is saturated (Figure 12.35). Therefore, the component of circumferential flux (storage flux) decreases to A''. Since the flux

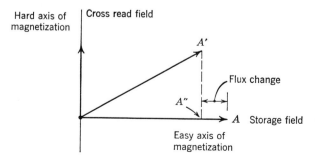

Figure 12.35. Behavior of the flux vector in non-destructive reading.

lines must be continuous, the magnitude of the storage flux outside of the region common to the linked cores, must also change and can be sensed by a read winding. This amounts to driving the storage core away from the remanent point, and it is clear that the flux in the storage core must not be driven over the knee of the hysteresis loop, or it will not return to its initial remanent point after reading. The output signal is small.

Another possibility capitalizes on the non-linear characteristic of the hysteresis loop about the remanent points. If two different radio-frequency signals are applied to the core, sum and difference frequencies will be formed. Their phase depends on the state of the core, i.e., at which of the remanent points it is. Again, the output signals are small (31).

A third possibility depends on subjecting the core to a very large but very short duration current drive. The resulting flux change seems to be an elastic change, and therefore, the storage flux reverts to its initial state after reading (32). The output signal is small.

In the practical case, non-destructive reading schemes are, for the most part, difficult to implement (33).

The Externally Selected Store

If the magnetic core is used as only a storage element, some suitable selection scheme must be devised to produce a practical store. Typically, this takes the form of a matrix selection arrangement (34). In Figure 12.36, a core and diode in series are inserted at each intersection of a rectangular array of wires. One dimension of this array is along the word; the other dimension, along a digit position of a word. As we see from the figure, a word can be selected by an appropriate signal (+10 volts), and in each column, a digit signal determines whether or not a current flows through the core winding. Clearly this scheme permits subjecting the core only to drive in one direction.

Another such selection arrangement could be used to drive the core in the other direction. Alternatively an extra winding threading all cores of one word can be used to set all cores to (say) 0, and the uni-directional column drive can write the 1's. The extra winding can also serve for the read operation; by driving all cores of a desired word to the 0-state, those which contained a 1 will switch and produce a voltage in the output winding. Notice that some selection scheme must also be provided for the extra group of clearing windings. Because the selection process is in terms of the word dimension, the store

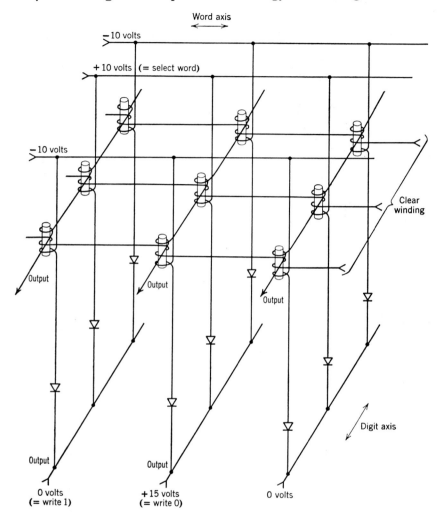

Figure 12.36. The externally selected core store.

is called a *word-select store*. It is also called a *word-organized store* because it is arranged in terms of a word (rather than character, or digit); each cycle of operation either writes or reads one word.

Practical constraints limit the usefulness of a core store with external selection. Windings almost certainly have to be used, rather than single wires, in order to bring the currents within range of high-speed switching diodes; the cost of the diode is a significant item. The inductance of the windings implies a large self-induced voltage which in turn implies an increased voltage capability in the driver. In small stores (for example, a few hundred words), these factors may be relatively unimportant. The externally selected core store does have the advantage that it can be read arbitrarily fast; because there is a separate winding for the reading, the current for reading can be made as large as desired. Access is random.

The Coincident Current Store

By proper choice of the magnetic material it is possible to combine the storage and selection function in the same core (35). The appropriate material is said to have a *square* or *rectangular hysteresis loop*. Figure 12.37 shows the important features of a rectangular material.

The points $+B_R$ and $-B_R$ are the two points of remanence; B_M is the saturation flux level. The ratio B_R/B_M is called the *squareness-ratio* of the material. Because of the steep vertical parts and the sharp knee, it is possible to drive the core with a current which does not cause switching ($I_S/2$ in the figure). Twice this current will cause the core to switch its state; $I_S/2$ is, therefore, called the *half-select current*. For typical ferrite materials driven from a single wire winding (36), the half-select current is from 300–600 ma.

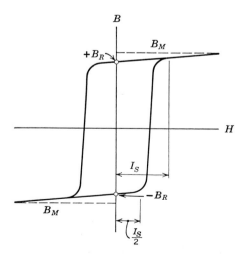

Figure 12.37. Information storage in a rectangular material.

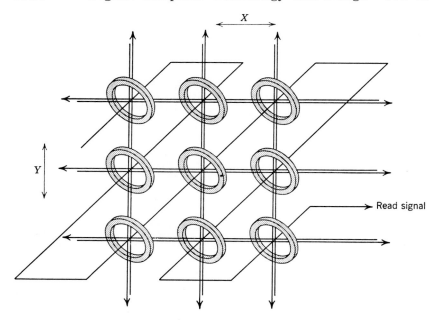

Figure 12.38. A magnetic core matrix.

In the coincident current store, the cores are assembled into a rectangular matrix (Figure 12.38). The two dimensions of the matrix are often called X and Y. If $I_s/2$ is applied to some X wire, and $I_s/2$ to some Y wire, the core which lies at the intersection will be subjected to full drive, but all other cores on the selected X and Y wires will be subject only to half-drive and will, therefore, not switch. The squareness of the hysteresis loop of the material makes the coincident current mode possible.

In order to permit setting the core to either of the remanent states (which incidentally will stand in 1-to-1 correspondence to the two binary digits), provision must be made for driving current in either direction on the X and Y wires, or two wires must be provided in each dimension (Figure 12.38).

Reading

For economic reasons the reading scheme is usually a destructive one. It consists of selecting the desired core and driving it to some reference state (say, the 1-state). If it contained a 1, there will be very little flux change; if a 0, a large flux change. An extra wire—the *read* or *sense winding*—will detect these events (Figure 12.38). In order to present a non-destructive read to the balance of the machine, the store system has means for automatically rewriting the information just read back into the cell from which it came. The complete read cycle, therefore, includes a portion for reading and a portion for rewriting.

Writing

A write operation is just like the part of the read cycle devoted to rewriting, except that the information to be written into the store comes from an external source rather than from within the store itself. As a matter of convenience, the write cycle of a store is generally the same as the read cycle, except that the information read from the store is ignored, and the new external information is written in during the second part of the cycle. Following the read part of the cycle, a core is left in the reference state (say, the 1-state). If the new digit to be written is a 1, nothing further need be done. If the new digit is 0, the two half-select currents must be established in the opposite direction, and the core will switch to the 0-state.

Addressing

Selection is simply a choice of the desired core by operating on the appropriate wires of the matrix. Addressing a store of this kind consists of specifying one of the X wires and one of the Y wires. If the *core matrix* or *core array* happens to be square, the same number of address digits will be required for each dimension; one half of the address will specify an X wire, and the other half, a Y wire. If the array happens to be rectangular, the address will be broken into appropriate parts.

EXAMPLE

In a square array of 1024 cores (32×32), five bits ($2^5 = 32$) of the address will determine the X line and the other five bits of the 10-bit address ($2^{10} = 1024$) will determine the Y line. Assuming that the X portion of the address

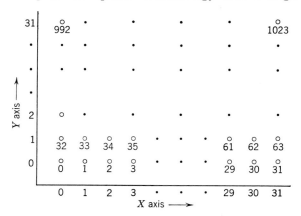

Figure 12.39. The correspondence between addresses and actual storage locations.

is the low order half, the actual storage locations in the matrix which correspond to the machine addresses are shown in Figure 12.39.

If the array happens to be rectangular (say $16 \times 64 = 1024$), four bits will be required for the 16-dimension (say, X) and thus six bits will specify the Y wire.

A Serial Store

Such a magnetic matrix, plane, or array can function as a serial store. In a 1024-core square array, the X dimension could represent the 32 bit positions of a word and the Y dimension, 32 different words. Reading (and writing) will consist of selecting a Y and operating in 32 successive cycles on the 32 X lines. Each cycle will consist of a destructive read followed by a rewrite. Because each cycle produces only 1 bit, this store can be called a *bit-organized store*.

The same 1024-core array can be organized into a serial binary-coded-decimal store. As before, the Y dimension is the word dimension, but the X dimension will be regarded as eight decimal digits of four bits each. In each cycle of operation, one Y line will be selected, but four adjacent X lines will be selected. Since four bits are expected to be read out, there must be four output terminals and thus four sense windings (Figure 12.40). One sense winding links bit position 1 of all decimal digits (X lines 0, 4, 8, 12, 16, 20, 24, 28); the second sense winding links bit position 2 of all decimal digits (X lines 1, 5, 9, 13, 17, 21, 25, 29); the third and fourth sense windings are obvious.

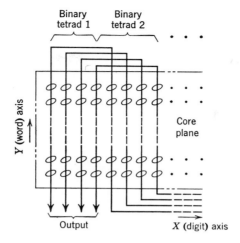

Figure 12.40. A serial binary-coded-decimal arrangement of sense windings.

This plane of 1024 cores, so far as organization is concerned, can be thought of as four 32 × 8 arrays intertwingled.

Since this store produces one digit per cycle, it can be called a *digit-* (or *character-*) *organized store,* but its selection is still coincident current; access to the first entry is random.

A Parallel Store

If the single 1024-core array is to be a 32-word, 32-bit parallel store, there must be 32 output terminals (one from each column), and selection could really be done—so far as reading is concerned—by driving all the current down the *Y* wire. This is reminiscent of the word-selected external selection store. In fact, with respect to reading, it is word select and is also sometimes called *end-fire.* However, writing will have to be coincident current, since each column must respond according to the digit to be stored. There is a possibility, however, of providing a very fast read cycle with a large *Y* current, but a somewhat slower write cycle with half-select currents in *X* and in *Y.*

A more interesting example is a 1024-word by 40-bit store. There must now be 40 planes of 1024 cores each. The *j*th plane will contain the 1024 digits from the *j*th place of the 1024 words. Figure 12.41 shows such a store schematically. As we see, corresponding *X* and *Y*

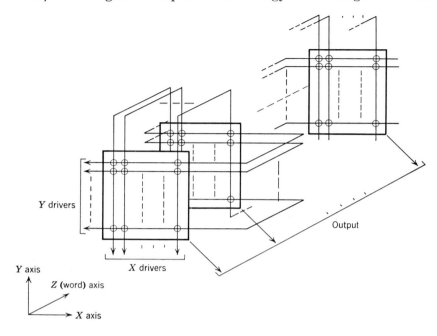

Figure 12.41. A parallel core store arrangement.

wires are all connected together. If this store is regarded from the end, the digits of a given word will lie one behind the other one along a line which is parallel to the *word* (or *Z*) *axis*.

The reading operation of this store follows from the previous discussion. An *X* and a *Y* are selected, and the several cores (one in each plane) emit their information in parallel to the output wires. Writing, however, is more complicated than it has been. Access is random.

Writing the Parallel Store

If the currents which drive the selected *X* and *Y* wires come from drivers which can supply a D-C component of current, the writing process is straightforward. Either do nothing in the write part of the cycle, or establish both currents in the sense opposite to that used for reading (Figure 12.42).

Frequently, however, transformers are used in the driving circuits in an effort to reduce the current demand on the driving elements.

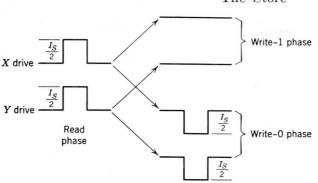

Figure 12.42. Writing the magnetic core.

Because the transformer cannot pass a D-C component of signal, it must always be driven through a symmetrical cycle of activity; otherwise, the current which it produces in the secondary may vary with duty cycle. Therefore, after such a transformer has produced the pulse of current for reading, it is obliged to produce an equal and opposite pulse. Since reading has left the core in the 1-state, this would appear to write a 0 always into the core.

There are two ways out of the problem. One is to permit the X and Y transformers to deliver their opposite polarity pulses in time sequence if writing of a 1 is desired; but simultaneously, if writing of a 0 is desired (Figure 12.43) (37). This has the disadvantage of increasing the cycle time. The other possibility is to provide another

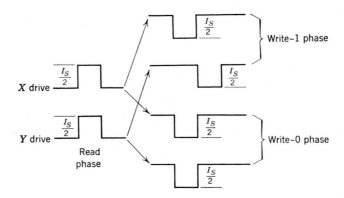

Figure 12.43. Concurrent or successive writing drives.

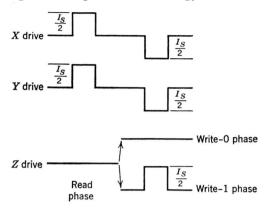

Figure 12.44. Z *winding writing.*

winding in each plane which threads all the cores—as does the sense winding. Logically the new winding could be the sense winding which is not in use during writing; for practical reasons it is usually a separate winding.

So far as the selected core is concerned, the new winding can contribute an extra unit of current. In this respect, it is a new selection coordinate and thus is usually called the *Z winding.* The transformers on the *X* and *Y* axis produce their opposite polarity pulses simultaneously; but if writing of a 1 is desired, a half-select current is put through the *Z* winding in such a sense as to buck the *X-Y* drive. The core algebraically sums all currents which link it, and therefore it feels a net current of only half-select value (Figure 12.44). If writing a 0 is desired, no current is established in the *Z* winding.

The Complete Cycle

As we have seen, a complete cycle of a store consists of a read operation followed by a write (Figure 12.45). If reading of the store is desired, the contents of the selected cell is read to an external register. From this register, the information flows to the rest of machine, but it also is the input for rewriting back into the same cell. Thus an overall non-destructive read is achieved.

If writing of the store is desired, the read cycle is spurious, and information from the machine is accepted by the store during the later part of the cycle. In principle, the read part and the write part can

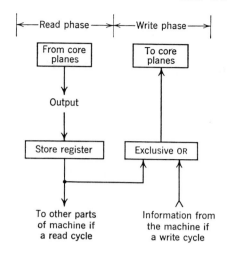

Figure 12.45.   The complete core store cycle.

be separated sufficiently in time to allow other machine operations. There could be a combined Read-Add-Write-into-the-Same-Cell instruction in a machine.

The Magnetic Core Switch

It is clear that the decoding required to convert the address (or part of it) into a choice of 1-of-n wires can be accomplished by means of a diode decoder (page 10.15). Diodes being what they are, the decoding must be done at low current levels; current amplification to the level required by the magnetic elements is accomplished after decoding. In an n-square array, $2n$ current drivers are required, where each driver must produce current in either polarity. Alternatively $4n$ drivers are required if there are two X and two Y wires through each core. In counting noses, we must include the drivers for the Z windings—one for each place in the word.

Often a *magnetic core switch* is used to combine partial decoding and current transformation (38). Figure 12.46 illustrates the principle of such a switch. For definiteness, assume that the core array is 64×64, and that the word length is 40 bits. Each switch (one X and one Y) will be a smaller 8×8 array. Through each core in the switch array passes three wires; sometimes these are many turn windings.

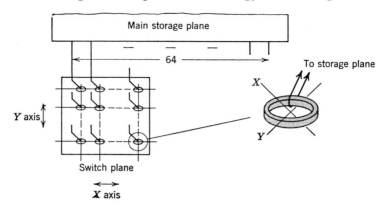

Figure 12.46. The magnetic core switch.

Two of the three are the coordinates of the switch array; and the third, an output winding to, say, an X wire of the storage array. The coordinate wires of the switch are driven by half-select current pulses. At the intersection of the driven X and Y wires, the switch core will transition. In so doing, it will provide a current pulse into the output winding for driving the storage array. In effect the 8×8 array accepts two octal digits (one X and one Y) and decodes them into 1-of-64 possibilities. The earlier decoding—from 3 binary digits to a 1-of-8 octal representation—can be done by conventional gating schemes.

The design of such a switch can be tricky. First of all, the switch core must be larger than the storage cores. The storage core and the associated driving wires dissipate energy which is supplied by the switch core. Therefore, a switch core must yield enough flux as it moves from one state to the other to supply the energy of transition of the storage core, plus the resistive losses in the connecting wires. The load which the switch faces varies widely. Each switch core drives a coordinate wire in the storage plane, which in principle passes through 64×40 (in our example) cores (see Figure 12.40). Of these 2560 cores, 40 of them will be selected ones and the other 2520, half-selected. Of the 40, some unknown number will be changing state; the information to be read (or written) might be all 0's or it might be all 1's or any combination in between. The large number of half-selected cores will also contribute some variability to the load. The number of turns on the output winding of the switch core can be adjusted to give the current transformation required.

The design of the switch as described may be so difficult that it cannot be built for large stores. As a practical matter, it may be necessary to provide a switch for each plane; a switch core then only faces one selected core which may or may not transition and (in our example) 63 half-select cores. The jth X wire (or Y wire) of a switch can be in series with the corresponding wire of all other switches, if the driver on this wire can tolerate whatever wide impedance fluctuations the switch cores themselves present.

After a switch core has been driven to provide a current pulse, it finds itself at the opposite remanence point. If driven again it would yield only the small output which corresponds to the elastic flux change in the saturation state. The switch core must, therefore, be reset to its original position before the next store cycle begins. One way to do this is to drive both the X and Y switches with equal positive and negative drives and use the resulting symmetrical output in a store cycle with Z winding writing. Alternatively the X and Y switches can be reset in time sequence. A supplementary bias winding threading every core in a switch can also be used to reset it. In this winding there will be a steady current equal to full select current but in the opposite sense. The coordinate drive currents are then unipolar but of full select amplitude (Figure 12.47).

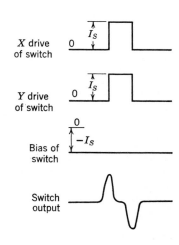

Figure 12.47. The output signal from the switch.

When they vanish, the bias snaps the switch core back. Notice that the bias and the select currents can be arbitrarily large so long as the bias is equal but opposite to the select current. Oversize current drive has the advantage of increasing the speed of transition of the switch.

Figure 12.48 shows another version of an n-way switch. There are $n + 2$ wires or windings for each core. Of these, n represents the number of bits to be decoded; one is a drive winding common to all cores in the switch, and the last one, the output. The true value of an input variable corresponds to no current and the false value, to negative full select current (or greater). The drive current is also of full select (or greater) value but of positive sense.

For any switch core which faces one or more false variables, a total

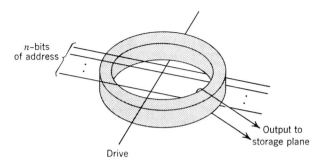

Figure 12.48. Address decoding in the switch core.

opposition current of one or more times full select current influences the core. For the one core which faces all true variables, there is no opposing current, and the core will switch in response to the drive current and provide an output. There is a reset requirement which must be satisfied somehow, perhaps with an additional bias winding.

Each switch core is really an n-way AND gate, and the inputs to the gate are the n Boolean variables which are being decoded. Each variable appears only once, either in its direct form or as the complement. Each core in such a switch responds to one and only one Boolean minterm of n variables.

In all of this core work, the sense of a current in a wire can always be reversed if the direction in which the wire threads the core is reversed.

The End-Fire Store

As we previously suggested, a store can be word select. For a 4096-word store there will have to be (in our example) a 64-by-64 switch; each of its 4096 outputs will feed one 40-bit string of storage cores. In principle, the switch decodes two base-64 inputs to a base-4096 output representation, in terms of which the words in the store are numbered (Figure 12.49). The advantage of this scheme is its high reading speed, because of the possibility of a large read current (greater than full select).

Although reading can be accomplished by an arbitrarily large current along one selection axis, writing must still be coincident current. There is a fundamental difference between reading and writing which accounts for this. Reading, in effect, is a special kind of write opera-

tion; all positions of the selected word are written to the same state—
the reference state for reading. Writing, however, requires that each
position of a word be individually selectable. One way of writing is
to arrange the switch so that it not only delivers a large current for
reading, but also a current of half-select magnitude for writing. The
other current of half-select magnitude will come from the Z winding
in each plane. An alternate way to arrange writing is to retain the
X and Y (and perhaps also the Z) windings in each plane, and use one
of the conventional coincident current writing schemes. Since the
end-fire switch may not take part in the write portion of the cycle, it
must somehow be reset in order to complete the symmetry of its cycle.

The end-fire arrangement provides a fast access time for reading,
but it shortens the overall store cycle only to the extent that the read
part of the cycle is shorter. Reading is still destructive and must be
followed by a rewrite. We have not yet considered the signal-to-noise

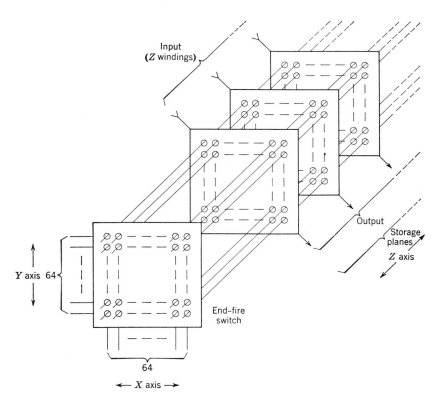

Figure 12.49. The end-fire store.

ratio in a coincident mode store, but we will see later that the end-fire scheme permits a much better ratio, and therefore larger stores can be built with this technique. Access is random.

The end-fire switch is difficult to build because of the wide load fluctuations it faces. Depending upon the digit content of a word, any number of cores between none and a word's worth can switch. One way out of this—but not neat—is to actually provide two storage cores per bit (39). The wiring can be arranged so that each such pair always stores opposite digits; therefore, no matter what the digit distribution in a word happens to be, the same number of cores—one word's worth —always change. The switch sees a constant load, and is, therefore, easier to design. Moreover, the spurious signals generated by a core tend to cancel by pairs. However, writing is a little troublesome to arrange because the two cores of a pair must always be in opposite states (see problem 12.10).

Reality

This is a good time to regain contact with the real world. In the two core-per-bit store, the load is not really constant; it is only more constant than it was. The constancy of the load which the switch sees depends very much on how uniform the cores are. Although the same number of cores will switch each time, it is not the same group of cores which switch each time. If cores are not sufficiently uniform, the load may still vary enough to make the design of an end-fire switch difficult. Obviously, one large end-fire switch can always be replaced with a multiplicity of switches—each one driving only a few planes of the store. The economics of any such situation, however, will have to be studied very carefully relative to the needs of the application. Non-uniformity of cores is also troublesome with respect to coincident current uses, as the next discussion will show.

Noise

What about all the half-selected cores? Do they really contribute zero signal to the common sense wire which links all cores in a given plane? If this is not true, it may be that the sum of their smallish contributions will override the desired signal from the selected core! And this is precisely the trouble. Cores do not have unity squareness ratio, and the half-select cores do contribute a small amount of signal.

The effectiveness with which such noise signals can be minimized will determine the largest plane which it is practical to construct (40).

A prescription for partially solving the noise problem is checkerboarding of the sense winding so that it links half the cores on each row and each column in opposite directions (Figure 12.50-a). Since the number n of coordinate wires is usually even (often a power of 2), an examination of Figure 12.50 shows that only $n - 2$ cores on a row or column can cancel although $n - 1$ are actually half selected. There will always be one core on the selected row and one on the selected column which will not be canceled. The signal produced by any half selected core depends not only on the state (0 or 1) in which it is but also on its immediate past history. The uncanceled noise component from a pair of half-selected cores which are in opposite states and link a common winding in opposite senses is generally called *delta noise* (V_δ).

In a selected row (or column) of an n-by-n array, there are $(n - 2)/2$ pairs of canceling cores. It is possible that the information stored in the selected row and column of a plane can be such that all cores which link the sense winding, say, in a positive sense are in the state which produces the maximum half-select noise signal, and all cores which link the sense winding in the negative sense are in the state which produces the minimum half-select noise. This is the worst case for non-cancellation of noise. The column and the row each contribute $(n - 2)/2$ pairs of half-selected cores; for each maximum noise core there is just one minimum noise core linking the sense winding in the opposite direction. Therefore, the total noise from the canceling pairs can be as large as $(n - 2)V_\delta$ which increases linearly with n. The desired signal still comes from just one core so that the signal-to-noise ratio varies inversely as n. This is the factor which limits the practical size of a core plane. Because it minimizes V_δ, core uniformity is clearly an important aspect of the noise problem in core planes.

An important by-product of a symmetrical checkerboard sense winding is that it also minimizes the air magnetic coupling to the X and Y wires which are being driven (Figure 12.50-b). Were this not true, a substantial noise component could be magnetically induced into the sense winding by the large X and Y currents.

Post-Write Disturb

Since the delta noise does depend on the immediate past history of a core, and particularly on whether a core has been half-selected after

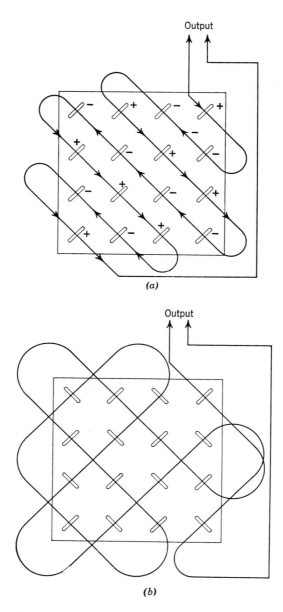

Figure 12.50.   Two checkerboarded sense windings.

it was written into, sometimes the whole plane is deliberately half-selected in order to get the first and biggest spurt of noise out of the system before the next read cycle. If the plane happens to have a Z winding, a half-select current on it will do the *post-write disturb* (41). This remedy extends the cycle time.

Multiple Sense Windings

It is possible to provide a multiplicity of sense windings in a large array (42). Using the output from only the sense winding which links the desired core decreases the effective size of the plane so far as noise is concerned.

EXAMPLE

Consider a 128×128 plane (Figure 12.51). If there are four sense windings, the large plane is effectively four 64×64 planes. A 14-bit address will be needed for the 16,384-cell plane; seven bits will choose one of 128 X lines and seven bits, one of 128 Y lines. The highest order bit of each 7-tuple will indicate in which group of 64 the desired line lies; therefore, by decoding the two bits which are the highest order places of the X and Y positions of the address, the appropriate sense winding can be determined.

This technique is not all gain, however. The signals from the sense windings are relatively small; and unless an adequate circuit for

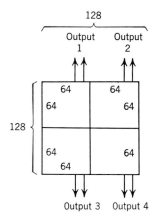

Figure 12.51. Multiple sense windings.

gating low level signals can be designed, a multiplicity of sense amplifiers will have to be provided.

Staggered Drives

At the expense of time, the signal-to-noise ratio can be improved by making the array non-square. The X and Y drives are then established time sequentially; the later one to come is on the shorter dimension of the plane and, therefore, produces substantially less noise (43).

EXAMPLE

Consider a 32×128 array (Figure 12.52). If the first drive appears on one of the 32 wires which stretch along the 128 dimension, the noise of the 127 undesired cores is ignored since there is not yet a fully selected core and, therefore, no reading signal. After all such noise has decayed, the drive on one of the 128 short wires appears, reads the desired core, but produces noise from only 31 half-selects. This is roughly the number of half-selects in a 16×16 conventional array. If core uniformity and quality is good enough, it may even be unnecessary to use a checkerboard sense winding.

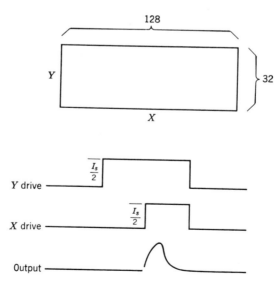

Figure 12.52.   A non-square array.

As usual, the gains in performance are not free. Aside from extra cycle time, more drivers are required for a non-square array than for a square array of the same number of cores. One drive must be fairly long in time, and it may not be possible to drive it from a core switch. A drive directly from an active element may be necessary.

End-Fire Noise

Inherent in a magnetic core technique of any kind is an amplitude discrimination problem. Magnetic materials do not have absolutely flat hysteresis loops, and hence there will always be a small output when reading a core in one state, in addition to the large output when reading it in the other state. To decide which state a single core is in requires a discrimination in amplitude between the two kinds of signals. So far as determining the output from one core is concerned, from the point of view of the information-receiver, there is a signal-to-noise problem, although it is not normally called that. In addition

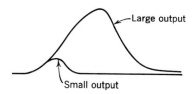

Figure 12.53. The two output signals from a core.

to this aspect, there is the one which we have just explored for coincident current stores—the addition of many noise components versus signal from just one source.

In the end-fire store, the signal-to-noise ratio is of the first kind described above. One and only one core contributes to the output signal on each output winding, and therefore the only problem is amplitude discrimination by the receiver. There is still a tolerance problem which is related to core uniformity. The smallest large-signal-state output (say, the 1-state) must be large enough compared to the largest small-signal-state output (the 0-state). Otherwise, it will be difficult to discriminate between them on an amplitude basis. Fortunately, the small signal output peaks earlier in time than the large signal output (Figure 12.53). Therefore, if the output winding is sampled (*strobed*) at about the time the large signal peaks, the apparent signal-to-noise ratio is much larger than the ratio of the signal to the noise at the time the noise is maximum. This feature, of course, also is true of the coincident current store, and represents another way to improve the ratio.

There are possible payoffs with an end-fire arrangement. Core uniformity is not as critical, and poorer quality cores can be used. Alternatively, for a given core quality, larger arrays can be constructed. There is the proviso, of course, that the end-fire switch can be designed, and perhaps also, that the requirements of the situation justify the possible extra cost.

Limiting Factors

The limit on the size of any one plane is set by the signal-to-noise ratio which is tolerable on the output signal. The signal-to-noise ratio in turn depends on the quality of the cores, their uniformity, the method of operating the cores, and the shrewdness of the designer in canceling or ignoring noise signals. His shrewdness is constrained, in part, by the speed region in which he must work. Tricks useful for slower stores (e.g., staggered drives, slower but squarer cores) are denied him in a fast store (44).

The speed limit of a core store is determined in part by heating problems. Each time a core switches, energy is dissipated. At high switching rates, the internal heat—if not removed—forces the material toward the Curie temperature at which point, it becomes non-magnetic. Long before the Curie point, however, the magnetic characteristics begin to degrade. Unfortunately core materials tend to be good thermal insulators, and heat removal may be troublesome.

Another factor which helps to determine speed is the material of the core and the mode in which the magnetism is reversed. Ferrite structures are such that they may be switched in two modes: domain wall movement or molecular rotation. The former is characteristic of bulk materials and occurs at half-select current levels of 300–500 ma. Rotational switching occurs very rapidly (few tens of millimicroseconds) at comparable current levels, but the currents must rise much faster. The switching mechanism in cores is a complex phenomenon and is not well understood.

Practical Matters

Select currents must be well controlled (perhaps $\pm 5\%$) and must be well-shaped rectangular pulses to avoid spurious effects. The sense amplifier is relatively straightforward except that with some arrangements of sense windings, the amplifier may have to handle bipolar signals. It may also be subject to large spurious input signals during writing (45).

The fabrication of, say, 36 or 40 planes, each of which contains perhaps 32,000 or even 65,000 cores, each core having 4 or more wires through it, is no trivial matter. Quite aside from testing, sorting, and selecting a few million cores for uniformity, the mechanics of threading so many cores requires considerable technique and time.

The minimum cycle time of a core store depends on the natural switching time of the core, and on the configuration of the store—coincident current, end-fire, or linear select, etc. As a rule of thumb, the minimum cycle time of a coincident current store is several times the natural switching time of the core; a linear select mode can reduce this to a few (two or three) times the natural time. If very short current drives are used, not all the material of a core will switch, and the apparent size of the core is much smaller than the real size. In such a partial switching mode, the total cycle time of a store might be of the same order as the natural switching time of the material (46).

The physical packaging of a store can play a very important part in determining its overall speed. For example, in a large parallel store, some wires will extend through all planes and thread a row (or column) of cores in each one. The inductance provided by the cores and the distributed shunt capacitance makes such a wire behave very much like a transmission line with finite velocity of propagation. Current drives may arrive at the far end of a store significantly delayed. Such delays in part determine how wide the current drives must be, and also determine the positioning of the strobe reading signal.

Other Geometries

The discrete magnetic core is not the only geometry possible. One other is the *ferrite plate* in which a continuous sheet of material containing holes in a rectangular array can function as an assembly of apparent cores (47). Since the magnetic field around a wire decays inversely with the distance from the wire, at some radius the field is too small to cause switching. Thus interaction between adjacent holes can be kept satisfactorily low. The fabrication problem is essentially that of weaving the windings through the holes; to some extent, printed wiring on the plates can substitute for actual wires.

A geometry which is particularly suitable to non-destructive reading is that of the biaxial element (48). As Figure 12.54 shows, this

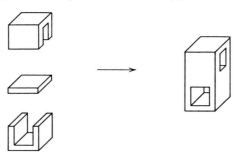

Figure 12.54. The biaxial storage element.

element is a rectangular variant of the linked toroidal cores (Figure 12.34). The two horseshoe-shaped closure paths can establish magnetic flux in the central slab in perpendicular directions. Thus one rectangular aperture (say, the lower) can be regarded as the usual storage element; the upper magnetic path establishes the cross-magnetic field for the non-destructive read.

Thin Films

Magnetic materials can be vacuum deposited onto suitable substrates. If deposited in a magnetic field, a film (typically of the order of 0.1 inch diameter by a few hundred Angstroms thick) exhibits both an easy direction of magnetization and the rectangular hysteresis loop needed for a storage element (49). Advantages of thin-film elements include: fast rotational switching (tens of millimicroseconds), the possibility of mass deposition of a whole array at once, and minimum heat problems because of the large ratio of surface to volume in the unit magnetic elements. The windings no longer actually thread the magnetic element, but simply pass near it. The magnetic flux path between winding and element is not closed, and the resulting air flux can create crosstalk problems. Furthermore, the coupling between drive lines and storage elements is lossy. Uniformity of characteristics from one film to the next is important.

The internal behavior of thin films is even more complex than that of such bulk materials as the ferrites. Not only are there axes of easy and hard magnetization, but the hysteresis loops along the two directions are quite different. Furthermore, the shape of the hysteresis loop depends on the switching mode of the internal flux state.

Various non-destructive read techniques try to capitalize on such differences.

One non-destructive reading scheme depends on the fact that magnetic flux is a vector quantity, and that the storage material is saturated (50). The scheme is similar to that used for the linked cores (Figure 12.34). A transverse field is used to swing the spatial position of the magnetic vector of the storage field. The resulting flux change is detected as an output signal. After the transverse field ceases, the storage field returns to its initial preferred direction of magnetization. Depending upon the material and its characteristics, the flux vector can be turned as little as $15°$ or nearly $90°$ without its failing to return to its original direction.

The thin-film technique can also be used in the geometry of a rod (51) rather than in a flat plane. The rod structure lends itself to the use of weaving-like techniques for fabrication of the windings and the arrays. Speed of operation of rod devices is in the range of a few tens of millimicroseconds.

Coincident Flux Devices

In a coincident current selection scheme, the drive current is necessarily limited to such a value that half-selected cores do not change state. Consider the arrangement of Figure 12.55. A D-C bias normally keeps the core far out on the saturation part of the loop; the X and Y drives are equal in amplitude to the bias current. Thus a half-selected core is driven only to point 1, but a fully selected core is driven to point 2. With such a large current driving the core, its response is very fast; the only trouble is that there is no storage because the bias current will return the core to its initial state when the X and Y drives decay.

A multiple-aperture magnetic structure can provide both rapid switching and storage (Figure 12.56) (52). Owing to the bias winding the initial state of magnetization in legs A and B is as shown. Now, let the X and Y currents be such as to fully saturate the core in a counterclockwise direction (Figure 12.57-a). Leg B reverses in direction, but legs C and D are each magnetized upward. By making the bias and the drive currents sufficiently large, the switching can be made to occur as rapidly as desired. When the drive currents decay, the bias winding returns leg B to its initial state. Since flux lines must be continuous, some change must also occur in either leg C or D. The reluctance from B to C is lower than from B to D; therefore, the changing flux in B completes itself through C and causes it also

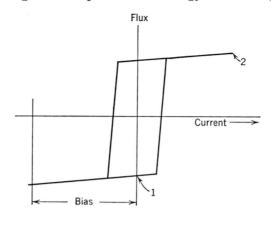

Figure 12.55. A core driven by large currents.

to reverse (Figure 12.57-b). After the cycle, flux lines circle each of
the vertical holes; the counterclockwise pattern of flux in legs C and
D can be defined as representing one stored state (say, 1).

Writing the other stored state is just the reverse of the previous
operation. The X and Y drives are established such as to completely
saturate the core in the clockwise direction (Figure 12.57-c). This
time, leg A changes and if leg D were in the 1 state, it also will change.

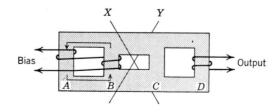

Figure 12.56. A coincident flux device.

Hence, reading is destructive. After the drives disappear, the bias winding returns leg A to its initial state. Since the reluctance from A to C is lower than from A to D, C changes along with A; this leads to a clockwise flux pattern around the right hole which corresponds to the other state (Figure 12.57-d).

Legs A and B always return to the same state. Thus the storage is in terms of the two flux patterns in legs C and D. Flux is switched from the left side of the core to the right for writing; hence the name—*coincident flux*—for this technique. Constructing an array of multiple aperture cores is more difficult than a conventional core array because of additional wiring complications. In return for this, the designer gets high speed—fractions of a microsecond—and a constant load for the current drivers. In the selected core, there are always two legs which flip. Another possibility for a multi-aperture structure is the circular geometry of the transfluxor device (53).

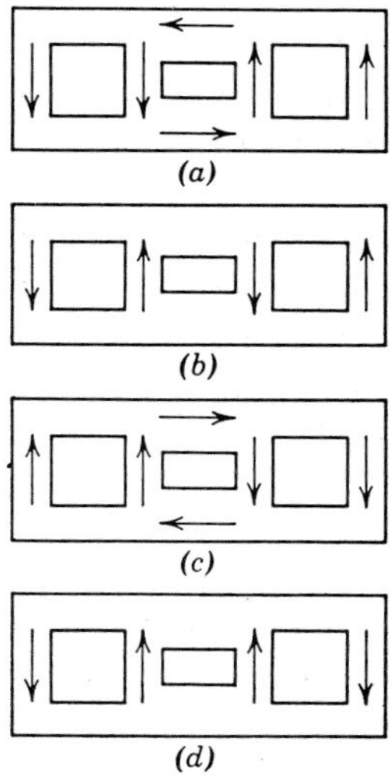

(a)

(b)

(c)

(d)

Figure 12.57. Flux patterns in a coincident flux device.

Bulk Storage

For some kinds of problems, storage of huge amounts of data is necessary. Sometimes such large stores are called *files* and organizationally are frequently in the secondary or tertiary level of storage. Most such devices depend on the magnetic tape or drum technique; the principle goal is low unit cost of storage with reasonable access time (54).

One possibility for bulk storage is a huge drum perhaps scanned by a single, moving, air-floated head (55). With such a head, machining tolerances of the drum are much freer. A multiplicity of smaller drums scanned by moving heads is also a possibility.

A variant of the drum is the *disc file* (56). A flat disc coated with magnetic material is read by a moving air-floated head. Often, recording is done on both sides of the disc, and often a large number of such discs are stacked on a single shaft. The moving head then darts to the selected disc, moves radially on the disc to the appropriate track, and waits for the right angular position of the disc. Several moving head read-write stations can be provided to improve the access time.

Another possible bulk store is a multiple tape file (57). Many relatively short lengths of tape (few hundred feet) are arranged side by side; each tape operates from its own storage bins rather than from reels. A moving head mechanism goes to the desired tape, and moves it to the desired position. A related possibility is a number of short lengths (perhaps few feet) of tape which are mechanically moved in and out of a storage cartridge.

Read-Only Storage

We have already suggested that the reading and the writing access times may be different. In some stores which we have discussed, the drum for example, the two times are in fact equal. In others, the core store, for example, the two times are different; the difference depends on the details of the operating cycle. In a *read-only store,* the machine under program control can only read from the store; it cannot write into the store. Since any store must somehow receive initial information, the implication is that some special action, perhaps external to the machine, is necessary to write into the store. Since the operating speed of the machine is not affected by the writing time of such a store, the ratio of reading- to writing-access time is of much less concern. The reading speed of course still must reflect the general speed range of the primary store, the control and arithmetic units. Some techniques offer reading speeds of fractional microseconds but writing speeds of minutes or hours.

We studied no programming example which required the storage of a large table. We did suggest, however, that a practical operating machine system will utilize a large number of routines which are standard, change only slowly over time, and belong to its library. For example, such routines will include the various assembly and compiler routines, and the subroutines for such standard functions as the trigonometric functions, the square root, multiple precision arithmetic, binary-decimal and decimal-binary conversion, diagnostic problems, etc. It is generally convenient for the programmer to have the whole library collection available, and often the library is kept in the magnetic tape level of the store hierarchy. Such routines have to be rewritten relatively infrequently, and therefore, it is appropriate to search for store techniques whose writing time is long, whose reading time is short, and which have an economic or operating advantage compared, say, to magnetic tapes. The programmer might expect to keep not only standard routines, but also large tables and dictionaries in read-only storage. A compiler, for example, in its operation will require tables of symbol equivalences in order to translate from the problem language to the machine language. If parts of the standard routines need to be rewritten during use, such parts can be kept in conventional storage. In addition to an economic advantage, with a read-only store we might also hope to get random access rather than the sequential access of the tape store.

A photographic technique is a natural suggestion for read-only storage. The density of information which can be written into a photographic emulsion is high; and after the developing process, the information is inviolate except for physical damage to the emulsion. The *photoscopic store* (Figure 12.58) utilizes a rapidly rotating glass disc to carry the emulsion (58). Such a store is read by a light-photocell arrangement, and the initial preparation of the disc requires equipment which is not normally part of the computer system. Access is sequential, but depending on the arrangement of the information tracks in the surface, the flow might be serial, serial-parallel, or even parallel.

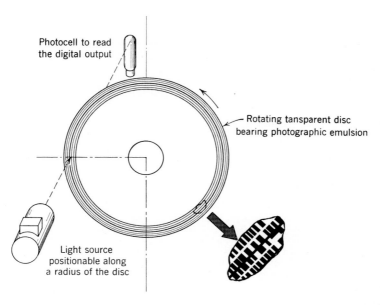

Photocell to read
the digital output

Rotating tansparent disc
bearing photographic emulsion

Light source
positionable along
a radius of the disc

Figure 12.58. A photoscopic store. (By permission of the Institute of Radio Engineers.)

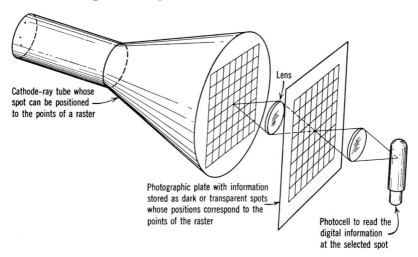

Cathode–ray tube whose spot can be positioned to the points of a raster

Lens

Photographic plate with information stored as dark or transparent spots whose positions correspond to the points of the raster

Photocell to read the digital information at the selected spot

Figure 12.59. A cathode-ray-tube read-only photographic store.

The scan rate of such a disc is in the low megacycle range, and hence the average access time is quite short.

Another photographic possibility is the use of a cathode-ray tube as a switchable light source (59). We have seen from the discussion of the electrostatic store how an electron beam can be positioned to any point in an array. If, instead of storing on the phosphor, the beam is used simply as a source of light to illuminate a pattern of information on a photographic plate in front of the tube, a read-only store results (Figure 12.59). Like the electrostatic store, this kind of photostorage can be organized for either serial or parallel access. A photocell can detect light coming through the photoplate, and hence information will be placed on it as clear or opaque areas. In the electrostatic store, interference effects between adjacent storage spots limited the density of storage. The spot spacing was sufficiently large that the precision of beam positioning presented no particular problem. In the corresponding read-only store, the cathode-ray tube is only a light source; there is no interference problem, and hence the density of storage is limited by the precision with which the beam can be positioned, and also by the fineness with which the beam can be focused as a visible spot. In a parallel form of such a store there will be one cathode-ray-tube light source for each column of the information to be stored. Although the deflection plates of tubes will be operated from the same voltage source, there may well be geometric differences from one tube to the next. Therefore, the beam position corresponding to a given address may vary a little from tube to tube. Such a tolerance problem may require that the initial writing of the photoplate be done by the same cathode-ray tube which will later read it. The deflection voltages must be sufficiently stable from the writing cycle to subsequent read cycles. To assist with the latter problem, a supplementary cathode-ray tube can be added to the system, and its deflection system driven as the rest from the same voltages. Instead, however, of reading stored information, its beam position will be compared to, say, a standard engraved plate, and a feedback servotechnique used to center its beam precisely on the desired area. In effect, the tolerance problems associated with the generation of the deflection voltages have been avoided by the introduction of extra equipment. The stability of beam positioning will depend on the dimensional stability of the engraved plate, and on the precision of the servosystem.

A different technique for read-only storage is really a derivative of the end-fire linearly selected core store. Suppose that the array of magnetic cores is replaced by an array of transformers (60). A transformer will be present to store one of the binary digits; absent, to store the other (Figure 12.60). The secondaries of all transformers

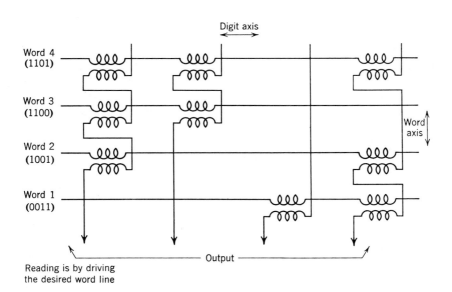

Figure 12.60. A transformer read-only store.

in a given plane will be linked in series to form the output winding. The primaries of all transformers in a given word will be linked in series and driven by one of the outputs of the end-switch. Writing in this store is clearly a reconnection of wires, although the physical construction might be arranged to expedite matters. For example, plug-in techniques might be used for insertion or removal of one or a group of transformers (61).

Conventional storage techniques can always be used in a read-only mode. If necessary, some special action, perhaps manual or perhaps under program control, can be taken to prevent writing into selected parts of a store. However, the cost of the writing feature has been paid, and the principal reason for locking out writing in a conventional store is to protect the information against accidental destruction or modification. Hence one of the attractive features, which we did not foresee for read-only techniques, is the security of the stored information against tampering, possibly as a result of machine malfunction, or program error. If the cost per unit of storage is low enough, read-only schemes may be good possibilities for large files, especially those files in which the information changes slowly compared to the write time of the read-only store (62). Conceivably, the useful life of such a semi-permanent file can be extended by keeping in conventional storage, a small file of changes to the main file. Occasionally, the main file will be updated. With some read-only storage, some things may be more convenient for the programmer because he can have random access to the information. On the other hand, some things will be a little more troublesome because he cannot write into part of the store.

Depending upon the size of a read-only store, and where it is in the store hierarchy, addressing will be handled differently. For a relatively small such store, its addresses might be a continuation of the address structure of the primary store. In effect, it is part of the primary store, although unwritable. For a large read-only file, addressing is likely to be like that of magnetic tapes—on a block or record basis. The addressing scheme will certainly be governed in part by the role that read-only storage is to play in the system—large file, library routine storage, or table storage. In table storage, for example, direct addressing is likely to be the most convenient. If the circumstances warrant, some hybrid addressing scheme might be arranged to provide a pseudodirect addressing arrangement. For example, the read-only part of the store might have enough additional equipment to find by itself the ith word of the jth block, given i and j from some other part of the machine.

STORE ORGANIZATION

A magnetic core store when present almost always serves as the primary level store. Sometimes small amounts of core storage which are separate from the main store function as a temporary repository between sections of a machine. Such *buffer storage* accommodates the uneven flow rates of two parts of a machine, or facilitates communication between parts of a machine which are not synchronized with each other. Buffer storage can also be used to improve transfer efficiency by batching information and transmitting it in a short burst at high speed.

The magnetic drum store can be primary storage for a slower machine or secondary storage for a faster machine. Some of its bulk-file variants may be in yet higher levels of storage. A drum can also serve the role of a buffer store.

The magnetic tape store can be second level for a slower machine; second or third level, for a faster machine. Some forms of tape systems which are intended for file storage could be in a yet higher level.

Interlayer Transfers

The most common arrangement for communicating between layers of storage is for all levels of storage to communicate with the primary level. A tape-to-drum transfer will generally use the primary store as a buffer to match the different flow rates of the drum and the tape.

The programmer generally has to be concerned about such inter-level transfers. It is his problem to move data among the several levels as needed. The machine may be such that he must always move data in *blocks* of a fixed number of words. Alternatively, it may be that the block is of variable length; it is to be specified on each occasion by the programmer. It might be that flow between primary and secondary levels is *variable block* length (as short as one word, and as large as the full contents of primary storage), but transfer between secondary and tertiary (via primary) is *fixed block* length.

In the case of variable length block transfers, the programmer must specify the length of the block, where it is in the store of origin, and where it is to go in the store of destination. There may be multiple parameter instructions for this purpose, or the programmer may have to assemble such parameters into one or more words and place such information in a particular part in the machine. A fixed block transfer is similar except that no measure of length need be given.

Addressing

Primary storage is generally all *directly addressable;* this implies that the address part of an instruction can specify any cell in the primary store. Sometimes the secondary storage is also directly addressable; its addresses are a continuation of the sequence of addresses used by the main store. The routine will never know which part of the store is being consulted except by the length of time required to get the information (63).

More often, the secondary store is accessible only through some special selection action. It has a set of addresses of its own, some of which may be the same as those of the main store. Such, say, *drum addresses* generally will not occur in the address part of an instruction because the address field for the drum will be longer than that for the smaller primary store. Such drum addresses must be positioned in particular parts of the machine by the routine. If the transfer is by fixed length blocks, drum addressing may consist only of specifying the block number.

The tertiary store generally is so voluminous that each cell in it cannot be directly addressed—the address field would be much too long. Location of information is likely to be on the basis of specifying, say, the ith word in the jth block; physically, the machine (by means of a routine or perhaps, special equipment) locates the information by counting the passage of blocks and words. Transfer to and from tertiary storage can be either fixed or variable block (or record) length. If variable, the length can generally be as short as one word.

Buffered Transfers

During the time that the primary store is being used as a buffer for transfers, say, from tape to drum, a machine often is not able to perform any other work on its problem. To maximize the efficiency of the arithmetic unit, sufficient autonomous control is sometimes provided so that interlayer storage transfers proceed on their own, once started by the routine. If the transfer happens to be to or from the primary store, it may be necessary to provide equipment interlocks so that the routine cannot accidentally get at information which is stale or is intended to be transferred. Alternatively, the programmer will program his own interlocks. The buffer storage required for such autonomous transfers may be a designated section of the main store or a specially provided auxiliary store.

EXAMPLE

A machine has autonomous tape-to-core transfer. The programmer, having located the particular record on the tape, specifies the first and last addresses of the cells which the block occupies (or is to occupy) in the core store. In going from tape to core, the autonomous control keeps a record of that portion of the designated area of the core store which has not yet been filled. The main control, by consulting the records of its helper control, can determine whether an address with which it is working specifies a cell which is not yet filled. If so, the main control must wait until the cell it desires has been filled with new information. Conversely, on the core-to-tape transfer, the main control is blocked from any region of the core store which has yet to be transferred to the tape.

Such a buffered transfer is especially helpful for input-output devices whose rate of flow is likely to be much lower than any other part of the machine.

As usual, there is a tradeoff in this arrangement. In return for the extra equipment and complexity of machine organization, there is increased utilization of the arithmetic unit, main store, and main control. The reasonableness of such an exchange can very easily depend on the class of problems for which a machine is intended.

Other Store Features

Besides the equipment for actual storage and for selection, a store system also will have a variety of gate circuits, perhaps a register or two, amplifiers, pulse sources, and local control. It may also have special counters such as those for tallying the number of words in a transfer, or those for keeping track of addresses on a drum. It may also have a small amount of arithmetic ability; for example, it may need to form check sums during buffered transfers.

It may also have error-detecting (or -correcting) equipment. The most common error check in a storage system is the parity check; additional equipment will be needed for generating parity digits on incoming messages and for verifying parity on outgoing messages.

OTHER STORAGE TECHNIQUES

There are other physical phenomena which have been used in a few stores or which appear to be promising. A brief discussion of some of them is included here for perspective.

One such is the diode-capacitor store (64). This is similar in principle to the word-select core store (Figure 12.34) and consists of a diode and capacitor in series for each bit. The charge on the capacitor is the representation of the stored information; the series diode functions both as part of the storage feature by providing a high impedance leakage path, and also as the selection mechanism. Depending on the leakage paths of the capacitor, the cyclic regeneration requirements may or may not be severe.

Ferroelectric Storage

Certain crystalline substances (e.g., barium titanate) respond to electric fields as a magnetic material responds to a magnetic field. The relation between the applied electric field and the internal polarization is the familiar rectangular hysteresis loop. A unit storage element can be made from a capacitor which contains a ferroelectric material for a dielectric. Ferroelectric storage is the dual of magnetic storage (65).

The ferroelectric technique is very attractive insofar as fabrication is concerned. Rectangular matrices can be formed by plating, depositing, or etching conducting paths on the ferroelectric substrate (Figure

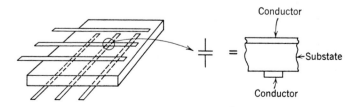

Figure 12.61.   A ferroelectric array.

12.61). However, there is considerable difficulty in getting sufficiently large pieces of suitable material; and unlike the windings on magnetic elements, it is not possible to thread another winding for the output. A supplementary capacitor is required.

Cryogenic Films

Some materials have the property that they become superconducting at sufficiently low temperatures; e.g., at liquid helium temperature (4° Kelvin), all resistance disappears. However, it is possible to return the material to the normal state by applying a sufficiently large magnetic field. Any magnetic flux which is in the material when it becomes superconducting is trapped because the zero resistivity of the material permits surface currents to flow without dissipation of energy. The states of trapped flux correspond to the information states (66).

The technique offers attractive fabrication possibilities. Superconducting materials can be deposited, as can insulating and normal conducting materials. However, the problems of multiple deposition are difficult; and the liquid helium operating environment contributes some problems. On the other hand, the technique offers the possibility of a very compact store which dissipates very little energy and operates at very high speeds (from a few microseconds to the low milli-microsecond range).

The Twistor

The twistor is a variant of the magnetic core technique (67). Magnetic wire of nickel-iron alloys develops a helical strain anisotropy when subjected to torsion; this leads to a preferred direction of magnetization. By arranging a group of stressed magnetic wires in a rectangular array with ordinary conducting wire in the other dimension, the effect of a small piece of magnetic material at each junction is obtained (Figure 12.62). The magnetic wire itself serves as the sense winding, but there are fabrication problems related to maintaining uniform torsion in all the wires. There is also some problem of interaction between adjacent bits. A variant of the stressed-wire technique avoids the necessity of twisting the wire. A flat magnetic strip is helically wound on a conducting, but insulated wire. The preferred axis of magnetization is obtained because the magnetic material is physically deposed in a helical structure.

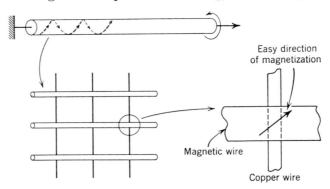

Figure 12.62. The twistor store.

Non-geometric Addressing

Stores as we have studied them are geometric in the sense that either explicitly or implicitly an address is associated with each cell. For the primary store, there is an explicit address; for a magnetic tape store, an implicit address in the form of, say, the ith word in the jth block. No information is available unless the address of its location is known (or perhaps the address of the address of the address . . .). If the address is unknown, a search for the information must be carried out. Human memory does not appear to be organized in this fashion. This has lead to the consideration of stores which are variously called *associative stores, tag stores, label stores,* or sometimes *doctor-in-the-house stores* (68).

In such a store, the storage mechanism in principle is no different, but the addressing is. In the doctor-in-the-house store, the store in effect is interrogated with the question: Is a given piece of information in there? The store is expected to answer "yes" or "no" without any information about location. If the information used in the question is, say, less than a word, the rest of the word can be regarded as associated information, or perhaps information which will lead to the location of the desired associated information. In what is commonly and generically called the associative store, a fragmentary piece of information is directed to the store; and if it contains that fragment, it is expected to reply with any information which it has associated with the fragment, perhaps part of a word or several words. The important point is that the rest of the machine, so to speak, asks for information by its name, rather than specifying the location of information. From the store's point of view, the information stored is unidentifiable and anonymous.

In a sense, any question directed to an associative store is directed to all cells at once, and any one (or more) which match the question respond. The ability to associate pieces of information together, one or more of which may be the basis for retrieving the information, must be under the control of the user. A conventional geometric store can always be programmed to behave like an associative store. The response to any interrogation involves a search procedure which may extend through the entire store. Therefore, the simulation of associative stores tends to be very slow even on fast machines. On the other hand, genuine associative stores contain enough extra equipment that all cells are interrogated simultaneously, and the response of the store is complete in one or a few cycles of operation.

Information in an associative store is filed away, so to speak, by a descriptor, a name, or an attribute which is relevant to the information itself. Another type of store organization with the same characteristic is the *list store*. Such a store is different only in addressing, and can be simulated by proper programming of a conventional store (69). All information in a list store is considered to be filed as a list of items. Typically, each storage cell contains an item, which itself might be ultimate information, or it might be the name or attribute of other information, or the name of another list. In effect, the individual cells of the store are chained together, but the length of the chains, the number of the chains, and the individual cells which each chain includes are under the control of the programmer. As with other associative stores, information is filed by an attribute, or on a list of a given name. It is retrieved in that fashion without knowledge of the address of the cell which it happens to occupy.

GENERAL COMMENTS

So far as the designer is concerned, there are both organizational decisions and detailed equipment decisions to be made (70). Not always is a given decision entirely one or the other kind. For example, one organizational problem is the number of layers in the store hierarchy. It is clear that this choice hinges in part on how cheaply various kinds of storage can be built. The organizational problem of addressing involves convenience to the user versus the cost of equipment to provide, say, some sophisticated addressing scheme. The choice of random versus sequential access involves cost since the randomly accessed store tends to involve more equipment, but certainly the random store contributes to a faster operating of the machine. There is some economic value attached to machine speed.

In a very general sense, the detailed decisions relating to the store (as well as to much of the rest of the machine) hinge on either convenience to the user, or suitability to a problem or class of problems versus cost. Cost may appear in an absolute sense; for example, a billion word random access store with a ten millimicrosecond access time would be a programmer's dream for certain kinds of problems, but the cost is unthinkable. Cost can also appear in a relative sense. For a machine intended to sell in a specified price range and to solve given kinds of problems, the overall budget of the machine is set by its market. A given store might be ruled out just because it cannot be constructed cheaply enough. The cost influence is relative because the store ruled out economically for one size and price of machine may fit well in a machine in a different price range or intended for some different class of user or problem.

To a considerable extent, the storage (and machine) organization tends to follow the discovery and exploitation of new techniques. For example, the earliest machines contained sequential access stores because techniques for parallel stores were not economically available. Programmers learned to cope with the variable access time and to maximize machine performance by placing the routine in the store other than in successive storage cells. Such *minimum latency programming* attempted to place each instruction so that it was at or close to the output point of the sequential store at the time it was needed (71). Unless a machine is intended for a fixed problem, the spacing between successive instructions will change from problem to problem. A simple instruction counter cannot provide the flexibility needed by the programmer, because in minimum latency programming, many instructions will have to be followed by jump instructions. Therefore, a multiaddress instruction format, in which one address field is the location of the next instruction, is very sensible. Available equipment techniques—in this case, sequential accessed stores only—reflect directly on preferred machine organizational characteristics—in this case, multiaddress instructions.

With the development of the electrostatic store, and later the core store, random access became economically feasible. Hence, single-address machine organization became sensible. More recently, large bulk stores have been developed, and read-only techniques have appeared. As programmers learn to exploit such new techniques, corresponding changes in machine organization are certain to occur. The important observation is this: the power and desirability of a new technique—storage or otherwise—can often not be completely foreseen; the ultimate judgment of value may very easily have to wait until programmers have learned how to use it. Here again, we observe the tight interplay between the programmer as the user of a machine and the engineer as the builder of a machine, and of the desirability of their close interaction, not only during the design but also during the research phase.

Traditionally in the computer field, the development of new hardware has led the exploitation by programmers. New machines have tended to appear more rapidly than features of existing machines have been fully exercised. The list store and the list processing languages which go with it are a good counter example. The incentive for the development of list languages was the application of machines to certain kinds of problems which involved, principally, manipulation of symbols rather than arithmetic operations. Game-playing routines such as chess, or theorem-proving routines such as those for geometry or logical calculus are typical of problems for which the allocation of storage space a priori is extremely difficult. In an effort to ameliorate the problem, and to make efficient use of storage space, the list languages were developed. Although conventional storage techniques can be used to build small list stores, large list stores await the discovery of new techniques for economic implementation. In this particular situation, the application happened to precede the development of hardware.

COLLATERAL READING

1. Siegel, P., *Understanding digital computers;* John Wiley and Sons, New York, 1961; chapter 12.

   Scott, N. R., *Analog and digital computer technology;* McGraw-Hill Book Co., New York, 1960; pp. 442–444.

   Bartee, T. C., *Digital computer fundamentals;* McGraw-Hill Book Co., New York, 1960; chapter 7.

   Flores, I., *Computer logic;* Prentice-Hall, Englewood Cliffs, N.J., 1960; chapter 13.

   Grabbe, E. M. *et al., Handbook of automation, computation and control;* John Wiley and Sons, New York, 1959; vol. 2, chapter 19.

   Smith, C. V. L., *Electronic digital computers;* McGraw-Hill Book Co., New York, 1959; chapters 11, 12.

   McCormick, E. H., *Digital computer primer;* McGraw-Hill Book Co., New York, 1959; chapter 8.

Ridenour, L. N., Computer memories; *Scientific American,* June, 1955; pp. 92 *ff. passim.*

Eckert, J. P., Jr., Survey of digital computer memory systems; *Proceedings of the IRE,* vol. 41, October, 1953; pp. 1393–1406.

Rajchman, J. A., Computer memories—a survey of the state-of-the-art; *Proceedings of the IRE,* vol. 49, January, 1961; pp. 104–127.

2. Richards, R. K., *Digital computer components and circuits;* D. Van Nostrand Co., Princeton, N.J., 1957; pp. 282–286.

3. Richards, R. K., *Digital computer components and circuits;* D. Van Nostrand Co., Princeton, N.J., 1957; pp. 294–296.

Millman, J. and H. Taub, *Pulse and digital circuits;* McGraw-Hill Book Co., New York, 1956; chapter 10.

Anderson, J. R., Electrical delay lines for digital computer applications; *IRE Transactions on Electronic Computers,* vol. EC-2, June, 1953; pp. 5–13.

Chance, B. *et al., Waveforms,* McGraw-Hill Book Co., New York, 1949; chapter 22.

4. Smith, C. V. L., *Electronic digital computers;* McGraw-Hill Book Co., New York, 1959; pp. 265–270.

Richards, R. K., *Digital computer components and circuits;* D. Van Nostrand Co., Princeton, N.J., 1957; pp. 286–289.

Auerbach, I. L. *et al.,* Mercury delay line memory using a pulse rate of several megacycles; *Proceedings of the IRE,* vol. 37, August, 1949; pp. 855–861.

Ryan, R. D., A mercury delay line memory unit; *Proceedings of the IRE* (Australia), vol. 15, April, 1954; pp. 89–95.

Chance, B. *et al., Waveforms,* McGraw-Hill Book Co., New York, 1949; chapter 23.

Lockhart, H. H., Delay lines; *Space/Astronautics Research and Development Handbook, 1961–62;* Conover-Mast Publications, New York.

5. Lockhart, H. H., Delay lines; *Space/Astronautics Research and Development Handbook, 1961–62;* Conover-Mast Publications, New York.

Smith, C. V. L., *Electronic digital computers;* McGraw-Hill Book Co., New York, 1959; pp. 270–273.

Richards, R. K., *Digital computer components and circuits;* D. Van Nostrand Co., Princeton, N.J., 1957; pp. 289–292.

Lockhart, H. H., Electronics associated with fused quartz delay lines; *Military Systems Design,* vol. 3, September/October, 1959.

6. Smith, C. V. L., *Electronic digital computers;* McGraw-Hill Book Co., New York, 1959; pp. 274–276.

Richards, R. K., *Digital computer components and circuits;* D. Van Nostrand Co., Princeton, N.J., 1957; pp. 292–294.

Lockhart, H. H., Delay lines; *Space/Astronautics Research and Development Handbook, 1961–62;* Conover-Mast Publications, New York.

Rothbart, A., Bibliography on magnetostrictive delay lines; *IRE Transactions on Electronic Computers,* vol. EC-10, June, 1961; p. 285.

Rothbart, A. and A. J. Brown, Magnetostrictive delay lines; *Electronics,* 13 April, 1962; pp. 55–59.

7. Scott, N. R., *Analog and digital computer technology;* McGraw-Hill Book Co., New York, 1960; pp. 483–494.

Smith, C. V. L., *Electronic digital computers;* McGraw-Hill Book Co., New York, 1959; pp. 277–286.

Richards, R. K., *Digital computer components and circuits;* D. Van Nostrand Co., Princeton, N.J., 1957; pp. 263–271.

Eckert, W. J. and R. Jones, *Faster, faster;* McGraw-Hill Book Co., New York, 1955; chapter 3.

Williams, F. C. and T. Kilburn, A storage system for use with binary digital computing machines; *Proceedings of the Institute of Electrical Engineers* (London), vol. 96, pt. II, April, 1949; pp. 183–202.

Thorenson, R., An improved cathode ray tube storage system; *Proceedings of the 1953 Western Joint Computer Conference,* Los Angeles, 4–6 February, 1953; pp. 167–173.

Wong, S. Y., High density Williams storage; *IRE Transactions on Electronic Computers,* vol. EC-4, December, 1955; pp. 156–158.

8. Eckert, J. P., Jr. *et al.,* A dynamically regenerated electrostatic memory system; *Proceedings of the IRE,* vol. 38, May, 1950; pp. 498–510.

9. Logue, J. C., Engineering experience in the design and operation of a large scale electrostatic memory; *IRE Convention Record,* pt. 7, 1953; pp. 21–29.

10. Richards, R. K., *Digital computer components and circuits;* D. Van Nostrand Co., Princeton, N.J., 1957; pp. 271–279.

Hines, M. E. *et al.,* Digital memory in barrier-grid storage tubes; *Bell System Technical Journal,* vol. 34, November, 1955; pp. 1241–1264.

Graham, M. *et al.,* The design of a large electrostatic memory; *IRE Transactions on Electronic Computers,* vol. EC-8, December, 1959; pp. 479–485.

11. Richards, R. K., *Digital computer components and circuits;* D. Van Nostrand Co., Princeton, N.J., 1957; pp. 279–282.

Rajchman, J. A., The selective electrostatic storage tube; *RCA Review,* vol. 12, May, 1951; pp. 53–97.

12. Ledley, R. S., *Digital computer and control engineering;* McGraw-Hill Book Co., New York, 1960; pp. 732–739.

Richards, R. K., *Digital computer components and circuits;* D. Van Nostrand Co., Princeton, N.J., 1957; chapter 7, especially pp. 336–342.

Smith, C. V. L., *Electronic digital computers;* McGraw-Hill Book Co., New York, 1959; pp. 256–259.

Murphy, J. S., *Basics of electronic computers;* John F. Rider Publisher, New York, 1958; vol. 3, pp. 1–8.

Cohen, A. A., Magnetic drum storage for digital information processing systems; *Mathematical Tables and Other Aids to Computation,* vol. 4, January, 1950; pp. 31–39.

May, M. *et al.,* A high speed small size magnetic drum memory for subminiature computers; *Proceedings of the 1959 Eastern Joint Computer Conference,* Boston, 1–3 December, 1959; pp. 190–199.

Coil, E. A., A multi-addressable random access file system; *IRE WESCON Convention Record,* pt. 4, 1960; pp. 42–47.

Schaffer, R. R. and D. W. Gill, Design and operation of a high speed increased capacity magnetic drum; *IRE Convention Record,* pt. 2, 1961; pp. 128–134.

13. Smith, C. V. L., *Electronic digital computers;* McGraw-Hill Book Co., New York, 1959; pp. 259–261.

Richards, R. K., *Digital computer components and circuits;* D. Van Nostrand Co., Princeton, N.J., 1957; pp. 318–320.

Brower, D. F., A one-turn magnetic reading and recording head for computer use; *IRE Convention Record,* pt. 4, 1955; pp. 95–100.

Hoagland, A. S., Magnetic recording head design; *Proceedings of the 1956 Western Joint Computer Conference,* San Francisco, 7–9 February, 1956; pp. 26–31.

Ferber, L. W., Flux responsive magnetic heads for low speed readout of data; *IRE Convention Record,* pt. 4, 1958; pp. 279–291.

Fau, G. J. Y., A study of the playback process of a magnetic ring head; *IBM Journal of Research and Development,* vol. 5, October, 1961; pp. 321–325.

Shew, L. F., High density magnetic head design for non-contact recording; *IRE Convention Record,* pt. 4, 1962; pp. 53–62.

14. Welsh, H. F. and V. J. Porter, A large capacity drum-file memory system; *Proceedings of the 1956 Eastern Joint Computer Conference,* New York, 10–12 December, 1956; pp. 136–139.

Farrand, W. A., An air floating disc magnetic memory unit; *IRE WESCON Convention Record,* vol. 1, pt. 4, 1957; pp. 227–230.

15. Scott, N. R., *Analog and digital computer technology;* McGraw-Hill Book Co., New York, 1960; pp. 495–500.

Ledley, R. S., *Digital computer and control engineering;* McGraw-Hill Book Co., New York, 1960; pp. 735–736.

Smith, C. V. L., *Electronic digital computers;* McGraw-Hill Book Co., New York, 1959; pp. 249–256.

Murphy, J. S., *Basics of electronic computers;* John F. Rider Publisher, New York, 1958; vol. 3, pp. 12–25.

Richards, R. K., *Digital computer components and circuits;* D. Van Nostrand Co., Princeton, N.J., 1957; pp. 320–328.

Miyata, J. J. and R. R. Hartel, The recording and reproduction of signals on a magnetic medium using saturation type recording; *IRE Transactions on Electronic Computers,* vol. EC-8, June, 1959; pp. 159–169.

Stein, I., Generalized pulse recording; *IRE Convention Record,* pt. 4, 1962; pp. 36–52.

16. Richards, R. K., *Digital computer components and circuits;* D. Van Nostrand Co., Princeton, N.J., 1957; pp. 328–330.

Lubkin, S., An improved reading system for magnetically recorded data; *IRE Transactions on Electronic Computers,* vol. EC-3, September, 1954; pp. 22–25.

Hoagland, A. S., A logical reading system for non-return-to-zero magnetic recording; *IRE Transactions on Electronic Computers,* vol. EC-4, September, 1955; pp. 93–95.

17. Richards, R. K., *Digital computer components and circuits;* D. Van Nostrand Co., Princeton, N.J., 1957; pp. 330–331.

Hoagland, A. S. and G. C. Bacon, High density digital magnetic recording techniques; *IRE Transactions on Electronic Computers,* vol. EC-9, March, 1960; pp. 2–11.

18. Smith, C. V. L., *Electronic digital computers,* McGraw-Hill Book Co., New York, 1959; pp. 252–253.

Williams, F. C. *et al.,* Universal high speed digital computers: a magnetic store; *Proceedings of the Institute of Electrical Engineers* (London), vol. 99, pt. 2, April, 1952; pp. 94–106.

19. Wallace, R. L., Jr., The reproduction of magnetically recorded signals; *Bell System Technical Journal,* vol. 30, October, 1951; pp. 1145–1173.

20. Potter, J. T. and P. C. Michel, A high density recording system; *IRE Transactions on Electronic Computers,* vol. PGEC-1, December, 1952; pp. 60–72.

Fuller, H. W. *et al.,* Techniques for increasing storage density of magnetic drum systems; *Proceedings of the 1954 Eastern Joint Computer Conference,* Philadelphia, 8–10 December, 1954; pp. 16–21

Seader, L. D., Magnetic recording head selection switch; *IBM Journal of Research and Development,* vol. 2, January, 1948; pp. 36–42.

Killen, D. E., Very high density digital magnetic recording; *IRE Convention Record,* pt. 2, 1960; pp. 109–113.

Hoagland, A. S. and G. C. Bacon, High density digital magnetic recording techniques; *Proceedings of the IRE,* vol. 49, January, 1961; pp. 258–267.

21. Welsh, H. F. and V. J. Porter, A large capacity drum-file memory system; *Proceedings of the 1956 Eastern Joint Computer Conference,* New York, 10–12 December, 1956; pp. 136–139.

Noyes, T. and W. E. Dickenson, Engineering design of a magnetic disc random access memory; *Proceedings of the 1956 Western Joint Computer Conference,* San Francisco, 7–9 February, 1956; pp. 42–44.

Axel, G. J., Univac ® Randex-II random access storage system; *Proceedings of the 1960 Eastern Joint Computer Conference,* New York, 13–15 December, 1960; pp. 189–204.

22. Murphy, J. S., *Basics of electronic computers;* John F. Rider Publisher, New York, 1958; vol. 3, pp. 10–11.

Richards, R. K., *Digital computer components and circuits;* D. Van Nostrand Co., Princeton, N.J., 1957; pp. 296–297.

23. Scott, N. R., *Analog and digital computer technology;* McGraw-Hill Book Co., New York, 1960; pp. 500–501.

Flores, I., *Computer logic;* Prentice-Hall, Englewood Cliffs, N.J., 1960; pp. 331–343.

Richards, R. K., *Digital computer components and circuits;* D. Van Nostrand Co., Princeton, N.J., 1957; pp. 342–347.

24. Buslik, W. S., The IBM magnetic tape reader and recorder; *Review of Input Output Equipment used in Digital Computing; Joint IRE-AIEE-ACM Conference,* New York, 10–12 December, 1952; pp. 86–90.

Brumbaugh, R., A new tape handler for computer applications; *Proceedings of the 1956 Western Joint Computer Conference,* San Francisco, 7–9 February, 1956; pp. 36–39.

Baybick, S. and R. E. Montijo, An RCA high performance tape transport equipment; *IRE Convention Record,* pt. 4, 1957; pp. 96–101.

25. Eckert, W. J. and R. Jones, *Faster, faster;* McGraw-Hill Book Co., New York, 1955; chapter 4.

Lawrance, R. B. *et al.,* Apparatus for magnetic storage on three-inch wide tapes; *Proceedings of the 1956 Eastern Joint Computer Conference,* New York, 10–12 December, 1956; pp. 84–90.

Lawrance, R. B., An advanced magnetic tape system for data processing;

Proceedings of the 1959 Eastern Joint Computer Conference, Boston, 1–3 December, 1959; pp. 181–189.

Baybick, S. and R. E. Montijo, An RCA high performance tape transport system; *Proceedings of the 1957 Western Joint Computer Conference,* Los Angeles, 26–28 February, 1957; pp. 52–56.

26. Thompson, B. W. and D. F. Eldridge, Achieving maximum pulse packing densities and transfer rates; *IRE WESCON Convention Record,* pt. 4, 1958; pp. 48–53.

27. Smith, C. V. L., *Electronic digital computers;* McGraw-Hill Book Co., New York, 1959; pp. 286–300.

Richards, R. K., *Digital computer components and circuits;* D. Van Nostrand Co., Princeton, N.J., 1957; chapter 8.

28. Bozorth, R. M., Magnetic materials; *Scientific American;* January, 1955; pp. 68 *ff. passim.*

Hogan, C. L., Ferrites; *Scientific American;* June, 1960; pp. 92 *ff. passim.*

Meyerhoff, A. J. *et al., Digital applications of magnetic devices;* John Wiley and Sons, New York, 1960; chapters 1–5.

29. Freeman, J. R., Pulse response of ferrite memory cores; *Proceedings of the IRE WESCON Computer Sessions,* Los Angeles, 25–27 August, 1954; pp. 50–61.

Meyerhoff, A. J. *et al., Digital applications of magnetic devices;* John Wiley and Sons, New York, 1960; p. 46.

30. Scott, N. R., *Analog and digital computer technology;* McGraw-Hill Book Co., New York, 1960; p. 473.

Richards, R. K., *Digital computer components and circuits;* D. Van Nostrand Co., Princeton, N.J., 1957; pp. 392–395.

Buck, D. A. and W. I. Frank, Non-destructive sensing of magnetic cores; *Transactions of the American Institute of Electrical Engineers,* pt. 1, Communications and electronics, vol. 72, January, 1954; pp. 822–830.

31. Widrow, B., A radio frequency non-destructive readout for magnetic core memories; *IRE Transactions on Electronic Computers;* vol. EC-3, December, 1954; pp. 12–15.

32. Thorenson, R. and W. R. Arsenault, A new non-destructive read for magnetic cores; *Proceedings of the 1955 Western Joint Computer Conference,* Los Angeles, 1–3 March, 1955; pp. 111–116.

33. Papoulis, A., Non-destructive readout of magnetic cores; *Proceedings of the IRE,* vol. 42, August, 1954; pp. 1283–1288.

Lambert, L. M., Non-destructive readout of metallic-tape computer cores; *IRE Transactions on Electronic Computers,* vol. EC-8, December, 1959; pp. 470–474.

Tillman, R. M., Fluxlock—a non-destructive . . . high speed memory technique . . . using cores; *IRE Transactions on Electronic Computers,* vol. EC-9, September, 1960; pp. 323–328.

34. Scott, N. R., *Analog and digital computer technology;* McGraw-Hill Book Co., New York, 1960; pp. 468–469.

Auerbach, I. L., Static memory for the ENIAC; *Proceedings of the Association for Computing Machinery,* Pittsburgh, 2–3 May, 1952; pp. 213–222.

35. Scott, N. R., *Analog and digital computer technology;* McGraw-Hill Book Co., New York, 1960; pp. 445–453.

Ledley, R. S., *Digital computer and control engineering;* McGraw-Hill Book Co., New York, 1960; pp. 724–726.

Murphy, J. S., *Basics of electronic computers;* John F. Rider Publisher, New York, 1958; vol. 2, pp. 78–87; vol. 3, pp. 26–36.

Meyerhoff, A. J. et al., *Digital applications of magnetic devices;* John Wiley and Sons, New York, 1960; chapters 22–26.

Smith, C. V. L., *Electronic digital computers;* McGraw-Hill Book Co., New York, 1959; pp. 286–300.

Forrester, J. W., Digital information storage in three dimensions; *Journal of Applied Physics,* vol. 22, January, 1951; pp. 44–48.

Papian, W. N., A coincidence current magnetic memory cell for the storage of digital information; *Proceedings of the IRE,* vol. 40, April, 1952; pp. 475–478.

Papian, W. N., The MIT magnetic core memory; *Proceedings of the 1953 Easter⌐ Joint Computer Conference,* Washington, 8–10 December, 1953; pp. 37–43.

Stuart-Williams, R., Magnetic cores, characteristics, and applications; *Automatic Control,* May, 1961; pp. 56 *ff. passim.*

36. Scott, N. R., *Analog and digital computer technology;* McGraw-Hill Book Co., New York, 1960; pp. 453–462.

Morgan, W. L., Bibliography of digital magnetic circuits and materials; *IRE Transactions on Electronic Computers,* vol. EC-8, January, 1959; pp. 148–158.

37. Rajchman, J. A., Myriabit magnetic core matrix memory; *Proceedings of the IRE,* vol. 41, October, 1953; pp. 1407–1421.

38. Scott, N. R., *Analog and digital computer technology;* McGraw-Hill Book Co., New York, 1960; pp. 463–468.

Richards, R. K., *Digital computer components and circuits;* D. Van Nostrand Co., Princeton, N.J., 1957; pp. 381–390.

Rajchman, J. A., Myriabit magnetic core matrix memory; *Proceedings of the IRE,* vol. 41, October, 1953; pp. 1407–1421.

Carter, I. P. V., A new core switch for magnetic matrix stores and other purposes; *IRE Transactions on Electronic Computers,* vol. EC-9, June, 1960; pp. 176–191.

Christopherson, W. A., Matrix switch system for a low-cost magnetic core memory; *IRE Transactions on Electronic Computers,* vol. EC-10, June, 1961; pp. 238–246.

Minnick, R. C. and J. L. Haynes, Magnetic core access switches; *IRE Transactions on Electronic Computers,* vol. EC-11, February, 1962; pp. 352–368.

39. Scott, N. R., *Analog and digital computer technology;* McGraw-Hill Book Co., New York, 1960; p. 470.

Edwards, D. B. G., Ferrite core memory systems with rapid cycle times; *Proceedings of the Institute of Electrical Engineers* (London), vol. 107, pt. B, November, 1960; pp. 585–598.

Raffel, J. and S. Bradspies, Experiments on a three-core cell for high speed memories; *IRE Convention Record,* pt. 4, 1955; pp. 64–69.

40. Meyerhoff, A. J. et al., *Digital applications of magnetic devices;* John Wiley and Sons, New York, 1960; p. 383.

Smith, C. V. L., *Electronic digital computers;* McGraw-Hill Book Co., New York, 1959; pp. 290–292.

41. Smith, C. V. L., *Electronic digital computers;* McGraw-Hill Book Co., New York, 1959; pp. 295–296.

Meyerhoff, A. J. et al., *Digital applications of magnetic devices;* John Wiley and Sons, New York, 1960; p. 384.

Papian, W. N., A coincidence current magnetic memory cell for the storage of digital information; *Proceedings of the IRE,* vol. 40, April, 1952; pp. 475–478.

42. Mitchell, J. L. and K. H. Olsen, TX-0, A transistor computer with a 256 × 256 memory; *Proceedings of the 1956 Eastern Joint Computer Conference,* New York, 10–12 December, 1956; pp. 93–101.

Best, R. L., Memory units in the Lincoln TX-2; *Proceedings of the 1957 Western Joint Computer Conference,* Los Angeles, 26–28 February, 1957; pp. 160–167.

Smith, C. V. L., *Electronic digital computers;* McGraw-Hill Book Co., New York, 1959; pp. 296–298.

43. Allen, C. A. et al., Three-dimensional core memory accommodates one million bits; *Electronics,* 12 May, 1961; pp. 68–71.

44. Haynes, M. K., Multi-dimensional magnetic memory selection systems; *IRE Transactions on Electronic Computers,* vol. PGEC-1, December, 1952; pp. 35–42.

Merwin, R. E., The IBM 705 EDPM memory system; *IRE Transactions on Electronic Computers,* vol. EC-5, December, 1956; pp. 219–223.

Bartik, W. J. and T. H. Bonn, A small coincident-current magnetic memory; *IRE Transactions on Electronic Computers,* vol. EC-5, June, 1956; pp. 73–78.

Foss, E. D. and R. S. Partridge, A 32,000 word magnetic core memory; *IBM Journal of Research and Development,* vol. 1, April, 1957; pp. 102–109.

Rhoades, W. H. et al., A 0.7-microsecond ferrite core memory; *IBM Journal of Research and Development,* vol. 5, July, 1961; pp. 174–182.

Allen, C. A. et al., A 2.18-microsecond megabit core storage unit; *IRE Transactions on Electronic Computers,* vol. EC-10, January, 1961; pp. 233–237.

McQuillan, J. D. R., The design problems of a megabit storage matrix for use in a high speed computer; *IRE Transactions on Electronic Computers,* vol. EC-11, February, 1962; pp. 390–404.

45. Goldstick, G. H. and E. F. Klein, Design of a memory sense amplifier; *IRE Transactions on Electronic Computers,* vol. EC-11, April, 1962; pp. 236–253.

46. McMahon, R. E., Impulse switching of ferrites; *Proceedings of the 1958 Eastern Joint Computer Conference,* Philadelphia, 3–5 December, 1958; pp. 31–33.

Sferrino, V. J., Transistor circuit technique for a core memory with 500-millimicrosecond cycle time; *IRE WESCON Convention Record,* pt. 4, August, 1959; pp. 3–15.

McMahon, R. E., Impulse switching of ferrites; *Proceedings of the Solid State Circuits Conference,* Philadelphia, February, 1959; pp. 16–17.

Stuart-Williams, R., An evaluation of partial switching in storage applications; *Solid State Journal,* vol. 2, November, 1961; pp. 25–32.

47. Rajchman, J. A., Ferrite aperture plate for random access memory; *Proceed-*

ings of the 1956 Eastern Joint Computer Conference, 10–12 December, 1956; pp. 107–115.

Rajchman, J. A., Ferrite aperture plate for random access memory; *Proceedings of the IRE,* vol. 45, March, 1957; pp. 325–334.

Rumble, W. G. and C. S. Warren, Coincident current applications of ferrite apertured plates; *IRE WESCON Convention Record,* pt. 4, 1958; pp. 62–65.

48. Wanlass, C. L. and S. D. Wanlass, BIAX high speed magnetic computer element; *IRE WESCON Convention Record,* pt. 4, 1959; pp. 40–44.

49. Pohm, A. V. and S. M. Rubens, A compact coincident current memory; *Proceedings of the 1956 Eastern Joint Computer Conference,* New York, 10–12 December, 1956; pp. 120–123.

Bittman, E. E., Thin film memories; *IRE Transactions on Electronic Computers,* vol. EC-8, June, 1959; pp. 92–97.

Raffel, J. I., Operating characteristics of a thin film memory; *Journal of Applied Physics,* vol. 30, April, 1959; pp. 605–625.

Dietrich, W. *et al.,* Nanosecond switching in thin magnetic films; *IBM Journal of Research and Development,* vol. 4, April, 1960; pp. 189–196.

Pohm, A. V. and E. N. Mitchell, Magnetic film memories—a survey; *IRE Transactions on Electronic Computers,* vol. EC-9, September, 1960; pp. 308–314.

Broadbent, K. D. *et al.,* Characteristics of a multiple magnetic plane thin film memory device; *Proceedings of the 1960 Western Joint Computer Conference,* San Francisco, 3–5 May, 1960; pp. 97–102.

Raffel, J. I. *et al.,* Magnetic film memory design; *Proceedings of the IRE,* vol. 49, January, 1961; pp. 155–164.

Looney, D. H., Magnetic devices for digital computers; *Datamation,* August, 1961; pp. 51–55.

Turnquist, R. D. *et al.,* A compact 166-kilobit film memory; *IRE Convention Record,* pt. 4, 1962; pp. 63–72.

50. Long, R., Electrodeposited memory elements for a non-destructive memory; *Journal of Applied Physics,* vol. 31, May, 1960; pp. 123–124.

51. Meier, D., Magnetic rod store element; *Journal of Applied Physics,* vol. 30, January, 1959; pp. 122–123. Also: *Proceedings of the Electronic Components Conference,* May, 1960; pp. 122–128.

52. Smith, C. V. L., *Electronic digital computers;* McGraw-Hill Book Co., New York, 1959; pp. 300–302.

Rajchman, J. A. and A. W. Lo, The transfluxor; *Proceedings of the 1956 Western Joint Computer Conference,* San Francisco, 7–9 February, 1956; pp. 109–118. Also: *Proceedings of the IRE,* vol. 44, March, 1956; pp. 321–332.

Lawrance, W. W., Jr., Recent developments in very high speed magnetic storage techniques; *Proceedings of the 1956 Eastern Joint Computer Conference,* New York, 10–12 December, 1956; pp. 101–103.

Rajchman, J. A., Magnetic switching; *Proceedings of the 1958 Western Joint Computer Conference,* Los Angeles, 6–8 May, 1958; pp. 107–117.

Hammel, D. G. *et al.,* A multiload transfluxor memory; *Proceedings of the 1959 Western Joint Computer Conference,* San Francisco, 3–5 March, 1959; pp. 14–21.

Petschauer, R. J. and R. D. Turnquist, A non-destructive readout film memory; *Proceedings of the 1961 Western Joint Computer Conference,* Los Angeles, 9–11 May, 1961; pp. 411–425.

53. Scott, N. R., *Analog and digital computer technology;* McGraw-Hill Book Co., New York, 1960; pp. 480–483.

   Rajchman, J. A. and A. W. Lo, The transfluxor; *Proceedings of the 1956 Western Joint Computer Conference,* San Francisco, 7–9 February, 1956; pp. 109–118.

54. Yovits, M. C., *Large capacity memory techniques for computing systems;* Macmillan Co., New York, 1962.

   Hoagland, A. S., Mass storage; *Proceedings of the IRE,* vol. 50, May, 1962; pp. 1087–1092.

55. Axel, G. J., Univac Randex-II random access storage system; *Proceedings of the 1960 Eastern Joint Computer Conference,* New York, 13–15 December, 1960; pp. 189–204.

   Hollander, G. L., Quasi-random access memory systems; *Proceedings of the 1956 Eastern Joint Computer Conference,* New York, 10–12 December, 1956; pp. 128–135.

   Fuller, H. W. *et al.,* The design and systems aspects of the high density file drum; *Proceedings of the 1958 Western Joint Computer Conference,* Los Angeles, 6–8 May, 1958; pp. 197–203.

56. Richards, R. K., *Digital computer components and circuits;* D. Van Nostrand Co., Princeton, N.J., 1957; pp. 349–350.

   Pearson, R. T., The development of the flexible disc magnetic recorder; *Proceedings of the IRE,* vol. 49, January, 1961; pp. 164–174.

   Hoagland, A. S., A high track-density servo-access system for magnetic recording disc storage; *IBM Journal of Research and Development,* vol. 5, October, 1961; pp. 287–296.

57. Macdonald, D. N., Datafile—A new tool for extensive file storage; *Proceedings of the 1956 Eastern Joint Computer Conference,* New York, 10–12 December, 1956; pp. 124–128.

58. King, G. W. *et al.,* Photographic techniques for information storage; *Proceedings of the IRE,* vol. 41, October, 1953; pp. 1421–1428.

59. Lovell, C. A., High speed high-capacity photographic memory; *Proceedings of the 1958 Eastern Joint Computer Conference,* Philadelphia, 3–5 December, 1958; pp. 34–38.

   Hoover, C. W., Jr. *et al.,* System design of the flying spot store; *Bell System Technical Journal,* vol. 38, March, 1959; pp. 365–401.

60. Wier, J. M., A high speed permanent storage device; *IRE Transactions on Electronic Computers,* vol. EC-4, March, 1955; pp. 16–20.

61. Kilburn, T. and R. N. Grimsdale, A digital computer store with very short read time; *Proceedings of the Institute of Electrical Engineers* (London), vol. 107, pt. B, January, 1960; pp. 17–18.

62. De Buske, J. J. *et al.,* A card changeable non-destructive readout twistor store; *Proceedings of the 1959 Western Joint Computer Conference,* San Francisco, 3–5 March, 1959; pp. 41–46.

   Penn, T. C. and D. G. Fischer, A word-oriented transistor driven non-destructive readout memory; *Proceedings of the 1960 Western Joint Computer Conference,* San Francisco, 3–5 May, 1960; pp. 83–90.

   Macpherson, D. H. and R. K. York, Semipermanent storage by capacitive coupling; *IRE Transactions on Electronic Computers,* vol. EC-10, September, 1961; pp. 446–451.

Gianola, U. F., Non-destructive memory employing a domain oriented steel wire; *Journal of Applied Physics,* vol. 29, May, 1958; pp. 849–853. Also: Yovits, M. C., *Large capacity memory techniques for computing systems;* Macmillan Co., New York, 1962; pp. 177–194.

Foglia, H. R. *et al.,* Card capacitor—a semipermanent read-only memory; *IBM Journal of Research and Development,* vol. 5, January, 1961; pp. 67–68.

Bloom, L. *et al.,* Card random access memory—function and use; *Proceedings of the 1961 Eastern Joint Computer Conference,* Washington, 12–14 December, 1961; pp. 147–157.

Ishidate, T. *et al.,* Eddycard memory—a semipermanent storage; *Proceedings of the 1961 Eastern Joint Computer Conference,* Washington, 12–14 December, 1961; pp. 144–208.

63. Kilburn, T. *et al.,* One-level storage system; *IRE Transactions on Electronic Computers,* vol. EC-11, April, 1962, pp. 233–237.

64. Richards, R. K., *Digital computer components and circuits;* D. Van Nostrand Co., Princeton, N.J., 1957; pp. 297–304.

Holt, A. W., An experimental rapid access memory using diodes and capacitors; *Proceedings of the Association for Computing Machinery,* Toronto, 12–14 September, 1952; pp. 133–141.

Holt, W. W., Prototype diode-capacitor memory; *Proceedings of the Argonne Conference on Digital Computers,* August, 1953.

65. Anderson, J. R., Ferroelectric elements for digital computers and switching systems; *Electrical Engineering,* vol. 71, October, 1952; pp. 916–922.

Pulvari, C. F., The snapping dipoles of ferroelectrics as a memory element for digital computers; *Proceedings of the 1953 Western Joint Computer Conference,* Los Angeles, 4–6 February, 1953; pp. 140–159.

Pulvari, C. F., Memory matrix using ferroelectric condensors as bistable elements; *Journal of the Association for Computing Machinery,* vol. 2, July, 1955; pp. 169–185.

66. Buck, D. A., The cryotron—superconductive computer component; *Proceedings of the IRE,* vol. 44, April, 1956; pp. 482–493.

Crowe, J. W., Trapped-flux superconducting memory; *IBM Journal of Research and Development,* vol. 1, October, 1957; pp. 294–303.

Gavin, R. L., An analysis of the operation of a persistent supercurrent memory cell; *IBM Journal of Research and Development,* vol. 1, October, 1957; pp. 304–308.

Matthias, B. T., Superconductivity; *Scientific American,* November, 1957; pp. 92 *ff. passim.*

Newhouse, V. L. *et al.,* The crossed-film cryotron and its application to digital computer circuits; *Proceedings of the 1959 Eastern Joint Computer Conference,* Boston, 1–3 December, 1959; pp. 255–260.

Johnston, R. C., Cryosar memory design; *IRE Transactions on Electronic Computers,* vol. EC-10, December, 1961; pp. 712–717.

Burns, L. L., Jr. *et al.,* Coincident-current superconductive memory; *IRE Transactions on Electronic Computers,* vol. EC-10, September, 1961; pp. 438–446.

Ittner, W. B., III and C. J. Kraus, Superconducting computers; *Scientific American*, July, 1961; pp. 124 *ff. passim.*

Macquire, T., Superconductive computers; *Electronics*, 24 November, 1961; pp. 45–51.

Davies, P. M., A superconductive associative memory; *Proceedings of the 1962 Spring Joint Computer Conference*, San Francisco, 1–3 May, 1962; pp. 79–88.

Newhouse, V. L. and R. E. Fruin, A cryogenic data-addressed memory; *Proceedings of the 1962 Spring Joint Computer Conference*, San Francisco, 1–3 May, 1962; pp. 89–100.

Bardeen, J., Review of the present status of the theory of superconductivity; *IBM Journal of Research and Development*, vol. 6, January, 1962; pp. 3–11.

67. Bobeck, A. H., A new element suitable for large sized memory arrays—the twistor; *Bell System Technical Journal*, vol. 36, November, 1957; pp. 1319–1340.

Schwartz, S. J. and J. S. Sallo, Electrodeposited twistor and bit wire components; *IRE Transactions on Electronic Computers*, vol. EC-8, December, 1959; pp. 465–469.

Looney, D. H., A twistor matrix memory for semipermanent information; *Proceedings of the 1959 Western Joint Computer Conference*, San Francisco, 3–5 March, 1959; pp. 36–41.

Gray, R. L., An electrically alterable non-destructive twistor memory; *IRE Transactions on Electronic Computers*, vol. EC-9, December, 1960; pp. 451–455.

Barrett, W. A. *et al.*, A card changeable permanent magnet twistor memory of large capacity; *IRE Transactions on Electronic Computers*, vol. EC-10, September, 1961; pp. 451–461.

68. Slade, A. E. and H. McMahon, A cryotron catalog memory system; *Proceedings of the 1956 Eastern Joint Computer Conference*, New York, 10–12 December, 1956; pp. 115–119.

Seeber, R. R., Jr., Associative self-sorting memory; *Proceedings of the 1960 Eastern Joint Computer Conference*, New York, 13–15 December, 1960; pp. 179–188.

Kiseda, J. R. *et al.*, A magnetic associative memory; *IBM Journal of Research and Development*, vol. 5, April, 1961; pp. 106–122.

Seeber, R. R., Jr. and A. B. Lindquist, Associative memory with ordered retrieval; *IBM Journal of Research and Development*, vol. 6, January, 1962; pp. 126–136.

Newhouse, V. L. and R. E. Fruin, A cryogenic data-addressed memory; *Proceedings of the 1962 Spring Joint Computer Conference*, San Francisco, 1–3 May, 1962; pp. 89–100. Also: *Electronics*, 4 May, 1962; pp. 31–36.

Davies, P. M., A superconductive associative memory; *Proceedings of the 1962 Spring Joint Computer Conference*, San Francisco, 1–3 May, 1962; pp. 79–88.

McDermid, W. L. and H. W. Peterson, A magnetic associative memory system; *IBM Journal of Research and Development*, vol. 5, January, 1961; pp. 59–62.

Kiesda, J. R. *et al.*, A magnetic associative memory system; *IBM Journal of Research and Development*, vol. 5, April, 1961; pp. 106–121.

69. Newell, A. (editor), *Information processing Language-V manual;* Prentice-Hall, Englewood Cliffs, N.J., 1961.
70. King, C. F., Factors affecting the choice of memory; *Proceedings of the 1961 Western Joint Computer Conference,* Los Angeles, 9–11 May, 1961; pp. 405–410.
71. Shiffman, B., Minimum time programming on a drum computer; *IRE Convention Record,* pt. 4, 1958; pp. 327–329.
   Knuth, D. E., Minimizing drum latency time; *Journal of the Association for Computing Machinery,* vol. 8, April, 1961; pp. 119–150.

EXERCISES

12.1. Sketch in detail the circuit diagram of the input logic of a delay store. Decide on a logical convention and select the appropriate diode gates. Repeat the above except use NOR gates.

12.2. Draw a block diagram showing all the necessary functional elements necessary to handle the addressing of a delay store. Include all information flow paths, gates including inputs from the control, registers, decoders, counters, etc. Assume that the store has the structure indicated in the example on page 12.6. Specify for your arrangement whether the address is to be delivered from the control serially or in parallel.

12.3. Describe how a delay store can be organized as a parallel store. As a serial-parallel store for a binary-coded-decimal machine. Indicate how information is arranged in the store, how the addressing is arranged, and draw a functional block diagram.

12.4. In order to address a delay store the origin or home position of the delay loop must be known. Must there be a special pattern of information in the loop to mark the origin? Must the origin be marked? How is this situation dealt with?

12.5. Consider an electrostatic storage tube with 1024 points on its face. A 10-bit address will be required to select a desired point. If the array of points is a square of 32×32, draw a block diagram illustrating how the address will be utilized to direct the beam to a desired position. Include all information flow paths, gates, registers, amplifiers, decoders, etc.

Suppose that the array has the following shape:

Repeat the above part. For your arrangement of the addressing circuit, indicate which address corresponds to what points on the tube.

12.6. Show how an electrostatic store can be arranged for a serial-parallel transmission of information. For the storage of 256 4-bit characters, how many tubes are required? How many output terminals are there?

12.7. Figure 12.6 is incomplete in some ways. For example, there is nothing to prevent more than one procedure from happening at the same time. Assume that the store contains two control toggles; one of them is used to designate whether the store is regenerating or not; and the other, whether the store is reading or writing. These toggles will, of course, be set by signals from the control. The store is to be regenerating unless it is reading or writing. Reading or writing will be as described on page 12.10.

Draw a logical diagram of the two toggles and all gates required to make the store function properly. The proper address must be supplied to the deflection circuits depending on the kind of cycle in process. For each kind of three cycles (read, write, regenerate), drawing a timing diagram which indicates when events start and stop; e.g., when are the deflection signals established, when must information be presented for writing, when can information be accepted during reading.

12.8. A magnetic head is obviously not a lossless device, since it dissipates energy whenever current flows through its windings. Hence energy is dissipated during the reading operation of a magnetic drum, tape, or disc. Does this energy come from the magnetic field associated with the stored information? If so, there is the risk that repeated reading of the stored information will gradually deplete the energy in the stored field, and hence eventually destroy the information. Where can this energy come from? Defend your answer.

12.9. Draw a functional block diagram showing how the addressing can be handled for each of the three cases in the example on page 12.17. Include all information flow paths, gates with control inputs, counters, decoders, etc. Assume that

    (a) only an origin mark is available,
    (b) a sufficient number of address tracks is available to record the complete address of each angular position.

Modify the arrangement to provide a 4-to-1 interlace. For each case above, specify the maximum and minimum access times. Take the drum rotation rate to be R revolutions per minute.

12.10. Reconsider exercise 12.4 in the light of the magnetic drum. Why is the origin position of the drum marked? Must it be marked? Suppose that neither an origin mark nor address tracks were available. Could the drum be addressed properly?

12.11. Suppose that HYPAC-I were to get a secondary store consisting of four drums of 2^{15} words each. Decide on the appropriate new kinds of instructions that will have to be added to the repertoire to provide

    (a) variable block lengths,
    (b) fixed block lengths.

Describe how each kind of instruction will work, and what the role of its address part will be. Indicate how addressing will be arranged for the secondary store.

12.12. Is an erase head required in an RZ recording scheme? Would there be any advantage to providing one? Could it be used for the various ways of organizing the information arrangement in a drum store?

12.13. Consider a return-to-bias recording scheme for a magnetic drum. Is an erase head required in order to have such a store operate properly. What is considered to be the "erased state" in this case? Is there a way to write both digits explicitly in a return-to-bias scheme? Keep in mind the requirement to write new information into cells.

12.14. The proposed drum store for HYPAC-I (exercise 12.11) is to provide full parallel flow of information. A complete HYPAC-I word will be stored, therefore, in nineteen tracks along an element of the drum parallel to the axis. In view of this, discuss the desirability of the various recording techniques, and select a technique which provides required features but is economically preferable. Does your answer depend on whether the transfer is fixed or variable block length?

12.15. Consider a drum with the same arrangement of storage loops (page 12.34) as that for the delay units in the example on page 12.6 one 256-word unit, etc. Describe in detail how the address selection is handled. Draw a functional block diagram including information flow paths, gates, toggles, decoders, etc.

12.16. Show that the corner digit in a rectangular parity check scheme for a magnetic-tape store can be made to be correct. What tape recording format is required? Does the format depend on the method of recording?

12.17. A magnetic-tape tertiary store is proposed for the HYPAC-I. It is to contain eight transports, and is to include a parity checking scheme. Information on the tape is to be grouped into records and into files. Decide on an appropriate format representing the information on tape—number of tracks, position of the parity check digit(s), the position of word information, etc. Decide on a method for indicating end-of-record and end-of-file positions. Keep in mind that information should be packed as efficiently as possible on the tape in order to maximize the flow rate. Decide on an appropriate set of operation parts to be added to the HYPAC-I repertoire, and describe how each kind of instruction will work and what will be the role of its address part.

Do this exercise for

    (a) fixed block length,

    (b) variable block length.

12.18. In a quadrature flux non-destructive reading scheme, how are the 1- and the 0-states distinguished?

12.19. Deduce the details of an operational cycle of the externally selected magnetic core store. Sketch the waveshape of the drive which is applied to each of the coordinate selection wires. Assume that a fast read cycle is to be provided. Describe both the read and the write cycles.

12.20. The primary store of HYPAC-I is to be a parallel magnetic core store. The control will furnish an address and a request to read or write. Describe the equipment necessary to make the store behave properly, and to present a non-destructive appearance to the rest of the machine.

Decide on a method for handling the write part of the cycle. Indicate why you have picked it. Sketch the waveshape of the X and the Y signals for a read and a write cycle. Diagram a group of pulse sources and a circuit for combining their outputs to supply the required X and Y drives. In particular, show the details of combining the signal sources to provide the write-0 and write-1 X and Y drives.

Draw a functional block diagram of the store as you have arranged it. Show all information flow paths, gates with control and timing inputs, decoders, timing signals, special registers, etc.

12.21. In the previous exercise, modify the arrangement of timing signals and the means for combining them to provide staggered drives for the X and Y drives during the read part of the cycle. Assume that the array is square.

12.22. Extend the previous exercise to include a post-write disturb signal within the store cycle.

12.23. Extend the previous exercise to include a write-strobe signal within the cycle. The strobe is to follow the second (and later) select current by some prescribed time interval. Indicate how you would arrange for such a delay.

12.24. Assume that the magnetic core store designed over the previous several exercises is to be driven by a magnetic switch. Since the dimension of the array (32) is not an even power of 2, the arrangement outlined on page 12.58 is not suitable. Deduce a scheme for using a core switch in a situation such as this one. If necessary, adapt your previous design to accommodate any special constraints that the core switch implies.

12.25. Consider a core store which is end-fire driven for reading. Describe one or more schemes for writing into such a store. Sketch the various driving signals into it.

12.26. Map the addresses of a 4096 ($= 2^{10}$) cell store onto a non-square core matrix of dimensions 16×64.

12.27. Sketch the wiring details of a square matrix containing 3-hole coincident flux devices. Keep in mind the problem of stray magnetic coupling between various windings and try to keep such spurious couplings to a minimum by appropriately arranging the geometry of the wiring.

12.28. Describe what special arrangements would have to be made to convert one fourth of HYPAC-I's core store to a read-only store.

12.29. Consider a non-destructive read scheme which elastically swings the flux vector through an angle θ. Estimate the magnitude of the output voltage compared to the destructive reading of the same magnetic element.

PROBLEMS

12.1. Draw the details of a circuit which will accept a 10-bit address, and produce the appropriate deflection voltages for an electrostatic store. The deflection voltages must be within 0.1% of their final position within 1 μsec. The precision of the voltage level generated for deflection must be ½ volt independent of the absolute level of voltage (and hence, independent of the address). The total peak deflection voltage must be 100 volts. (If you elect transistor technology, assume that a linear amplifier with a gain of 10 is available). See pages 8.92 to 8.93 for appropriate characteristics curves.

12.2. For the recording scheme selected in exercise 12.14, indicate how you would recover the information from the read-back signals from the heads. Draw a functional block diagram and then a detailed logical diagram showing all information flow paths, all gates with control inputs, all address selection and routing circuits, toggles, etc. necessary to completely govern both reading and writing of the drum.

12.3. Discuss and contrast the several ways of recording information in a magnetic surface from the point of view of such factors as

(a) density of storage,
(b) heating problems in the heads,
(c) power demands in the write drivers,
(d) amplification requirements in the read amplifier,
(e) possible economics in the design of either write or read amplifiers,
(f) sensitivity to the timing signals which control reading or writing,
(g) cost of head design,
(h) amount of electronics required.

Does there appear to be one scheme which is markedly superior to all others? Defend your answer.

12.4. In an effort to shorten the initial access time to the proposed HYPAC-I drum store (exercise 12.11), four heads are spaced 90° apart over each track. Draw a block diagram of the circuit necessary to select the appropriate head to read from. Include necessary information flow paths, gates, toggles, registers, etc. Such a circuit must compare the given address with the angular position of the drum and decide which of the four heads is to be used.

Is there some particular scheme of arranging address selection or of addressing the drum that is preferable from the viewpoint of multiple heads? Detail the circuit, using first diode logic and second, NOR logic.

12.5. The proposed tape store for HYPAC-I (exercise 12.17) is to have an independent searching mode. Each transport will be given information which locates a desired position along the tape. (The details of such information will depend on how you designed the tape system in exercise 12.17.)

Describe what equipment each tape transport must have in order to procede (either backward or forward as required) to the desired position and stop. Parity checking, if it is necessary during search, is to be included. Describe appropriate operation part(s) for controlling such a search mode. Describe what kind of instructions the repertoire must include to permit the control to query a desired transport to see if it is in the desired position.

Block diagram the array of equipment which you have decided on; include information flow paths, toggles, gates with control inputs, special registers, etc.

12.6. Deduce how the special registers for combatting skew (page 12.39) operate. What features must such registers have?

12.7. Describe what extra equipment or features must be added to the tape store of exercise 12.17 in order to read backward as well as forward. Are there any special timing problems which might arise during reverse reading?

12.8. The magnetic-tape store of exercise 12.17 is to have a check sum for each record as well as the parity check scheme you have decided on. The check sum is to be formed as information flows to or from the tape. If writing is in progress, the one-word check sum is to be written onto the tape at the end of the record. If reading is in progress, the check sum from the tape is to be compared with the check sum which has been formed as the record streamed from the tape. An indication is to be given that reading occurred correctly or not. During reading, the check-sum circuit may have to realize that the last item read is the check sum itself and not one of the words in the record. On the other hand, the programmer may not know, and hence cannot specify, the record length.

Describe the extra equipment necessary for adding this error-detecting check sum scheme. Draw a functional block diagram of the equipment including information flow paths, gates with control inputs, toggles, special registers, special adders, etc. Indicate any special timing constraints that must be observed.

12.9. Of the several ways to handle the write part of the cycle of a magnetic core store, is there one that is markedly superior to the others? Consider such factors as the cost of the drivers, the complexity of the control logic, the length of the cycle, the feasibility of core switches, the necessity of direct drive, etc. Justify your answer.

12.10. Work out the details of the two-core-per-bit end-fire store. Describe the wiring pattern of each core plane, specify the operating cycle of such a store, and discuss feasible operating speeds.

12.11. Consider the problem of providing drive currents to a magnetic core store. Such currents typically are of the order of 500 ma and must be regulated to be constant within a few percent from that figure.

Give your suggestions for designing a circuit which can economically meet the regulation requirement at such a high current level.

12.12. Consider a bulk store which consists of several magnetic discs and which is very much larger than the primary store. Why cannot it be directly addressed by means of address parts in instructions? Describe several ways in which addressing of the disc store might be arranged. How would you arrange the addressing to maximize the flow rate of information blocks whose length exceeds the capacity of one disc? (*Hint:* consider the ways in which drum or tape stores are addressed.)

12.13. Suppose that HYPAC-I were to have a disc store such as considered in the previous problem. Suppose that the size of each set of discs were 2^{20} words and that there are 8 sets of double-sided discs. Describe an appropriate addressing scheme consistent with other HYPAC-I charatceristics, including the augmentation of the store by drum and tape levels (exercises 12.11 and 12.17).

Describe a set of operation parts which the repertoire must contain to efficiently handle the flow of information between the disc and the primary store.

12.14. Means are to be provided for establishing part of HYPAC-I's core store as read-only. Two special registers are provided which can be loaded under program control. The two registers contain the addresses of the ends of the block which is to be read-only.

Describe what equipment must be added to the store and draw a functional block diagram. Include all information flow paths, gates with control and timing inputs, toggles, registers, etc. If the control attempts to write into the locked-out region, a special signal is to be sent back by the store.

12.15. By this time, in addition to its core storage (see exercises 12.11 and 12.17), HYPAC-I may well have drum, tape, and disc storage—if not read-only storage. The exchange between any level and the core level is to be autonomous in the sense of the example on page 12.81.

Describe the detailed operation of such autonomous transfers for each kind of storage. Describe the events that the autonomous "helper" control must govern and monitor. List these events in the sequence in which they must be attended to.

Draw a functional block diagram of the autonomous control. Include all information flow paths, gates, toggles, interactions with the main control and other parts of the machine, special registers, special adders, etc.

12.16. Describe how to make an associative store with conventional magnetic core techniques. Assume that half of the word is descriptive information and that the other half is associated information. A half-word of information is presented to all of the cells in the store simultaneously. Each cell which matches this half-word in corresponding columns is, so to speak, to raise a flag. All cells whose flags are up are to be read again to obtain the full word. Reading, in case of multiple matches, is to occur in the order of ascending absolute addresses.

Are coincident flux devices or cryotron devices useful for such a store? If so, describe how to make such a store from them.

12.17. Describe how to make a list store with conventional magnetic core techniques. Extra equipment is to be added to each storage cell, not for purposes of additional storage, but for the purpose of linking the cell to any other cell in the store.

It must be possible to chain together any number of cells. The number of chains, the length of chains, and the particular cells which constitute a particular chain must be controllable from the program. Are coincident flux devices or cryotrons useful for a list store? If so, describe how to utilize them.

12.18. Consider Figure 12.60. It would appear that there are sneak circuits in the array. Suppose that word 4 is selected and driven. An output is developed in the first column properly. Through a transformer in the lower right corner of the network, this output is coupled onto the undriven word-1 line. Through a second transformer on the word-1 line, some output is coupled into the third column—where there should be none.

Is this analysis correct? Do these sneak circuits exist? If so, they influence the signal-to-noise ratio on the output lines. Can you visualize any remedies for this situation?

thirteen

Control

REVIEW

The control unit of a machine is perhaps its most heterogeneous part, from both the hardware and logical point of view (1). Other sections of the machine—arithmetic unit and store, for instance—tend to have a great deal of repetition; for example, each column of a parallel adder is substantially the same as any other column. The job of control, however, is to fetch each instruction in turn from the store, to interpret each instruction, and then to activate and sequence such other parts of the machine as are necessary to execute the current instruction. Control must thus do such kinds of operations as:

1. make decisions concerning the content of an instruction or concerning some state of events in the machine;

2. establish switching paths between functional parts and within each functional part of the machine;

3. sequence events in the machine; and

4. fetch instructions from the store in the sequence intended by the programmer.

The Instruction Register

For its job, control requires a certain minimum number of functions. From the operation part of each instruction, the control must derive information which determines which information flow paths are appropriate, and what sequence of events is necessary for the given instruction. In particular, the destination and handling of the address part cannot be determined until the operation part is analyzed. The control needs access to the information in an instruction over some period of time. Hence, since the read-out signals from a store are transient, an *instruction register* is normally provided to hold statically each instruction for as long as necessary. Generally, this is until the next instruction is fetched. Even though the store may itself contain a register (as for example, one from which the store rewrites to overcome an inherent destructive reading), this register cannot be used to staticize the instruction because the store will be reused in the course of executing many instructions.

Under special circumstances, it might be possible to omit the instruction register. For example, in a serial machine, the operation part of an instruction can be analyzed as the instruction flows serially from the store. In effect, instead of staticizing the instruction, the consequences of the instruction are staticized. To obtain the address part, a second access to the same cell of the store will be required. Such a machine is slower because the fetching of each instruction requires two consultations of the store instead of one. The tradeoff is clear: at the cost of a slower machine, equipment has been saved.

Generally, however, there is an instruction register of some length. It could be long enough to accommodate only an address part; but most often it is one instruction long, and occasionally two instructions long. Such a register is similar to the ones of the arithmetic unit. It includes a group of storage devices (toggles), gates for writing information in, gates for reading information out. The instruction register does not usually require shifting properties, although if particular circumstances require it, such a feature can be added. The principal difference between the instruction register and a simple arithmetic register is likely to be the length.

Decoder

The operation part for each instruction contains all the information which the control will need to completely execute the instruction. As we know, the operation part is expressed in a numeric code; and from the information in this group of digits, the control must (in effect) derive new information which will be used to establish information flow paths, sequence operations in other parts of the machine, and perhaps even determine future events within the control proper. The network which inspects the digital information in the operation part and produces unique information for each one is called the *de-*

coder. There may be secondary decoding operations in complex instructions. For example, a given instruction may use a short address field to select one of a group of input-output devices. After the decoder has established that a given instruction is an input (or output) one, the short address field will have to be decoded to determine which input (or output) device is to be connected to the main information channels of the machine. Conceivably, the control may have more than one decoder, or may time sequentially use the same one for different purposes.

Suppose that the operation part is six bits in length. Sixty-four different binary 6-tuples are available and can be used to identify up to sixty-four different kinds of instructions. The sixty-four groups are the numeric symbols (i.e., *machine alphabet*) which represent the operation parts. There is another point from which to view this.

Each column of the 6-tuple can contain either 0 or 1. Hence each column can be regarded as representing a Boolean variable, and in a given instance, the column contains the current value of that variable. Call the six columns (in our example) *A*, *B*, *C*, *D*, *E*, and *F*, and let the variables represented have the same symbolic names. The decoder detects the sixty-four minterms of the six Boolean variables. Hence one way to build a decoder is as a decoding matrix (see page 10.15). In this example, the tetrads are decoded to a 1-of-64 representation; the binary information is decoded into a base-64 representation. Because such a matrix accepts a group of digits as inputs but produces only one output at a time, it is sometimes called a *many-to-one matrix*. Because it implements Boolean logical processes, a decoder is one of a class of circuits which are categorically called *logical networks*. We expect the decoder to be constructed from the gates described in Chapter 9.

For each minterm (and, therefore, type of instruction), the internal configuration of the machine must be established to execute the instruction at hand. The outputs from the decoder will determine such things as the routing of the address part, the choice of reading or writing of the store, the selection of communication paths, the selection of end-to-end register connections, and the routing or sequencing of signals. The outputs from the decoder considered as logical variables, become inputs to AND gates and in this way exert their influence.

EXAMPLE

Figure 13.1 shows a few operation parts from HYPAC-I, their symbolic representation as 6-tuples, and the corresponding minterms. For the Add, the

	SYMBOLIC REPRESENTATION	
OPERATION PART	(*ABCDEF*)	MINTERM
Add	010001	$\bar{A}B\bar{C}\bar{D}E\bar{F}$
Multiply	011000	$\bar{A}BC\bar{D}\bar{E}\bar{F}$
Store Acc	010100	$\bar{A}B\bar{C}D\bar{E}\bar{F}$
Right Shift Accumulator and MQ	101100	$A\bar{B}CD\bar{E}\bar{F}$

Figure 13.1.   Decoding the operation part.

Multiply, and the Store Accumulator, the address part of the instruction must be routed to the store. For the first two, the store is to be read but for the third, it is to be written. For the Right Shift Accumulator and MQ, the address part is routed to a counter. For the Multiply and the Shift, there must be an end-to-end connection between the Accumulator and the MQ. For these representative parts of these four instructions, Figure 13.2 shows an arrangement of gates which will do the job.

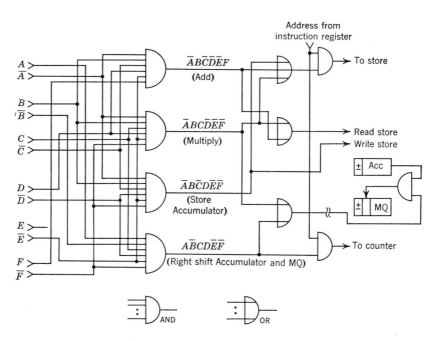

Figure 13.2.   Part of possible decoder.

Sometimes, the decoder does not have to respond to complete min-terms. In such a case, it is of course simpler. For example, if the operation part is much longer than is necessary to specify the desired number of instruction types, individual digits of the operation part may signify specific features of an instruction. Considered as a Boolean variable, an individual digit directly controls some aspect of the instruction; it does not have to be combined with other variables.

EXAMPLE

A machine has an 8-bit operation part but only forty operations in its reper-toire. One particular bit can be assigned to indicate whether the Multiply or Divide is to be rounded. Only for a few kinds of instructions, therefore, will this bit be a 1. Most of the time, it will be a 0, e.g., for a Branch, Jump, Input, Output, Store. Another bit, when a 1, might indicate that the absolute value of the information coming from the store is to be used.

If all 2^8 instruction types exist, it is unlikely that such a specific meaning can in general be ascribed to specific positions in the operation part. Each bit will have to be 1 for half of the 2^8 kinds of instructions and 0 for the other half. Various properties of the operations probably will not follow such a half-and-half split; e.g., rounding almost certainly will not be a part of exactly half the instruction types.

Instruction Counter

We now know in a broad sense what the control does with each instruction, but how does it obtain the instructions in the sequence intended by the programmer? In a multiaddress instruction format, one of the address parts might be the location of the next instruction. If so, each instruction "tells" where the next one is. Without such explicit information, some ground rule is adopted which indicates where successive instructions are located relative to each other. Such a situation is necessary for a single-address machine, and may be true for a multiaddress one. The most common situation is that instructions are placed in cells whose addresses are numerically consecutive. The control is given the location of the start of the sequence, and must thereafter deduce for itself the addresses which specify the cells containing the remaining instructions. Given a starting address, the control is expected to thread its way through a sequence of cells whose addresses are each one larger than the preceding.

A convenient way to generate a sequence of consecutive numerical addresses is with a simple counter; hence the control contains an *instruction counter* whose contents will be used by the control as an address of a cell from which to fetch an instruction. The initial number in this counter must be the address of the first instruction to be executed in the routine. After the completion of each instruction, the counter is advanced by 1, and its contents, therefore, can be used as the address of the next instruction. There is a delicacy of interpretation here. The numbers in the instruction counter form a sequence of natural numbers; specifically, in a binary machine, a sequence of the natural binary numbers. Because of the way these numbers are used by the control—in other words, interpreted by the control—they serve as addresses with which to consult the store. The numbers are interpreted as addresses. Loosely, we say that they are addresses.

As we already know, the address part within a Branch or Jump instruction affects the instruction counter. For every Jump or every satisfied Branch, the address part within the instruction is inserted into the instruction counter in place of its current value. The counter is expected to proceed sequentially after each such situation. It is in this way that the programmer with the Branch and Jump instructions directs the control to fetch instructions from various parts of the store. The instruction counter can also be set to an initial value from the console. This allows the operator to manually direct the machine to fetch specified instructions.

We will discuss the details of counters later in this chapter. However, we can observe at this point that the instruction counter must be capable of generating numbers which when interpreted as addresses, permit the control to reach any cell of the store. The instruction counter must generate the same sequence of numbers which are used as address parts within instructions. Hence the length of the counter will be dictated by the size of the store which must be addressed from the counter.

Arithmetic Counter

The control has other counting chores to do. It must tally the steps of a multiplication (or division) and terminate either of these instructions when all places of the multiplier (or the dividend) have been exhausted. It must tally the number of shifts which have taken place in the arithmetic register, e.g., during shift instructions or floating-point arithmetic. Since the control will lose its place in the routine if the contents of the instruction counter are ever destroyed, a separate *arithmetic counter* is provided.

Recognition of the end-count can be done in several ways. The counter can simply record the number of events which has happened —shifts or steps of an operation. When the count matches the desired endpoint (which must be stored somewhere in the control), a comparison circuit indicates a match and that part of the instruction is terminated. Alternatively, the desired end-count can be inserted into the counter at the start, and the counter made to go backwards one step each time an event occurs. When the counter reaches zero, the desired number of events has occurred. Alternatively, let the initial value be the true complement of the end-count. Count forward one step for each event. When the counter reaches zero, the desired number of events has occurred.

The arithmetic counter can be used for various other counting functions. For instance, it might be used to tally the number of words which are handled in a Block Transfer operation, or it might count address positions when consulting a drum store. The arithmetic counter can be used to do a counting job whenever it is not already busy.

Sequencing

It is apparent that the execution of each instruction requires that selected events in the machine occur in the proper sequence. While the decoder will have determined which events are going to occur, some other feature of the control must cause them to occur and in the right order. Hence the control will contain a variety of pulse or other signal sources which actually initiate action in parts of the machine. These signals are distributed to the right place on each occasion by means of the gates which have been enabled by the decoder. For example, in Figure 13.2, the activating signals might be introduced as an additional input to each of the AND gates. A given AND, so to speak, is primed by its logical inputs, but the timing signal input determines exactly when it does become satisfied, and produce an output.

We see here only the necessity for such timing or sequencing signals. We have yet to determine how to organize and produce them.

Control of the Control

We know that there are two kinds of instructions with which the programmer can influence the control's own business—the Jump and the Branch. Each of these modifies the instruction counter. There are other parts of the control to which the programmer has no direct access; e.g., he cannot influence the sequencing properties of the control; he cannot store the value in the instruction register. Yet, it is apparent that the control is sequencing itself through what amounts to a small fetch subroutine:

> Fetch Instruction
> Interpret Instruction
> Execute Instruction
> Modify Instruction Counter
> Jump (back to the Fetch step)

This subroutine is trickier than it appears. For example, if the execute step happens to change the value in the instruction counter because the instruction happened to be a Jump, then the following step (Modify Counter) must be skipped. The programmer has no access to this level of activity in the control.

The sequence of events for fetching is provided for the control by the designer and builder. There are no explicit instruction types in the machine repertoire to determine this loop of events. Rather, special equipment over and above that required to interpret and execute an instruction is provided. There is a wired-in pattern of response which internally governs part of the activity of the control.

We can conceive in a broad sense how this might be done. Suppose that there is a chain of five toggles. Only one at a time is to be in the 1-state, and when it is, it establishes a gate which when activated by some timing signal turns the toggle back to the 0-state and advances the next one in line to the 1-state. We might call this a ring-of-5. Each toggle controls all the events of the corresponding step in the fetch loop. We have the effect of a decoder which is systematically cycled through a chain of steps. For example, the first toggle directs a read request to the store, sends the contents of the instruction counter along to the store with the read request, and gates the information from the store into the instruction register. Obviously we still have the sequencing problem, and timing signals of some kind are required. After the new instruction is registered, the toggle chain steps along. The second toggle gates information from the instruction register to the decoder, and may gate the output from the decoder into certain other toggles, e.g., for secondary decoding steps, for staticizing routing information, for establishing sequencing information. The third toggle releases the activitating signals along the various paths which by this time have been established. Among other things, it must also arrange for the next step of the fetch loop to be skipped in case the current instruction is a Jump or a satisfied Branch. It can do this by setting a toggle in case either of these two events occur. This toggle may either completely skip over the next step by rerouting the chain-advance signal one stage further ahead, or alternatively, it may only block the signal which the fourth step directs to the instruction counter. The third step will very likely be of variable duration according to the kind of instruction under execution. By the fifth step, the instruction is completed, and the control is set-up to obtain the next one. Before returning to the beginning, however, all toggles which have just participated in executing the instruction must be reset. So to speak, the control must be reset to its home-state.

We will see later that a binary counter of n stages can generate the first 2^n natural binary numbers. A two-stage counter can, therefore, control a four-step fetch loop. The toggles of the counter behave precisely like the part of the instruction register which holds the operation part. Hence a small decoder maps the four states of the counter (00, 01, 10, 11) onto a 1-of-4 representation. Each output of the decoder determines the events which are appropriate to that step in the loop.

THE SYNCHRONOUS CONTROL

From a logical point of view, the control determines only the sequence of which events occur. From a practical point of view, the control must also determine the precise time at which events occur because various events take different lengths of time, either because of the nature of the event or because of uncontrollable delays through circuit elements. One way to time a machine is to *synchronize* all events which happen at a given time from a central source of timing signals, the *clock* or *master clock*. In effect, the clock specifies a fixed sequence of positions in time at which events can occur; which events do occur are determined by decisions made either by the control or locally in other parts of the machine.

EXAMPLES

1. The decisions related to proper handling of the address part for each instruction are made by the control.

2. The decision related to proper handling of the multiplicand for each multiplier digit is made by some local autonomy within the arithmetic unit; such local autonomy is sometimes called *local control*.

In the *synchronous* (or *clocked*) *computer* (2), events are initiated by timing signals directly from the clock, or sometimes by signals derived from clock signals. Generally speaking, events take place when a clock signal occurs (at *clock time*); e.g., toggles change, a register shifts, or a carry occurs. Between clock signals, transients decay; gating networks and toggles settle down in preparation for the group of events which are to occur at the next clock time. For the most part, the set of events which occur at a given clock time is determined by the events which occurred or obtained at the previous clock time. Thus the computer can be regarded as a sequential switching network whose configuration at any time is determined by the immediately previous state of affairs. In the synchronous computer, transition from one configuration to the next occurs on a rigid schedule under the control of a signal whose sole purpose is to maintain the schedule by acting as the initiator of events.

The Clock

In the synchronous machine, the time required for each event is—so to speak—rounded in an upward direction to the nearest clock time. There may be tolerances associated with time intervals and time delays; the clock interval will reflect such tolerance problems. Sometimes a control is organized so that each kind of instruction always takes a fixed number of clock intervals. It can also be organized so that the time required for a given kind of instruction varies, but even so, must always consume an integral number of clock intervals. Whatever the detailed structure of the timing, sufficient leeway must be allowed to accommodate what tolerances there may be in the completion time of events.

EXAMPLE

In binary multiplication, a 1 in the multiplier requires an addition followed by a shift, but a 0 requires only a shift. Multiplication can be implemented so that each step is an add and shift, in which case the time required to execute a multiplication is always the same and does not depend on the digit content of the multiplier. Multiplication can also be implemented so that the multiplier digit determines whether add and shift or just shift will be done. In this case, the length of the multiply instruction depends on the digit content of the multiplier. The control can still be synchronous because each step of the multiplication is initiated by a clock pulse, and the total time is, therefore, always an integral number of clock intervals. Such a control is sometimes said to have *variable execution time*.

The simplest kind of clock provides a sequence of equally spaced signals. If, in a particular part of the machine, some event takes longer than one clock interval, one or more clock pulses must be skipped at that point; more logic of some kind is implied. Figure 13.3 suggests one way of skipping a clock pulse. This situation arises often enough that it is generally convenient to provide more than one sequence of signals from the clock.

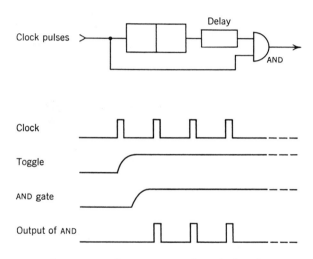

Figure 13.3. One way to omit a clock pulse.

The *n*-Phase Clock

Let there be a pulse source of frequency $f (= 1/\Delta t)$. Distribute these signals onto n wires by an electronic commutator; every nth pulse, therefore, appears on a given wire (Figure 13.4). The pulse rate on any wire is then f/n, and the spacing of pulses on that wire is $n\Delta t$. Each pulse on the jth wire (of the n) then lags the corresponding pulse on the $(j - 1)$st wire by Δt, the $(j - 2)$nd by $2\Delta t$, etc.

A clock which provides a multiplicity of outputs in this way is often called an *n-phase clock* (3). The several sequences of pulses are distributed throughout the machine, and signals from appropriate phases are selected to time the machine.

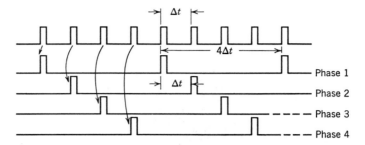

Figure 13.4.   A 4-phase clock.

The frequency of the initial source may imply an incorrect estimate of overall machine speed. While there may be signals in the clock which occur every Δt, it is not necessarily true that some event in the machine occurs every Δt. It might be that the machine is organized around a basic cycle time of $n\Delta t$; this uncertainty can be resolved only from a rather detailed knowledge of the system.

EXAMPLES

1. Consider a double-ranked register which is to be shifted. Assume that gating is done by first clearing the destination register to 0, and then gating into it any 1's which are in the source register (Figure 13.5-a). Such a two-step transfer of information from a source to a destination is often referred to as *clear and gate*. A shift of one place then consists of:

   (1) Clear temporary register to 0.
   (2) Gate down 1's from the permanent register.
   (3) Clear permanent register to 0.
   (4) Gate diagonally up the 1's from the temporary register.

   Clearly a 4-phase clock will very conveniently do this. However, else-where in the control, the arithmetic counter must be sampled to see if another shift cycle is to be done. The shift instruction must be terminated after the proper number of shifts. The arithmetic counter can be advanced by the first phase, and the fourth phase can be used to sample the counter. This allows the time between phase one and phase four for the counter and the comparison circuits to operate (Figure 13.5-b).

2. Consider the problem of presenting a number to an adder, waiting for the carry to finish, and then gating the sum from the adder to some destination. Suppose that the clock is a 4-phase one, and that both writing-in and reading-out must occur at 1-phase time. Figure 13.6 shows one way this might be done. The symbol Add is the name of a Boolean vari-

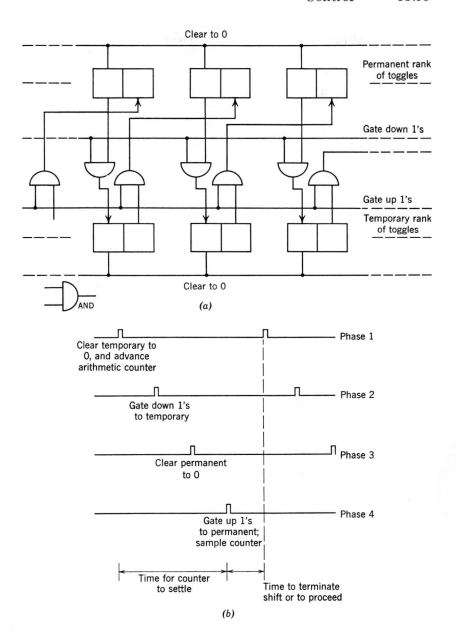

Figure 13.5. Timing in the shift of a double-ranked register.

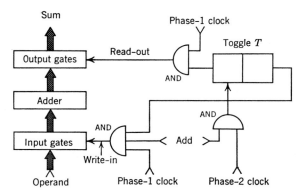

Figure 13.6. Timing part of an Add instruction.

able which is true when the decoder has found the information that an addition instruction is to be executed. Toggle T is an auxiliary toggle which is set by phase-2 and thereby enables the first phase-1 pulse to write-in but the next one to read-out. Such auxiliary toggles must be reset following the completion of the instruction.

3. A machine has a store with a 10-μsec cycle. The designer is, therefore, inclined to organize the machine around a basic 10-μsec interval for all operations; each instruction-type, for instance will be completed in an integral number of 10-μsec intervals. However, for some instruction types time will be seriously wasted by not having timing signals which are more frequent than every 10 μsec. For instance, suppose that the carry time of the adder is somewhat less than 2 μsec. A convenient arrangement is a 500-Kcps pulse source ($= 2$-μsec pulse spacing) distributed onto five buses, each of which will then have a 100-Kcps ($= 10$-μsec pulse spacing) pulse rate. Each of the five clock phases will lag the previous phase by 2 μsec.

Terminology is imprecise. Sometimes the original pulse source is referred to as the clock and its rate quoted as the clock frequency, but sometimes the whole ensemble of timing signals is referred to as the clock.

The Drum Clock

It is clear that certain kinds of storage devices operate with respect to absolute time; e.g., the magnetic drum is paced by its rotation rate, and the acoustic store is paced by the velocity of sound in the storage medium. Insofar as communicating with such a store is concerned, the rest of the machine must be synchronous during the communication interval. It is generally convenient to organize the whole machine synchronously, and therefore the frequency of the clock must be made compatible with the absolute time scale of the store.

One way to do this of course, is to servo the store to the clock; e.g., adjust the rotation rate of the drum so that the time to turn one revolution is an integral number of clock intervals. Another way is to let the time scale of the store determine the clock rate.

In the case of the drum, this means that some of its tracks are reserved solely for the clock function and never act as part of the store. The desired clock signals are written into such special tracks, and the time scale of the whole machine will follow any fluctuation in drum speed. Since signals can be recorded into these clock tracks wherever desired, there is great flexibility in the kind and number of clock signals which can be provided.

EXAMPLES

1. One clock track can provide a sequence of equally spaced signals.

2. One clock track can provide a signal at the beginning (or end) of every word.

3. One clock track can provide signals for every digit position except the first of a word.

4. One clock track can provide some sequence of signals which are time displaced any fraction of a clock interval behind any other clock track.

In order to provide the fastest machine, a machine will be timed as closely as possible consistent with expected tolerances in time delays and circuit response time. If some change in sequencing is necessary at a later date, or if an extra operation must be inserted into the execution of some instruction, we find that the synchronous control exhibits a structural rigidity which can make such modifications troublesome or tedious. The time slot in which each event occurs is fixed relative to other events and, moreover, will have been chosen to optimize the overall speed of the machine. In all likelihood there is no spare time available in the timing sequence. Hence modification of the sequencing of events probably means retiming major sections of the machine.

Local Clocks

Sometimes it is convenient to provide more than one clock in a machine. For instance, the store might be sequenced and timed by its clock, but the arithmetic unit timed by a separate one. The two parts of the machine are asynchronous with respect to each other although each is synchronous in itself. In order to communicate between two devices which are relatively asynchronous, either the two devices must be temporarily synchronized, or buffer storage must be provided.

A magnetic core store might reasonably have its local clock. Such a store is electrically quiescent except during interrogation; therefore, the clock in the store probably will run only when the store is being accessed. Such a clock might be a chain of triggered pulse sources rather than a free running source. A local clock might also be expected in a magnetic drum store which is the secondary level of a storage hierarchy.

Design of the Synchronous Control

For each instruction type in a machine, it is possible to list each event which must occur, and also the sequence in which events must occur. At the outset we need either direct knowledge or an estimate of the time required for each event to complete. We can then construct a timing chart which schedules all events necessary to complete each instruction. From the timing charts for all instructions, we can look for things which are common to more than one instruction and which, therefore, represent a potential saving in equipment. We will probably find that some events can be scheduled in alternate positions, or in earlier positions. We may also find events which can be concurrent with other events. By juggling and rejuggling the timing charts, we evolve toward a schedule of the events within each instruction. At all times, we are attempting to compress the time schedule in the interests of the fastest machine.

At this stage of the game, we may have only estimates of event times. If the development schedule permits, we may await the completion of other parts of the machine in order to obtain realistic measured times. It may well be that we cannot wait, in which case we proceed with the design knowing that refinements and changes are very likely later on. Either way we have a good feel for the overall time structure of the machine.

Next comes the tolerance problem. As component parameters drift and time passes, we know full well that the response time of circuits and the completion time of events will vary; in particular, event times can lengthen. Unless we have measured experimental evidence, our knowledge of the expected time tolerances will be estimates which depend on the tolerances assigned to other parts of the machine. In adjusting the timing schedule to accommodate anticipated changes in event times, we may find it expedient to reschedule some events. For example, an event which does not have to occur at some specific time but only before some given time, might be scheduled earlier to give it the maximum leeway.

After we have molded the machine and its events into some time frame, we now begin to look for time intervals which are characteristic of many events. Such time intervals suggest the structure which the clock must have. In reconciling the timing charts with some set of fixed time intervals, we may find it necessary to readjust the scheduling of some things. Eventually, with enough iteration and readjustment, we converge on a clock and a set of outputs from it which satisfy the needs of the other parts of the machine. The whole thing can work in reverse. Given the clock characteristics, the circuit speeds required elsewhere in the machine can be deduced.

The internal fetch loop of the control gets roughly the same treatment. The list of events and its sequence is timed, adjusted for tolerances, meshed with other timing events, and fitted into the timing scheme which has been evolved. Possibly some detail arises at this point which forces revision of earlier decisions, and if so, some more iteration occurs.

The following examples suggest some typical aspects of the design of a control.

EXAMPLES

1. Once the contents of the instruction counter has been used to fetch an instruction, it probably does not matter when it is advanced by 1. The incrementing of the counter might be done concurrently with the execute phase, as an entirely separate step, or wherever convenient. It might be advanced at the same time that the auxiliary toggles in the control are reset.

2. In a Reset Add instruction, the Accumulator can be cleared any time prior to the appearance of information from the store. The clearing might be initiated concurrently with the start of the access to the store; it might be done part way through the store cycle if such happens to be

convenient. It might also be done as a distinct step, concurrent with nothing else. If the store happens to contain its own clock, one of the signals from it might be used to perform the clearing. Other signals from the store clock might be used for other purposes in, say, the arithmetic unit.

3. The end-to-end register connection in a shift can be established at any time prior to the beginning of the actual shifting.

4. Input-output devices are often self-synchronous, and when such a device communicates with, say, the store, the clock signals which operate the store may have to be used to initiate certain things in, say, an input device. The central machine must sense when the input device is ready to transmit information, and then and only then, must route certain signals. Figure 13.7 shows one way that this can be done. Toggle T_1 is set by the input device when it is ready. When set, it enables a gate which directs clock signals to a second toggle T_2. If T_1 happens to set at such a time that less than a full clock signal is delivered to T_2, the latter may not set. However, it will set on the following clock pulse, and thereby enable whatever other gates or paths are necessary to transmit information into the machine.

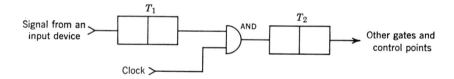

Figure 13.7. A possible synchronizing circuit.

5. The No Operation instruction does nothing except to run the control around the fetch loop once. The Jump instruction transfers the address part of itself from the instruction register into the instruction counter. One way to implement a Branch-on-Sign is as follows: sense the sign and according as the Branch is satisfied or not, in effect convert the Branch into a Jump or into a No Operation. This might be an explicit conversion in the sense that the operation part of the instruction register might actually be altered to the operation part of the Jump or the No Operation. This choice has the shortcoming that if the machine happens to stop on the instruction, the operator (or programmer) will be misled as to what instruction the machine was actually doing. The conversion might be implicit in the sense that the timing schedule of the Branch merges into that of either the Jump or the No Operation (but not both), but no modification of the instruction register or of the decoder is done. In any case, there will be large parts of the Jump, Branch, and No Operation instructions which are the same.

Another example of two instructions with much in common is the Reset Add and Add; they are alike except for the preclearing of the Accumulator in the Reset Add.   Each obtains a word from the store and adds it into the Accumulator, cleared or not.   As a result of constructing timing charts for each instruction, we hope to locate groups of events (such as illustrated here) which are common to two or more instructions. Otherwise we may needlessly duplicate equipment.

In the light of the final example just above, we now understand the observation that some instructions appear in a machine repertoire because they are inexpensive to implement.   Such cheap instructions may require a sequence of events which is a subset of some other instruction, or else they require a sequence of events which is only slightly different from some other instruction.

Once the scheduling of events is completed, the rest of the design is reasonably straightforward.   Appropriate Boolean variables can be defined, necessary functions described by truth tables, and the gating networks implemented.   We can appreciate that AND gates will be used to combine Boolean variables with timing signals; OR gates will be used to combine several inputs which lead to the same destination. It may be necessary to introduce auxiliary toggles to store a record of the occurrence of some event, or to decide which of two or more possibilities some future event follows.

We recognize that a machine which performs serial arithmetic and uses serial transmission of information will, unless there is some unusual circumstance, also include some form of serial storage.   In the serial machine, information is always on the move, either traveling along some information channel or propagating through a serial store.   The essence of the information is time position, and therefore all events in a serial machine must occur on a common time schedule if intercommunication between parts of the machine is to be possible.   Hence the serial machine typically is a synchronous machine and includes one or more clocks to provide a common time base for all its parts.

THE ASYNCHRONOUS CONTROL

In the light of our discussion of the synchronous control, we can surmise that the asynchronous control somehow avoids the problem of timing the details of each event (4).   It must still govern the sequencing of events, because only the control has the information necessary to do this; this information is contained in the instruction currently under execution. Timing of each event is related to the event itself. Hence the control simply initiates (invites) an event to occur. The event then takes place, governed only by its own natural time constants of inherent characteristics. When finished, it reports a completion signal to the control which then invites the next event in the sequence to occur. The asynchronous control does not have the rigidity in time that a synchronous one has.

There is neither a discrete nor a fixed time scale. The asynchronous control does not contain a clock, or other source of timing signals. It may contain sources of pulse or other signals, but such sources do not operate at a regular rate as in a synchronous design. Therefore, if a particular event happens to take longer than it did the last time, nothing catastrophic happens. All subsequent events patiently wait in line for their turn. It is clear, of course, that if an event in a synchronous machine overruns the time set aside for it, all chaos breaks loose, and failure surely follows.

Some problems become more tractable; some new ones appear. We can be much less concerned about the tolerances on event times. Since the control is quite agreeable to a variable event time, we need make no special precaution in the design of the control to protect against it. On the other hand, this very nicety implies that the duty cycle of an electrical signal will be less predictable than ever. We can never know, at the time of design, what kind of malfunction or change of circumstance will drastically alter the time scale of some event; hence we know nothing about the duty cycle of signals except that it is unknown. In the face of this, it is virtually mandatory that all circuits be direct coupled.

Because the time scale is so pliable in an asynchronous organization, modification, insertion, or deletion of operations is relatively easy. Since each event takes whatever time it needs, and since each event awaits the completion of the previous one, a chain of events can be severed and other events (i.e., time) can be added or deleted. Because of this feature we can proceed with the design of the asynchronous control somewhat earlier in the machine development cycle. We can be more certain that subsequent change will not be necessary because in the large, we are not concerned with the timing of individual events.

Design of the Asynchronous Control

Assume for the moment that we can derive a completion signal from each event. How do we design the asynchronous control? First of all, we make the same analysis of each instruction as for a synchronous control. We identify the events which must occur for each kind of instruction, and determine the ordering. We try to collect groups of events together to minimize the amount of equipment, and we may make some rough estimates of event times to get a little feel for what things we might consider inviting to happen concurrently.

The control must be constructed so that all events except the one that is invited at the moment, are prevented from happening. One possibility is a chain of toggles, much like the chain that we envisioned for the fetch loop of the synchronous control. Each toggle controls an event, is set by the completion signal of the previous event, and is reset by the completion signal of its own event. There need be just one such chain of toggles. According to the information which the decoder finds in the operation part of the instruction, the chain of toggles is mapped onto the sequence of events for the particular instruction. The first toggle controls the first event of whatever instruction is being executed; the second toggle, the second event of each instruction; etc. Each toggle clearly can receive inputs from a large number of sources, and will supply outputs to many destinations. For example, if the first event of twenty kinds of instructions is different in each one, the first toggle in the chain must accept reset signals from twenty different sources. Hence any such toggles will receive information through a large number of AND gates which are ORed together at the toggle and will supply information to a large number of output AND gates. Which input and output AND gates are concerned with a given occasion is determined by the output from the instruction decoder.

In this simple visualization, the toggle chain represents the current status of the instruction execution by virtue of the one toggle which is in the set state. At the interpretation phase of each instruction, the decoder enables certain AND gates which connect the toggle chain to the events pertinent to the instruction. As the control passes from the interpretation phase to the execution phase, the first toggle in the chain is set and the first event is invited. Whenever it completes, the first toggle is reset and the second one set by the completion signal. If any event fails to complete, the execution of the instruction stalls at the point of failure. In a synchronous control, time marches on, failure or not. Information which might be useful to diagnose trouble is lost in the passage of time.

A better implementation because it represents more efficient use of equipment replaces the chain of toggles with a counter. As we see later in this chapter, a binary counter of length n can progressively generate the first 2^n natural binary numbers. These 2^n numbers can be mapped onto the events of each instruction. A decoding matrix which responds to the n inputs from the counter maps the binary representation onto a 1-of-2^n representation. These outputs can be used to invite events. The completion signal of each event is used to advance the counter by 1.

A second smaller counter or ring of toggles can sequence the fetch loop. Be it counter or ring that controls sequencing, there will undoubtedly be an arrangement for short cycling it, i.e., returning it to the home state before it completes all advances. Otherwise, the counter or ring would have to proceed to its endpoint for every instruction, and not every instruction will contain the same number of events. This is not a hard problem to deal with. It only means that the instruction decoder designates which toggle of the ring (or state of the counter) is the last one in each circumstance. The completion signal from the last event is then routed to the fetch-loop control to signify completion of execution, rather than advancing the execution phase to its next state.

There are some ticklish practical problems. Most electrical signals in a machine are exponential in nature, and there is always a question of just when an event is really completed. Some care must be exercised in deciding how to generate the completion signal. There is an overlap problem to be watched. As the execution control stages from one state to the next, the signal which has invited one event is in transition to the $\overline{\text{Invite}}$ state (false state), whereas another signal is in transition from false to true (Figure 13.8). At some time, the two signals are at the same potential, and it can happen that the following event gets started while the preceding one is still stopping. Trouble may or may not occur depending on the events.

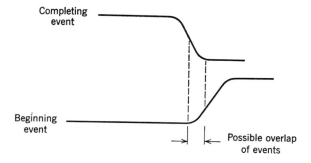

Figure 13.8. A possible trouble in an asynchronous control.

It is necessary to guarantee that as invitation, completion, and interlocking signals change from one state to another, no gate accidentally produces a spurious signal. Consider the situation in which one input of an AND gate changes from false to true, but the other one changes from true to false. Under normal circumstances, the second input becomes false before the first becomes true; therefore, the gate remains false as it should. Suppose that the second signal is later than usual, perhaps because the signal has arrived from a different source or along a different path, or has passed through a different number of gates. The gate may become temporarily and spuriously true, and perhaps invite some unrelated event or invite an event prematurely. A problem of this kind generally cannot occur in a synchronous control, because the timing schedule is adjusted to permit some tolerances in the arrival time of signals.

The asynchronous control must effect the same sequence of events no matter in what order signals arrive at any of the gating elements. Boolean algebra, because it does not represent time effects, is a relatively ineffective tool for the detailed design of asynchronous controls. Boolean algebra is useful for the synchronous control only because time has artificially been quantized by the clock. Hence Boolean difference equations can be written which relate the state of variables at one time interval to their state in the following time interval. To some extent, tools based on the theory of groups are useful in the design of asynchronous circuits (5).

Completion Signals

We now have to demonstrate that an event can be made to report its endpoint of activity. We might derive such a signal logically. For example, an AND gate will indicate when a group of variables have each attained the true state. From a practical view, there is indeterminacy in the output of such a gate. Its signal has a finite rate-of-change of voltage, and therefore the precise instant of time at which completion is thought to have occurred depends on the amplitude discrimination characteristic of whatever responds to the output of the gate. This is a form of the tolerance problem. Another way to generate a completion signal is to provide an auxiliary circuit whose time constants and the drifts in its performance incited by environmental changes are similar to those of the event to be timed. The passage of some voltage across a reference potential typically will signify completion.

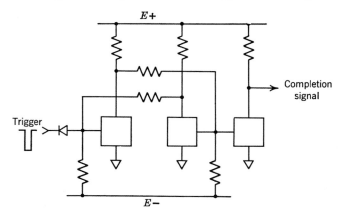

Figure 13.9. One form of completion signal from a toggle.

EXAMPLES

1. A toggle must be flipped. The completion signal can be the recognition that some element of the toggle has reached a predetermined level. In Figure 13.9 the grounded-emitter toggle is to be flipped by a negative signal on the left control. The completion signal can be the recognition that the right control voltage has come within some prescribed distance of its final new position. As shown in the figure, a completion signal is derived from the grounded-emitter stage, which begins to develop an output signal only when the right control voltage of the toggle is sufficiently close to ground potential.

   Whether or not such a completion signal is a good indicator of toggle status depends on the detailed characteristics of the toggle. If the toggle is well past the mid-point of uncertainty when the upcoming control voltage approaches ground, our choice of this particular completion signal is a good one.

2. A register of n toggles is to be cleared. A completion signal can be derived from each toggle, and the n such signals collected through an n-way AND gate.

3. Alternatively, in example 2 an auxiliary toggle can be provided which is just like those in the register. Its time constants are, therefore, similar and the behavior of the timing toggle responds to environmental changes (supply voltages, driving signals) in the same way as the register toggles. A completion signal can be derived from this timing toggle and used to indicate completion of the register operation. This particular scheme critically depends on the timing toggle being as slow as the slowest of the n toggles in the register. While the timing toggle will change its

transition characteristics in the same way as the register toggles with respect to all environmental conditions which are common to the register and to the timing toggle, it obviously will not respond to component drifts which take place only in the register toggles.   The desirability of this particular method will depend on whether we are concerned about drifting of components in individual toggles or about fluctuations of common environmental conditions.

A Specific Case

Consider Figure 13.10.   Assume that the invitation signal from the control section is at $+5$ volts but dips to -10 volts when the event is to start; the timing toggle is initially conducting on the right side. When the invitation signal appears, the current in the left section of the 3-way current switch transfers to the center section which then

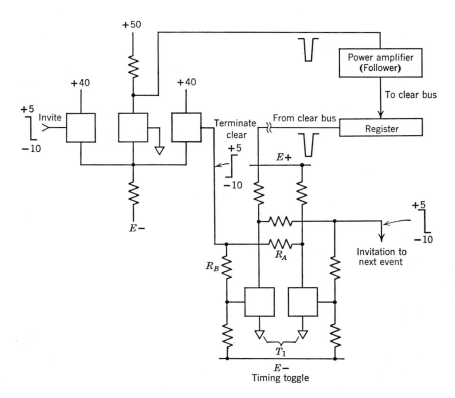

Figure 13.10.   Self-timing of a clearing operation.

develops a negative signal at its collector. This signal is passed through a suitable power amplifier and applied to the clear bus of the register. A connection from the clear bus also applies the same clearing signal to the timing toggle which then begins to flip. As the timing toggle finishes flipping, the output from its left side passes from -10 volts through 0 to $+5$ volts, and the current switches from the center section to the right section of the current switch. This terminates the negative clearing signal. A signal can be derived from the opposite side of the timing toggle to invite the next event.

In real life, the timing toggle probably must be slightly slower than

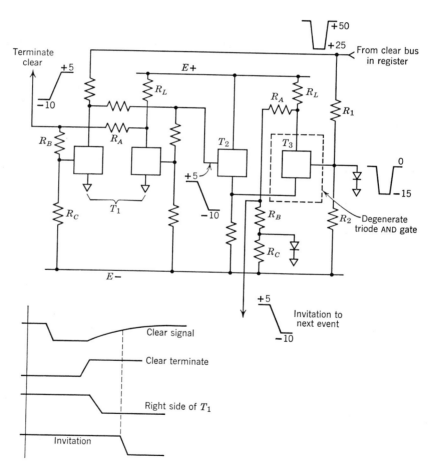

Figure 13.11. Self-timing of clearing with an extra interlock.

the slowest of the register toggles. Furthermore, if there is any substantial delay in the return of the clear bus to its quiescent level due
to a lazy trailing edge, it may be desirable to require that the bus
voltage return to its quiescent position within some prescribed interval
before inviting the next event. Otherwise, not all internal conditions,
say, in the register toggles will be normal, and some of them may fail
to respond to a subsequent gating operation. Figure 13.11 shows an
example of such an interlock.

As before, T_1 is the timing toggle to which is applied the clear signal
from the clear bus in the register. The clear-terminate signal is
derived from the left side of this toggle. However, the invitation-for-
the-next-event signal is no longer derived directly from the right side
of the toggle. Instead the down-going signal on the right side of the
toggle is used to drive (through the follower T_2) one input of a
degenerate triode AND gate. The signal on the clear bus is positioned
with respect to D-C level by the resistor divider (R_1 and R_2) and
applied to the other input of the AND gate. Hence the invitation
signal appears only when the timing toggle output has reached some
level *and* the clear bus has returned to some prescribed level.

Why Asynchronous

An asynchronous control can make expansion and modification of a
machine somewhat easier. To some extent, it can also make detection
of trouble easier because if the machine fails to complete an operation,
the asynchronous machine generally stops precisely as it was when
the trouble occurred.

On the other hand, the asynchronous organization is likely to require
more equipment because of the ancillary completion detection and
interlocking circuits. It may be troublesome to design because of the
race situations which give rise to spurious signals. We do not have
the complete set of design tools that Boolean methods provide for the
design of the synchronous control.

The asynchronous control does offer some advantages. Since it
can be held in suspended animation by withholding a completion
signal, interaction with devices external to the machine is often simplified. For example, suppose that a machine is accepting data from
some experimental apparatus, e.g., windtunnel, motor test mount. The
data will come at irregular intervals and not at times which the machine can determine. An asynchronously organized control can trans-

mit an invitation signal to such a data source, and remain quiescent until the source responds with a completion signal. Thus uncontrollable and changing increments of time delays between the two devices can be accommodated.

More importantly, the asynchronous control tolerates time delays which are variable. As we push basic circuit speeds faster and faster, the unavoidable time delays become a larger and larger part of the total response time of the circuit. The jitter in time position of a signal will not change significantly as the signal becomes narrower and narrower, i.e., as the circuit speeds become faster and faster. Hence the relative uncertainty in the time position of signals increases with increasing circuit speed. Uncertainty in timing is the one thing that troubles the synchronous control most, and it is the very thing that the asynchronous control is intended for. In a parallel machine, the situation will deteriorate more rapidly than in a serial one. As information is transmitted from place to place in such a machine, it is supposed to travel company front. Inevitably the line of advance is ragged because of variable delays or transmission times, and information does not arrive at its destination simultaneously in all columns. We may find that as our circuit technology advances, the time delay problem is so severe and so uncontrollable that the asynchronous arrangement may be the only way to organize a machine.

It can happen that the implementation of an instruction while it is correct, turns out to be inefficient. Such trouble might not appear until the operational life of the machine. Furthermore, the solution of certain problems might place a premium on the execution efficiency of certain instructions. Such a thing would likely not be foreseen during design. The point is that it may be either necessary or desirable to modify the execution details of some kinds of instructions after the machine is completed. Since the asynchronous control is so tolerant of detailed scheduling of time, such changes can be made with relative ease. It can be true that desirable changes will not be made in a synchronous control simply because a complete retiming of the whole control is necessary and is hence infeasible because of cost or lost time.

Mixed Systems

There is every reason why a hybrid system is feasible. The mixture might be in a spatial sense, e.g., one part of the machine synchronous but another part, asynchronous. The mixture might be in a time sense, e.g., a part of the machine sometimes synchronous and sometimes asynchronous. Different parts of a machine might each be self-synchronous but asynchronous relative to each other.

EXAMPLE

A core store operates by some fixed sequence of signals. These signals can be collectively regarded as a clock which is started when the store is consulted. Hence the store is synchronous. Such a store when communicating with an asynchronously controlled arithmetic unit, temporarily slaves the asynchronous part to its synchronous self for the communication interval.

In our discussion of the asynchronous control, we referred to "sequences of events." At the time, we regarded an event as some fundamental operation such as clearing a register, performing a gating operation, or initiating a store cycle. An event might also be something much larger; it might itself be a collection of events under the control of a local clock, it might be a lengthy routine executed in a machine which itself may be either synchronous or asynchronous. We can visualize a machine organization in which an asynchronous master control presides over a number of lesser controls which themselves may be some synchronous, some not. In a larger sense, it is conceivable that the asynchronous philosophy is the appropriate way to organize a supercontrol whose domain is not such functional units as the store or arithmetic unit, but rather whole other machines and other devices.

The asynchronous philosophy is handy when time delays are unknown, uncontrollable, or too variable. It requires direct-coupled circuits, and as a side benefit, the dependence on waveshape decreases. There is a reasonable analogy between the operation of an asynchronous control and the problem of trying to do parts of a computation concurrently in machines with more than one of a functional unit, e.g., a machine with two arithmetic units. Each part of a computation will contain loops of loops of loops of operations, and the time through each part may be poorly known, or widely variable. Yet the parts must mesh in order to yield the proper solution. Perhaps the concepts of the asynchronous control, and the tools which evolve to deal with the race conditions in it, will give some insight into the problem of programming concurrent computations, or perhaps will suggest some ideas for the design of special equipment to handle the situation.

SPECIFIC CASE HISTORIES

To extend our insight into the events which must occur for the execution of an instruction, let us follow the sequence of information flow for typical instructions in a single-address machine such as HYPAC-I. We will not concern ourselves in this discussion with the timing of events.

An Add

Consider fetching and executing an Add instruction. Assume that the previous instruction has just been completed, and the control has returned to the beginning of the fetch loop. A read request together with the present contents of the instruction counter as the address is sent to the store; the information channel from the store is connected to the instruction register. A gating operation writes the instruction into the register. The control passes to the interpret phase. While it is convenient for us to think of interpretation as a separate phase functionally, it may in reality overlap over functional operations. For example, the decoder action might commence as soon as the instruction register fills, and perhaps in parallel with the advance of the instruction counter.

The part of the instruction register which contains the operation part passes its information to the decoder which then establishes information paths and routes for timing signals. In the case of an Add, for example, the channel from the store is coupled to the Accumulator, and appropriate toggles and/or gates are prepared to carry out the details of an addition. The control passes to the execute phase; again it is convenient to consider this as a distinct time phase functionally, but it is not necessarily so in reality.

The execution of the addition requires the following sequence of events. The address contained in the part of the instruction register which represents the address part is sent together with a read request to the store. The information read-out is delivered to the Accumulator, together with whatever signals are required to cause the Accumulator to add the new information to its previous contents, and replace the previous contents with the new sum. The operation of the Accumulator (depending on the design) can involve a sequence such as: read the new information (from the store) into the adder; wait for a carry to propagate (in a parallel machine); register the new sum in place of the previous contents. The registration operation itself might require just a simple gating or a clear-gate operation.

Eventually the accumulation will be finished. In a synchronous control, the timing signals will have been chosen to allow enough time. In an asynchronous control, the Accumulator will report that it is finished; alternatively, whatever it is that sequences the Accumulator through its steps will report that it has delivered all necessary signals to the Accumulator for one cycle of addition. The control now passes to readying itself for the next fetch cycle.

If the instruction counter has not been previously advanced, it will now be incremented by 1. Several auxiliary toggles may have become set during the execution of the addition. In the asynchronous control, for example, toggles may have been used to govern the sequencing of events. All such toggles will have to be reset in preparation for the next instruction. The current instruction is no longer of interest, and so the instruction register can be cleared in preparation for receiving the next instruction. If there are toggles associated with the decoder, these will be reset. But some toggle (or perhaps some timing signal) indicates that the control is in the clean-up phase and will shortly revert to the beginning of the fetch loop. When this toggle is reset, or when the appropriate timing signal occurs, the fetch loop begins again.

A Shift

Suppose that the control has already fetched the instruction, has interpreted it, and is entering the execute phase. If the Shift happens to involve more than one register, end-to-end connections will have been established in the interpret phase. The interpret phase (in response to the particular operation part currently in the instruction register) will have also set up the gates which determine what the "end" of the register is. For example, in the hypac-i Right Shift Accumulator and MQ, the end-to-end connection will read information from the rightmost stage of the Accumulator, but will write information into the MQ stage just to the right of the sign position. In a Permutation Right Shift Accumulator and MQ, the same end-to-end connection will read from the right end of the Accumulator, but will write into the sign position of the MQ. Thus this particular end connection between Accumulator and MQ couples to (at least) two AND gates, one into the sign position of MQ and one into the next stage to the right. One and only one of the two ANDs will have been selected by the decoder on the basis of the operation part it is working with.

The execution continues. The address part of the instruction register is transferred into the arithmetic counter. The control now circles around a small loop of activity as follows:

> Shift one place
> Decrement the arithmetic counter
> by 1, perhaps concurrently with
> the shift, perhaps not
> Test the counter for 0
> Begin again

This cycle continues until the counter becomes 0, at which time execution is complete, and the control passes to the clean-up phase.

Fine and dandy, but we already have discovered some complications of Shift instructions. For example, if a Shift is longer than the number of places in a register, the register becomes and stays 0. The number of shifts, however, is specified by the address part of an instruction; this might have been a value computed by the routine and inserted in the address part of a Shift. In HYPAC-I, the address is 12-bits long, and the maximum number of places that can be shifted is 4095 ($2^{12} - 1$). It is useless to shift more than nineteen places for one HYPAC register or thirty-eight places for two; the machine will consume enormous amounts of time doing nothing. Hence we are well advised to have the control verify that the number of places to be shifted is no larger than thirty-eight. We might even consider the single-register and double-register shifts separately; in one case we check the number of places to be shifted against nineteen; in the other case, against thirty-eight.

The only technique that we have for investigating the size of a number is to subtract it from the proper quantity and inspect the sign of the difference. For example, we might subtract the given address which specifies the number of places to be shifted from thirty-eight; if the difference is negative, we need do no shifting per se, but only clear the register(s) concerned to 0, and conclude the execute phase.

Evidently we need to give the control an accumulator whose length is that of the address part. If there is enough other uses for the extra equipment so that it is an economic expansion, we may do so. If the extra accumulator happens to represent inefficient usage or we are reluctant to add it, we can compromise as follows. Suppose that the machine (HYPAC-I for instance) executes all shifts by actual shifting up through and including sixty-three places. After thirty-eight places, nothing useful is happening but this is part of the compromise. Shifts of sixty-four and more are to result in clearing of the register(s) to 0 but no shifting. An address part of 64 or larger will have at least one 1 in places seven and beyond. A many-way OR gate having inputs from places seven and beyond of the address part of the instruction register will detect the too large address. When it is satisfied it changes the whole pattern of control behavior for the rest of the execution.

In any case, the implementation of the Shift is more complicated than it looked at first. The complication arises not because the instruction is particularly difficult to execute, but because operational circumstances can arise which needlessly waste machine time. We want to make the machine efficient internally, but we do not want to levy restrictions on the programmer. This is the sort of situation which might be overlooked completely during design, and flushed only during the operational life of the machine. Such a design error or oversight is sometimes called a *logical error*. The Shift situation is one that might well be hard to correct in a synchronous control because a large number of extra events need to be added to the sequence.

A Branch

Suppose that the control has fetched the instruction, has interpreted it, and is entering the execute phase. Assume that the Branch responds to the sign of the Accumulator.

The sign toggle of the Accumulator must be sensed to determine its state. This is done of course, by ANDing the output of the toggle with a query signal from the control. If the Branch is supposed to be satisfied on a positive sign, then the corresponding state of the sign toggle (say, the 0-state) will enable the AND gate, and there will be a true signal returned to the control. If the sign toggle is in the 1-state (negative sign), a false signal will be returned to the control.

As we observed before, once the sign is sensed, either a No Operation or a Jump instruction is executed. In a synchronous control, there may be a toggle which determines this choice. One possibility is to have the 0-state of such a toggle result in the No Operation. If all toggles of the control are reset to the 0-state at the beginning of the fetch loop, then so to speak, the Branch instruction is primed to be unsatisfied. When the sign is positive, the sign-sensing AND gate becomes true, and its output will be used to set the control toggle to the 1-state.

The important observation for the synchronous control is that in one case (negative sign), no specific information has to be returned to the control. The absence of information from the sign-sensing gate permitted the control to proceed in the direction it was primed for—the unsatisfied condition—and to complete a No Operation. In the asynchronous control, the situation is different. Every signal that goes out from the control must always come back. This is the way that the asynchronous organization keeps track of completed events; it asks a question, and it must always receive an answer or it cannot proceed along the sequence. Thus there will be two AND gates connected to the sign toggle; one or the other but not both will always be enabled by the toggle. The toggle plus the two gates give the effect of an exclusive OR. The query signal from the control will enter each of the AND gates. Whichever gate is enabled from the toggle will become satisfied in the presence of the query signal and return a signal to the control. Thus the state of the toggle results in a signal returning to the control on one of two paths. Each path leads to the appropriate sequence of events.

In the synchronous control, the sign-sensing is in the form of one signal (i.e., Boolean variable) which is in the false state for one sign but the true state for the other. In the asynchronous control, there are two variables; each is the complement of the other, and one of them is always in the true state.

If the Accumulator sign is negative, completion of the No Operation is straightforward. The instruction counter is incremented by 1, clean-up completed, and the fetch loop reentered.

If the sign is positive, the address part of the instruction register is transferred into the instruction counter. Clean-up phase begins immediately without incrementing of the counter, and the fetch cycle restarted.

Console Control

It is usually possible to interfere with the normal behavior of the control from the console. For example, in the asynchronous control, by withholding or artificially delaying completion signals, it is possible to advance the control one step at a time or at a slower than normal rate. It may also be possible by inhibiting the instruction counter advance and preventing an automatic reentry into the fetch loop, to execute repeatedly the same instruction.

Similar things can be done in the synchronous control, but the situation is trickier. Even though the control is inactive, the clock is still running. Therefore, anytime the execution of an instruction or a step of an instruction is called for from the console, there is a synchronizing problem. The clock signals have to be recoupled to the rest of the machine in proper phase in order that timing signals reach proper destinations. A certain amount of equipment—toggles and gates—will be required to handle the problem of stopping and restarting the control without upsetting the relative timing between the clock and other parts of the machine.

For example, suppose that a clock happens to be ten phase, and that execution in some situation is supposed to start on phase 7. Suppose that the control has been led through the fetch step and the interpret step from the console. When the operator commands the execute step, the clock must not be reconnected to the control until the instant at which the signal on phase 7 is present, i.e., phase-7 time. Otherwise, some parts of the control may receive signals out of step in time and, therefore, operate out of sequence. One way to handle such a situation is to synchronize a counter at phase-1 time (see Figure 13.7) and have it count the signals on all phases. When the counter has received six counts, a toggle can be set which reconnects the clock to the control at the upcoming phase-7 time.

A practical aspect of the console design problem is the physical separation between the control itself and the console. Generally the separation is such that high-speed signals cannot be trafficked to and from the console without risk of serious time delays or capacitance loading of circuits. Much of the interaction of the console with the control and other parts of the machine is often through relays which are physically within the machine, but which are controlled from the console. Sometimes the relay is literally that; but in high-speed circuits it may also be a toggle and associated gates. The toggle is set and reset from the console, but it controls machine activity by means of the gates which it drives.

SPECIAL FEATURES

The control may have large amounts of equipment beyond that required for its minimal performance. As in any other part of the machine, the prime consideration for the addition of more equipment is the cost of the equipment versus what it buys for machine performance. Machine performance may be reflected as convenience for the user, as increased efficiency on problems, or simply as an increased rate of instruction completion.

Indexing and Address Modification

The programming examples in Chapter 6 suggested several situations in which the address part of one or more instructions was repeatedly modified. In actual programming, there are numerous situations in which the address part of an instruction must be modified before execution. Sometimes the change is systematic in some way, e.g., a progression through consecutive addresses, or through a sequence of even addresses. In a simple machine, address modification must be done by manipulating the instruction in the arithmetic unit. The writing and execution of several instructions is necessary for each modification. To improve user convenience, special features are often provided to expedite the situation. When such features are present, address modification is accomplished completely within the control by means of one or more *index registers* * and a local adder. Indexing contributes to machine performance both by decreasing the time required to modify an address, and by shortening the amount of routine that must be devoted to the job (6).

An index register contains a numeric quantity which is added to (or subtracted from) the address part (*base address*) of a fetched instruction before it is executed. The resulting *effective address* (or *absolute address*) is then used to consult the store for the information needed by the instruction. The original unmodified instruction is still intact in the store, and available for subsequent modification or use as is. The index register may also have the feature that it can act as a counter; a special kind of instruction (among other things) causes the register to increment (or possibly decrement) by 1. Conceivably the index register could be provided with an adder so that it can be incremented by any desired quantity. This amounts to indexing the index register. More complicated arrangements are possible. For example, *multiple indexing* permits adding the contents of more than one index register to the not yet used base address of the instruction. There might be an option whereby the programmer can write the effective address back into the storage cell from which the original instruction came.

It is clear that a whole group of special operation parts will be necessary to properly control the indexing operation. Often, every

---

* Other terms are *B register* or *B box*.

instruction will have indexing as an option. If so, there must be information within each instruction to specify whether or not it is to be indexed. If it is to be indexed, there must be information which specifies what the indexing quantity is, or alternatively, the location of the indexing quantity. Hence an instruction may carry within itself the quantity (the *increment* or the *decrement*) by which the address is to be modified; or it may contain a short address part which specifies, say, which one of several index registers contains the indexing value. An instruction might even contain both items.

EXAMPLES

1. Given only one index register, a single bit in the instruction is sufficient to indicate whether or not the particular instruction is to have its address modified before execution. This single bit acts as a flag and might be within the operation field, or an extra place in the address field. If there is a multiplicity of index registers, a short address field will be needed to indicate which register (if any) is to be used on a given occasion. Such a short address field will probably be considered a second address field in the instruction format. For example, a 3-bit address field can specify 1-of-7 index registers, as well as the no-index condition.

   There might also be a second flag bit in each instruction which indicates whether or not a given index register is to be counted or incremented by some specified quantity.

2. There must be an operation part to load each index register. If there are *n* index registers, there may be *n* such Load-Index-Register operation parts: Load Index Register 1, Load Index Register 2, etc. The address part of such a Load instruction might be the location of information in the store—the normal interpretation of an address part. However, since an index register is to be used to modify an address part, its length will be exactly that of the address part itself. Therefore, the address part of the Load-Index-Register instruction might directly be the information to be placed in the specified register. This is an example of a *zero-address instruction*.

3. Branch instructions are generally provided which respond to the contents of a specified index register. For example, there might be branches which are satisfied under one of the following conditions:

   (1) The contents of a given index register is zero.
   (2) The contents of the given index register is equal to a given quantity.
   (3) The contents of a given index register is greater than (or less than) a given quantity.

   The reference quantity in points (2) and (3) above might be, say, in a special register in the control. If such a special register(s) exists, there must be operation parts for loading it, and perhaps also for storing it. The reference quantity also might be in the main store in which case its location must be given. The address part of the Branch can be used to address the given reference quantity; if so, the Branch is really a Branch-and-Skip (see the Sense-and-Skip instruction on page 5.45). The cell next after the Branch will contain the address to which the satisfied Branch goes. Another possibility is to use one of the index registers to contain the address of the reference quantity; its length is correct for such a usage. In this case, the instruction might contain two short address fields, one to specify the index register whose contents is the address of the reference quantity, and the second to specify the index register whose contents is to be compared against the reference quantity for equality.

4. Branch instructions, whatever their fine structure, can be arranged so that when satisfied (or unsatisfied), the indicated index register is counted after the Branch has sensed it.

5. There may not be an indexing option in each instruction. The programmer may have to insert a special Index instruction ahead of each instruction to be indexed. Such an Index instruction may directly contain the indexing quantity (a zero-address format) or its address may locate the indexing quantity in the store.

6. There might be a generalized Branch instruction with the following format.

OPERATION PART	BRANCH
2-bit field	Condition on which to branch 00—equal to zero 01—equal to or greater than zero 10—equal to a reference quantity 11—greater than a reference quantity
3-bit field	Which of eight index registers is to be sensed.
3-bit field	Which of eight index registers contains the address of the reference quantity.
1-bit field	Whether the index register is to be counted by 1 every time it is sensed, or counted by 1 only if the branch is unsatisfied.
Address part	The location to which the satisfied branch proceeds for the next instruction.

Such an instruction is very complex and very powerful; it provides the programmer with a large number of possibilities. As we have previously observed (page 13.19), instructions often are included in a repertoire because they are inexpensive to implement, once certain other instructions have already been included. A priori, therefore, it may not be clear that all possibilities such as those suggested above are useful, but they may be included on the chance that profitable uses will be discovered by adventuresome programmers.

The sixth example given illustrates the complexity that can appear in a single instruction. It also suggests the tendency to include powerful and complex instructions in a machine repertoire in order to assist the programmer.

It is clear that the indexing operation is a prefix to any details of execution which we have already discussed. It is also clear that for instructions which contain an indexing option, the decoder may have to inspect some other part of the instruction. In particular it will have to inspect the short address field specifying which index register, if any. In the case of the explicit Index instruction, its address part or the contents of the cell located by its address part must be stored in some special place in the control until the next instruction is fetched.

No matter what the details of the indexing feature, a genuine addition must be performed within the control. The base address of the fetched instruction must be added to the indexing quantity (wherever it comes from) to form the effective address. The control must sequence a series of events to accomplish this end. In effect, the control first executes an Add instruction within itself before proceeding with the execution of the instruction proper. Hence a typical way to implement indexing is to convert the part of the instruction register which holds the address part to an accumulator—of the same design perhaps that is in the arithmetic unit. The address part of the instruction register becomes the register part of the special accumulator. The indexing quantity from one of several index registers, or from within another part of the instruction, or from a special register which may have held the quantity from a previous instruction, is presented to the other input to the adder. Following the addition—including the carry propagation—the effective address appears in the accumulator in place of the address part of the original instruction. The control now proceeds with execution of the main instruction.

In the case of a machine with a specific zero-address instruction, here is an economic way to implement the operation. The quantity in the address field is the indexing quantity, and is not needed to complete the execution of the Index instruction. Let us arrange the control so that the part of the instruction register which contains the address field is not cleared upon completion of the Index instruction. We will also have converted the address part of the instruction register to an accumulator. As the next instruction is fetched, let the address part of it be added into the corresponding part of the instruction register. The effective address is automatically in place in the instruction register ready for use during execution. However, suppose that for some reason, the machine stopped during the execution of the instruction. What information is available to the operator or to the programmer to diagnose the trouble?

The instruction register does not contain the original instruction. Both the address part of the original instruction and the indexing quantity have been lost. It is true that each of these items is still in the store, but there may be no ready access to the store from the console, and there may be no ready record of the location of items in the store. To make matters worse, suppose that the instruction which had just been indexed and partly completed happened to be a satisfied Branch. Suppose, furthermore, that the execution has proceeded to the point at which the instruction counter has been altered so that it contains the effective address from the instruction register. The programmer is really lost. The instruction register holds an instruction which is not in the store; it has been constructed from two items of information which were in the store. The instruction counter has been changed, so that the programmer does not even know the cell from which the Branch came. He has virtually no useful information to help diagnose the trouble.

This leads to a new point for us. In implementing the execution of instructions, we may arrange things optimally for the design, but accidentally or prematurely destroy information potentially of great value to the user. We may have to modify the implementation in order to preserve information which on some occasions will be needed by the programmer.

As we penetrate more and more deeply into the control and discover the intricacies of its behavior, we notice the similarity between the job which it does and the loops, branches, and tests which a routine incorporates. The significant difference is that during design all of the possible situations which the control can traverse must be completely defined, and the corresponding behavior wired—rather than programmed—into the equipment.

Figure 13.12 summarizes the concepts which we have so far developed.

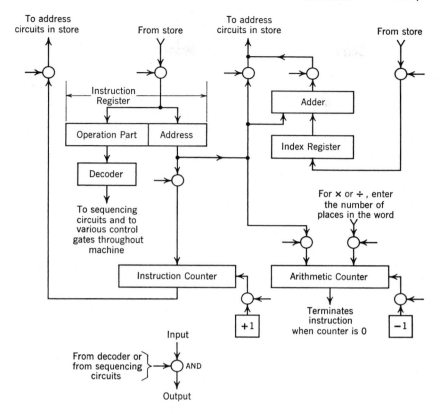

Figure 13.12.   The major information flow paths of an indexing control.

Error Correction and Detection

The control governs the sequencing of events as well as manipulating digital expressions both arithmetically and logically. Arithmetic which may be involved in indexing can be checked just as arithmetic elsewhere is checked. It is another story to verify that the proper sequence of events did happen and with the right timing. It may be very difficult (or costly) to devise schemes to make the control extensively self-checked. Such things as parity or casting-out checks are generally not useful for verifying sequencing or timing.

One possibility is to set a group of monitor toggles for each instruction as it is interpreted. The group will change from instruction to instruction, and will represent in each case, the sequence of events to be performed. As each event is completed, a completion signal resets the corresponding toggle. At the completion of the instruction, all monitor toggles should have been reset, and no new monitor toggles should have been set. A many-way OR gate can detect whether any one of them is set.

The control may contain the equipment for monitoring the error problem elsewhere in the machine. For example, if a machine contains an error-correcting feature, the control may tally the number of times an error has been corrected in various parts of the machine. Such information is useful for maintenance purposes. The control may also contain the equipment which governs what happens in the machine when an error has simply been detected someplace.

Look Ahead

It is apparent by now that roughly speaking, a machine alternately fetches an instruction and executes it. Time could certainly be gained by *overlapping the fetch* of the next instruction with the execution of the present one. Once the present instruction is safely written into the instruction register, and any consultation of the store which it needs has been made, the control can proceed concurrently to execute one instruction, and to advance the instruction counter and fetch the next one. A second instruction register is required. It is also true that the advance-fetched instruction may sometimes be unwanted. For example, if the present instruction turns out to be a satisfied Branch, the next instruction needed will not be the one directly next to the present one in storage.

Additional time can be saved if more work is done on an instruction prior to execution. More than one instruction ahead can be obtained, interpreted, indexed, and generally prepared for execution. Needed operands can be obtained in advance. Features of this sort will imply extra registers, decoders, index facilities, perhaps counters, and other equipment in the control. As with overlapped fetching, such a *look-ahead* sometimes produces unusable information (7). If one of the, say, four instructions ahead happens to be a branch, some or all of the advance information may be useless. For sufficient equipment, the look-ahead can proceed on each path of the branch.

The object of fetch overlapping or look ahead is to maximize the utilization of all equipment within the machine. In particular, of course, the arithmetic unit will be busy a larger part of the time. Machine speed has been increased by improving the internal organization of the machine, rather than by developing faster circuits. Such extra features in the control are generally not subject to program control but operate automatically.

Interlock Registers

It is often convenient for the programmer to deny the control access to part of the store. For example, in buffered transfer of information between levels of the store (see page 12.80), a part of the store must be protected against writing or reading while the transfer is in progress. Perhaps more than one routine is in the store at one time. To protect one routine against accidental infiltration by the other one—due either to an error in the routine or a machine malfunction—the control can be denied both reading and writing access to the part of the store containing other routines. Denial is accomplished by specifying the addresses of the end cells of the block to be protected. There may be more than one pair of *interlock* or *limit registers* to hold the extra addresses (8). There may also be a toggle or two whose states indicate whether denial is for writing, reading or both. Instruction types for loading (and perhaps also storing) interlock registers are, of course, required.

As with indexing, execution of the interlock aspect is a prefix to the execution of the instruction proper. The interlock phase follows the indexing phase because it is the effective address which is used to consult the store. The control must compare the effective address with the contents of the two limit registers and in effect answer the question: Is the given address equal to either of the limit addresses or between them? We know how to program such a question. Subtract the given address from the lower limit; if the difference is positive, we are safe and can proceed. If the difference is zero, we cannot proceed. If the difference is negative, we may be in trouble. Next subtract the given address from the upper limit. If the difference is positive, we are in trouble and cannot proceed. If the difference is zero, we cannot proceed, but if the difference is negative, we are safe.

To implement the interlock phase, we must sequence and wire in the same series of events. An adder (or subtractor) is necessary and conceivably it can be the same one used for indexing if it is not concurrently busy. Extra gates are necessary for routing information; extra toggles will be required to maintain the sequencing.

The control has other options to investigate. If denial is for writing only, but the current instruction reads the store, no interlock check need be made. Hence the decoder plays a part in determining whether in a given case the interlock is required.

What happens if the interlock check denies access to the store? The machine may simply wait until other processes have been completed and the denial is removed. In some situations, no other processes are in operation. Rather than stall the control, a toggle may be set to indicate an unexpected condition has arisen, or the control may automatically branch to some fixed and predetermined place in the store. This is often known as *trapping*. Having trapped to some particular cell, the machine must be directed by its routine to assess the situation and take appropriate action.

At the expense of extra word length, a more flexible scheme can be provided for protecting information against accidental misuse. Special flag bits can be included within each word to indicate whether it is currently available for use within the machine, or for what kinds of operations it is currently available. Obviously, the programmer can change the status of a word by altering the state of one or more such flags.

Interrupt

By now we realize that many situations can arise within a machine which are of concern to the programmer. An interlock check may appear; an overflow may occur; the machine may have trapped; a parity check may have occurred; an improper division may have been attempted. Up to now, we have tended to introduce Branch instructions which respond to the situation. Unfortunately, if the number of situations is large, the programmer will be forced to incorporate an enormous number of branches in his routine.

Most of the time, trouble or the unusual situation is not expected. Hence if the programmer is not bothered except when the unusual does occur, he can afford to search for the situation which is abnormal rather than having it immediately apparent. The situation *interrupts* the normal progress of the routine (9). A common way of handling the interrupt is to combine all the situation-indicating toggles into a register. One place in the register responds to the overflow, another to the underflow, another to the parity check, and so on. If any indicator is set by the appearance of the corresponding situation, there is an automatic diversion of the control away from the problem routine. One possibility is to trap the machine to a given storage cell, say cell 0. Implementation is easy. An OR gate monitors the many toggles of the *situation register;* if any input becomes true, an output appears which can be used to clear the instruction counter to 0.

There is more to the story. If the counter is simply cleared to 0, there is no record of the point in the routine from which trapping occurred. Prior to clearing the counter, therefore, its contents must be stored in some place known to the programmer, so that he can later recover his place in the routine. For example, the contents of the instruction counter might be stored in the cell next to the trapped cell, cell 1 in our example. From cell 0, the programmer must proceed with his routine to search the situation register in order to determine what condition(s) is present. On the basis of such a search, remedial action can be taken and the main problem routine reentered.

There are other uses for the interrupt feature. It can be used to signal that some external device requires attention and is ready to deliver information or requires some. Such external devices might be individual consoles for users, or they might be data acquisition devices. There are other ways to react to an interrupt situation. Rather than being trapped to a predetermined cell, the programmer may be able to specify the cell to which the interrupt refers him. For example, there can be one or more registers which can be loaded by the routine, and which contain addresses to which referral occurs. Some situations trap to the contents of one such register, while other situations will trap to the contents of other such registers. In an extreme case, there might be one register (i.e., trap address) for each situation which can arise. In principle, we can give the programmer the ability to adjust by the routine the correspondence between the situation toggles and the various trapping registers.

Variable-Length Instructions

Not all kinds of instructions implicitly require the same number of address parts. While an arithmetic instruction may naturally require three address parts, a shift instruction may more naturally fit a single- or possibly double-address format. Sometimes the information with which a machine deals is naturally less than one word long. For instance, quantities for address modification need only be as long as the address part. Sometimes, therefore, it is convenient to put the information itself rather than an address in the address part of a zero-address instruction. Very complex instructions may naturally require more than three address parts.

A machine can be organized to deal with instructions which differ in format. If such is the case, the control will contain a great deal of extra equipment of various kinds.

Decentralized Control

It may be appropriate to organize control in a hierarchal way. For instance, a transfer of information to or from a tape unit requires continuous monitoring and control at a low level; there are various decisions which may have to be made depending on circumstances that arise during the tape activity. While the main control can concern itself with such a problem, generally a certain amount of *local control* is provided at several places in the machine. Such local control is rather specialized in nature and is responsive to the *master control* or *central control*.

EXAMPLE

Master control may specify the number of a tape unit, the position of information on the tape, and its destination in primary storage; tape local control will then carry out all of the details of this activity, including perhaps attention to error problems. Meanwhile the master control and other parts of the machine may be productively busy. Among other kinds of extra equipment, there might be interlocks which prevent master control from invading regions of the primary store which have been delegated for some need of a locally controlled operation.

As machines continue to grow in size and capability, the amount of decentralization of control is likely to increase. The level of detail handled by each local control is likely also to increase, perhaps even so far as executing sequences of instructions which have been assigned to it by the master control. Meanwhile the level of activity in master control will also have been raised; it will be busy with the assignment of various parts of a complex machine to parts of several problems, with the interlace of work within the machine, with the resolution of simultaneous demands for the same part of a machine, with the assignment of priorities to problems or parts of problems, and so on.

In the limit, the control may in its own right become a large computer or *information processor* intended only for the manipulation of symbols and for making complicated and involved decisions. Conceivably, the structure of the control might be adapted to each problem by having the structure modifiable by the routine itself (10).

COUNTERS

The counter as a device is a special item of equipment which we have not yet discussed. Although in principle it might have been discussed as one of the miscellaneous circuits of Chapter 10, it is better treated here since some of our knowledge about the behavior of an adder is relevant to the operation of a counter. It is included in this chapter on control because historically the counter was spawned principally by the needs of the control (11).

The One-Stage Counter

Consider first the behavior of a single-stage counter which operates in the binary number system. There are only two one-place binary numbers—0 and 1; therefore, a single-place *binary counter* must alternate between the 0-state and the 1-state for as long as input signals continue to come. To the best of its ability, it counts the incoming signals. It is clear that a toggle driven through its complementing input will behave exactly as required; thus a complementing toggle is sometimes loosely called a *binary counter* or *counting toggle* and the complementing input, the *binary-counter input* or *counting input*.

0000
0001
0010
0011
0100
0101
0110
0111
1000
1001
1010
1011
1100
1101
1110
1111

Figure 13.13. A sequence of natural binary numbers.

Consider now the sequence of natural binary numbers in Figure 13.13. The first (right-most or least significant) column changes every time, the next column to the left changes every other time, the third column changes every fourth time, the fourth column every eighth time, and so on. In a sequence of n-place binary numbers, the jth column will change every $2^{(j-1)}$ times; or to put it another way, in the jth column, there are $2^{(j-1)}$ consecutive 0's, then $2^{(j-1)}$ consecutive 1's, etc. Such behavior is a direct consequence of the positional notational scheme of representing numbers.

The Many-Stage Counter

A binary counter of length n will be able to count from 00 . . . 0 to $2^n - 1$ which is a total of 2^n counts. On the (2^n)th input, the counter will return to 0, just as a set of mechanical counting wheels will eventually turn over and return to 0. A binary counter of length n, therefore, counts modulo 2^n.* From an inspection of Figure 13.13, we see that any column must change its state (either $0 \rightarrow 1$ or $1 \rightarrow 0$) as the column to its right changes from 1 to 0. This makes sense because a change from 1 to 0 in any column of a binary numerical expression implies that a carry is to be passed to the next more significant column.

In principle, therefore, a binary counter could be built from a string of complementing toggles. The jth toggle is driven from the $(j-1)$st in such a way that a transition from 0 to 1 in the $(j-1)$st is ignored, but a transition from 1 to 0 causes the jth to change state.

Figure 13.14 shows a typical arrangement. The complementing toggle is the one discussed in Chapter 8; the interstage network is a differentiation network plus a follower to handle the current load of the complementing input. The output terminal at each stage is that collector which moves negatively as the stage changes from the 1-state to the 0-state. In a practical case it might be necessary to provide a pulse-shaping feature in the interstage network.

Such an arrangement is not necessarily a good one practically, because (1) the complementing mode of a toggle may be very sensitive to the waveshape of the driving signal, and (2) the precise waveshape of any point in a toggle (especially the rise time) can depend on the parameters of every component in the circuit. A counter built of a chain of complementing toggles can really be a case of the blind lead-

---

* For a total number of inputs greater than 2^n, the count will be short by some multiple of 2^n.

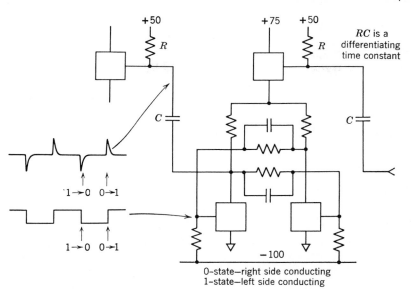

Figure 13.14. A complementing-toggle counter stage.

ing the blind. Be that as it may, many counters of cascaded complementing toggles have been built and are operating (12). Frequently,
they are used as scalers for nuclear physics applications where a mis-
count one way or the other is not significant, if even detected. Many
of the techniques described in the literature for the design of counters
are acceptable for scalers but cannot produce the reliable well-behaved
device required by the computer.

A Storage Requirement

Because any stage of a counter must respond to a "change your state"
signal rather than a "go to this state" signal, the requirement for
temporary storage is the same in a counter as it is in a complementing
toggle. Each stage of a counter must know for a little while, at least,
in what state it was so that it knows into which state to go. As with
other situations in which the same problem arose—for instance, the
shift register—the temporary storage can be provided by an element
such as a capacitor, whose storage life is time dependent, or by an element such as an auxiliary toggle, whose storage is independent of time.

CHARACTERISTICS OF A COUNTER

There are two important features of a counter which must be kept in mind when deciding upon its detailed structure. The first of these is the maximum rate at which the counter can accept input signals. This does not imply a steady sequence of inputs; a counter must be prepared to accept signals arriving in a sporadic fashion.

EXAMPLE

Consider the multiplication scheme which either add-shifts or simply shifts according to the value of the multiplier digit. If the add time of a machine is t_1 and the shift time is t_2, signals to the arithmetic counter which tallies the steps of the multiplication can arrive spaced either by t_2 or by $t_1 + t_2$. Which it is depends on the multiplier digit. Thus we have no a priori knowledge of what will happen to the counter at any time. There is no choice but to design the counter so that it can accept signals which come at any time but are never closer together in time than t_2.

If a counter will properly respond to a pair of inputs spaced by Δt, then the minimum value of Δt for which the counter will operate properly is called the *resolution time*. Unless there are circuits whose recovery times are too long, the same counter will operate at a maximum steady input rate of $1/(\Delta t)_{min}$ pulses per sec. In an unusual case there might be some characteristic pattern of the inputs, and it might be possible to build a counter which will respond properly to some given number of input signals spaced by Δt, but which would not respond to a steady input rate of $1/\Delta t$.

Notice how the tolerance problem can turn up here. The spacing between two signals can depend on time constants sprinkled throughout some large other part of the machine; some knowledge of the variation in the spacing must be available before a counter can be thoroughly designed.

Settling Time

The second significant property of the counter is the time required to completely settle after an input signal has been received. A counter is of no use unless its contents can be made available to other electronic circuits. Following an input signal, all transients must have settled sufficiently completely before the contents of the counter can be read out. A counter frequently progresses through the natural binary numbers. Thus, at some point, the counter will advance from, say, 011111 to 100000; a carry will have propagated nearly the whole length of the counter, and therefore the carry behavior of a counter is involved in the settling time.

The carry situation in a counter is somewhat different than in an adder. A carry can be initiated only at the first stage because this is the point at which information is entered into a counter. Any carry which starts will propagate as far as there is a consecutive string of 1's; the last thing that the carry will cause is a change from 0 to 1 in the stage just beyond the end of the string of 1's.

EXAMPLES

1. Suppose that a machine requires a time interval t_1 to shift its registers one place. Therefore, the arithmetic counter must accept inputs spaced as closely as t_1. However, suppose that it takes a time interval t_2 for other circuits to decide on the basis of the count, whether the shift instruction is to be terminated or continued. The settling time, t_3, must therefore be $\leq (t_1 - t_2)$. If it exceeds this limit, the decision circuit will not be able to react before the next place of shifting has begun, and the shift instruction may not be terminated at the appropriate time.

2. A counter is to tally the forty steps of a multiplication. It must therefore be six stages long, since $(2^6 - 1) > 40$. If the initial value in the counter is set to 24, the counter will read 63 at the 39th step and will return to 0 at the 40th step; proper termination of the multiplication operation in this case will depend on the recognition of the all-0's state. Therefore, the carry time of all six places of the counter can be involved in the settling time. Alternatively, if the initial reading in the counter is 40 but the counter runs backward, at the 40th step, the carry (actually a borrow) which occurs is only 1 place long, and the settling time is correspondingly shorter.

    In the case of the counter which starts at 24 and counts upward to zero, there is actually a carry out of the sixth stage just as the all-0's state is forming. The presence of this carry can be used to determine the completion of the multiplication.

The Toggle Counter

Consider a counter each state of which is a complementing toggle of some sort. Assume that there is some appropriate interstage network. It is clear that the maximum input rate of such a counter is determined by the characteristics of the first stage toggle. However, the toggle in each of the following stages need operate only half as fast as its previous neighbor; each stage receives an input half as often as its previous neighbors. Advantage might be taken of this and slower, cheaper toggles used in the higher stages of the counter.

The carry is ripple in nature but unfavorable in a time sense; it occurs as each toggle changes and passes some signal along. At most, the carry (for n stages) is n * times the switching time of one toggle (if they are all similar). It may be less than this but probably not less than $\sqrt{n}$ † times the flip time of one toggle. For a long counter— perhaps as many as fifteen stages for the instruction counter of a machine with a 32,768-word store—the carry time might be prohibitively long.

The worst that can happen is that a carry progresses the full length of the counter, causing the final stage to change. The maximum settling time is, therefore, the full length carry time plus the settling time of one toggle.

HOW TO MAKE ONE

First of all, a complementing flip-flop of some kind is needed. Consider the one shown in Figure 13.15; the external logical networks are sometimes called *steering networks*. The temporary storage is provided by the resistance-capacitance time constants of the steering logic;

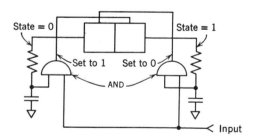

Figure 13.15. A steering-gate counter stage.

---

* This is an upper limit, because a given toggle can begin to flip while its neighbor is still finishing its transition.

† This estimate is based on the behavior of an n-stage cascaded linear amplifier. The rise time of the overall amplifier is $\sqrt{n}$ times the rise time of one stage.

the capacitance may only be the distributed capacitance. Were it not for such information storage, the toggle change will be felt at the gate before the driving pulse is finished; thereby the gate will change to a false state before the complete driving signal has passed through. The circuit as shown is satisfactory for the first stage, but it is obvious that the pulse width must be short compared to the delays. Otherwise the gate on the opposite side can leak a pulse which will tend to reset the toggle.

EXAMPLE

The names on the various connections in Figure 13.15 are the Boolean variables which are represented. Suppose that the two voltage levels of the toggle outputs are 0 volts and -10 volts, and that the 0 volts level represents the true position. The right output when at 0 volts indicates that the proposition "the toggle is in the 1-state" is true. Because of the antisymmetry of the toggle outputs, the left output is at -10 volts if the right one is 0 volts, and this indicates that the proposition "the toggle is in the 0-state" is false.

Suppose that the toggle is in the 1-state. The right output is then in the true state and when the input signal appears, the right gate becomes satisfied. Its output goes to the true state, which then sets the toggle to the 0-state. The delay introduced by the resistance-capacitance network prevents the input from the toggle to the gates from changing too quickly.

Each stage is supposed to change as the prior stage goes from 1 to 0. Alternatively, if the prior stage is 1 and will shortly change to 0, we know that the next stage must change state, and it might as well change state simultaneously with the prior stage. This implies

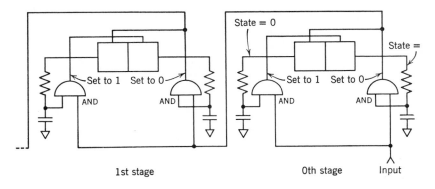

Figure 13.16. A counter with 2-input steering gates.

that the pulse which changes the first stage from 1 to 0 can also be used to change the state of the second stage; the pulse which changes the second stage from 1 to 0 can be used to change the state of the third state, and so on. This leads to the configuration of Figure 13.16 which has only 2-input steering gates, but which has the disadvantage that the signals to the later stages have passed through many layers of logical elements and may have lost some vigor. It may be necessary to insert pulse amplifiers along the way. In a sense this counter exhibits the feature of bypass carry (see Chapter 11, page 11.12). Any stage which presently contains a 1 has established its external steering gates so that the next input signal passes right through to the next stage. In this regard, the time to propagate the input along the cascade of gates plays the role of a carry time.

A Variant

Figure 13.17 shows a similar type of counter in which the number of inputs to the AND gates increases by one at each stage. It is clear that the jth stage of a counter is to change state when all of $(j-1)$st stages contain a 1; the many-way AND gates implement this observation. It is clear that all toggles of this counter which are supposed to change, change in unison. There appears to be no effect which is propagated. This should not be surprising because time has been exchanged for equipment; the extra gates perform simultaneous decision making rather than the sequential decision making of a normal carry process.

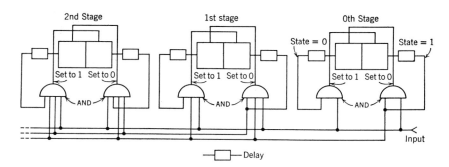

Figure 13.17. A counter with many-input steering gates.

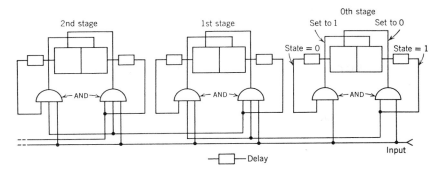

Figure 13.18. A disjoint counter.

A Second Variant

A similar counter which avoids the disadvantage of propagating the input signal through many gates uses 3-input ANDs for the steering function (Figure 13.18). Again there appears to be no effect which propagates along the chain after the input signal and, therefore, no carry-like behavior. There are, however, changes in the inputs to the gate circuits; and these will determine the behavior of the counter when the next input appears. Such gating changes occur simultaneously in all stages of the counter and do not propagate from state to stage. This appears to be a violation of the carry phenomenon, but again—sequential decision making has been exchanged for simultaneous decision making at the expense of additional equipment (see problem 11.1, Chapter 11). This arrangement is not a counter in the usual sense (Figure 13.19). It does not proceed through the natural binary numbers and in fact has only half of the expected number of states. However, the mapping between the contents of the device and the true binary numbers can be deduced, and perhaps this pseudo-counter can be effectively used in particular situations. Devices which progress through a set of states, even though the set may not be a consecutive sequence of binary (or other radix) numbers, are still generally referred to as counters. The set of states may depend on the initial state of the counter.

If the counter of Figure 13.18 is started from a number which does not happen to be among the first set of eight, we see (Figure 13.20) that it proceeds through a second set of eight states whose intersection with the first set is zero; i.e., there are no common members. This

DECIMAL COUNT	BINARY COUNT	DECIMAL COUNT	BINARY COUNT
0	0000	3	0011
1	0001	4	0100
2	0010	13	1101
7	0111	6	0110
8	1000	11	1011
9	1001	12	1100
10	1010	5	0101
15	1111	14	1110

Figure 13.19. A sequence of counts in a disjoint counter.   *Figure 13.20. A second sequence of counts in a disjoint counter.*

device partitions the first sixteen natural binary numbers into two disjoint sets of eight each.

With longer counters, other connections between the stages, and more complex logic, the natural numbers can be partitioned in various ways. Such a device might be the basis of the decoding and sequencing part of the control (13). For example, suppose that the counter is designed so that it partitions the natural binary numbers into as many disjoint groups as there are operation parts. As each instruction is fetched, the operation part will be written into the counter which then will cycle through a sequence of steps which is unique for each instruction. Perhaps the successive steps of the counter can do some or all of the sequencing of events to execute the given instruction.

The Half-Adder Counter

Recall the manner of operation of the Accumulator which is in the arithmetic section, and consider repeatedly adding a 1 into the least significant place. The Accumulator will obviously progress through the natural binary numbers, i.e., count. Thus any of the schemes for building an accumulator can also be used to build a counter. The adder part, however, can be simplified.

The least significant adder stage of such a counter needs but two inputs: the input signal which is to be counted and the digit input from the corresponding position in the register part. Any other stage of the adder part also has, in distinction to the adder part of a true accumulator, only two inputs: the digit input from the corresponding place in the register part and the carry from the next less significant stage. Thus the adder part of an accumulator-type counter need only have a half-adder in each column.

The carry process is favorable because it is the ripple of a signal along the string of half-adder stages; specifically no toggle turnover-times are involved in the carry propagation, and thus the carry can be made to occur as fast as the switching networks can be made to respond. Registration of the adder output into the register part occurs simultaneously in all columns. Thus a counting cycle includes the carry time plus a toggle flip time plus any settling time needed for the toggles.

Since a new counting cycle cannot commence until the previous adder output is safely registered, it follows that the resolution of this type of counter is the same as the settling time. The carry time of the half-adder chain is, therefore, directly involved in determining the maximum input rate of the accumulator (or half-adder) type counter.

The Hybrid Counter

Generally speaking, it is easier to build a many-stage half-adder with a given carry time than to construct a toggle chain of the same length which will have the same carry propagation speed. Since the carry time of the half-adder chain increases with the length of a counter, there eventually comes a length of counter for which the total cycle time of a half-adder counter is greater than the flip time of one or of a few cascaded toggles.

A hybrid counter nicely compromises the conflicting demands set by a short resolution time and a short settling time. Each stage of the toggle-chain counter divides the rate by two. Therefore, the trick is to use a few stages of a cascaded-toggle counter in front of a half-adder counter. The number of stages is chosen such that the input rate is divided down far enough to match the cycle time of the half-adder counter.

The Double-Ranked Counter

In a toggle-chain counter, the temporary storage required for the complementing property can be provided by an auxiliary toggle in each stage rather than by a capacitor (see page 11.38) (14). A counter with this feature has some new and useful properties.

Consider Figure 13.21; the names on the connections have the same meanings as described in the example on page 13.53. The gating is such that a 1 or 0 is transmitted from the top to the bottom toggle as a 1 or 0, but from the bottom to the top, as a 0 or 1. Thus a 0 in the top goes to a 0 in the bottom but returns as a 1 to the top. A cycle of operation consists of a vertical down-gate followed by a vertical up-gate. It is clear that either toggle (in particular, the top) will alternate between the 0- and 1-states as a single-stage binary counter should; the two toggles are in opposite states after each cycle. It is clear that only the up or the down (but not both) gate may operate at a given time. Thus a typical input signal consists of a pair of time-spaced pulses. Such a two-part signal is sometimes called a *two-beat* signal; the input rate is the rate of occurrence of the pulse pairs.

Call the top toggle the *true* one and the bottom one *false*. If the state of the true toggle is used to control the gating of a second such stage, we see that the overall behavior is that of a two-stage counter (Figure 13.22). As the true toggle in stage 1 changes from 0 to 1, it enables the down gate in stage 2; as the true toggle in stage 1 changes from 1 to 0, it enables the up gate. Thus the second-stage true toggle changes state when the first stage changes from 1 to 0; as we previously noticed, this is the desired pattern of response.

In a many stage counter of this kind, the transition of the jth true toggle may enable the up gate in the $(j + 1)$st stage, which may in

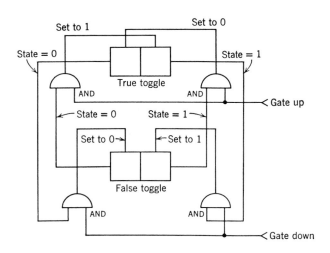

Figure 13.21. A single stage double-ranked counter.

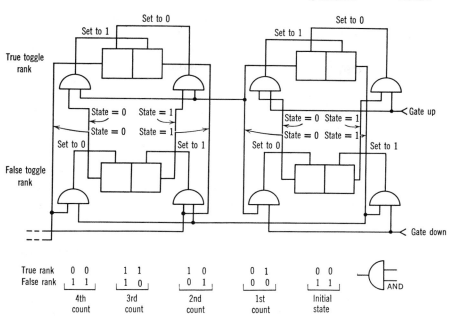

Figure 13.22. Two stages of double-ranked counter.

turn enable the up gate in the $(j+2)$nd stage, and so on. Thus, as in the ordinary cascaded toggle counter, the carry propagation is, in effect, the sequential turnover of a chain of toggles. The *double-ranked counter* has no advantage here; its settling time roughly is be-tween $\sqrt{n}$ and n times the flipping time of one toggle. Furthermore, the maximum input rate (or the resolution time) depends only on the characteristics of the first stage.

A New Property

Suppose that some number is in the true rank of such a counter. There is a unique *dual number* which must be in the false rank; assume that it is there. Notice that there can be no carry-like activity in the false rank. As a carry propagates through the true rank, it changes all the true toggles except the one at the end of the carry from 1 to 0. This is the change in true which enables the false-to-true gating, and thus the corresponding false toggles cannot have changed. In the final stage of the carry, there is a true toggle change from 0 to 1; in the next stage, this enables the true-to-false transfer which thereby changes that false toggle. Thus, beyond the first stage, one and only one false toggle can change at a time; the first stage false toggle changes on the other beat of the input signal. Thus the false rank counts in a reflected binary system (see page 2.20), but on every beat of the input signal, i.e., at double the input rate. One change occurs in the false rank for each beat of the input signal. This is sometimes a convenience which can be exploited (15).

The true and the false toggles of the input stage each change on every other beat of the input signals. So far as counting in normal binary is concerned, the maximum counting rate is the rate of occurrence of pairs of input signals; i.e., the resolution is the time between a given beat of one input pair and the same beat of the next input pair.

With additional intrastage gating, the double-ranked counter can also be made to count backward (subtracting counter) or to start from an arbitrary origin. The latter is slightly more complicated than simply gating the desired starting number into the true rank; the appropriate and unique dual number must be created in the false rank.

The Decimal Counter

As with other parts of a binary-coded-decimal machine, a decimal counter is basically a binary device which has been fudged to behave as a ten-stated device (16). Each stage of such a counter must count 0 through 9 and then return to 0 as it produces a carry. Each decimal stage thus is really a 4-stage binary counter; some special provision is made to return the counter stage to 0 and to emit a carry following the 9-state. Usually this takes the form of some special gating which recognizes the 9-state, and then so routes the next input signal (to that stage) that it clears the stage to 0 and produces a carry. Alternatively, special connections within the four stages can be used to short cycle the normal group of sixteen states. If more than a pulse indication of a carry is necessary, an auxiliary toggle might be used to provide the carry output.

To build a binary-coded-decimal counter, typically we take a 4-stage binary counter for each decimal digit and make special arrangements for the decimal carry and for discarding six states. A 4-stage binary counter operates in effect in the 8, 4, 2, 1 code. If a particular machine happens to use other than the 8, 4, 2, 1 code, the output of the binary-coded-decimal counter might have to be translated to the other code if the contents of the counter were to be used elsewhere in the machine. Alternatively, a counter might be designed to operate directly, say, in the 5, 4, 2, 1 code.

EXAMPLE

A binary-coded-decimal machine uses the 2*, 4, 2, 1 code. This means that address parts of instructions appear in this code, and therefore that the address selecting part of the store must respond to this code. The usual binary-coded-decimal counter works in the 8, 4, 2, 1 code, and therefore the contents of such an instruction counter are not acceptable to the store as an address. Among other problems, an 8, 4, 2, 1 counter will legitimately produce tetrads which are forbidden in the 2*, 4, 2, 1 code. Either the counter output must be translated to the appropriate code, or the store must be provided with a second address selection part which responds to 8, 4, 2, 1 code groups, or an entirely different kind of counter must be designed which operates directly in the 2*, 4, 2, 1 code.

Even at this late date in our discussion, we suddenly come across a factor which might be influential in determining the code chosen for a decimal machine!

For some speed ranges, special devices are available which are truly decimal in that they directly possess ten stable states (17). However, if such a counter is immersed in an otherwise binary-coded-decimal machine, the decimal counter output will have to be encoded into the proper form.

The Serial Counter

The foregoing discussion has been principally concerned with counters for parallel machines. However, much of it still applies to the serial counter, i.e., a counter for a serial machine (18). For example, a serial accumulator equipped with a half- (rather than full) adder will operate as a serial counter. The several stages of a spatially deployed parallel counter can be reconsidered as a single stage acting in time sequence on a string of information. The characteristic differences between parallel and serial behavior still obtain. For example, the carry problem largely evaporates as it did in the serial adder; there must be temporary storage for carry information produced at one time interval but needed later. The settling time of the counter is really one word time, although use of the count perhaps can be overlapped with forming the count. Possibly the digits of the count can be utilized as fast as they are formed. Since only one stage of equipment is used time sequentially, the resolution time is at best one word time.

Special Counters

Many special forms of counters are possible and may be required. One might be a counter which both counts forward and backward (adding and subtracting counter). In the accumulator-derived counter, this can be accomplished by providing both a half-adder and a half-subtractor; additional gating will be necessary to permit only one of them to operate at a time. The double-ranked counter can be bidirectional also.

Another special counter might be one which counts from an arbitrary initial count. Except in the case of the double-ranked counter, this implies only that an arbitrary number can be written into the counter, and hence write gates must be provided.

The double-ranked counter permits very complicated configurations. Given two counters of which only one need operate at a given time, it is possible to make one false rank serve both true ranks, and in fact, to use the false rank as the output of the counter (19). Any true rank which is at any moment unused retains the point at which it stopped counting and can resume from this point when connected to a false rank. Furthermore, several false ranks can be switched among a multiplicity of true ranks to provide a complex of counters with several output terminals (the false ranks); each false rank can resume counting with any true rank to which it is connected.

Other special counters include those for counting in unusual number systems (e.g., base 5), in special codes (reflected or binary-coded-decimal) or in some unusual sequence (even integers). There are also other techniques for building counters. For example, a *ring counter* uses one (or possibly two) storage devices per state of the counter and there are as many states as the counter is expected to register (20). A decimal ring-of-10, for example, may have twenty tubes for storage purposes plus gating elements. A mechanical counting wheel is analogous to a ring counter. It assumes a succession of angular positions for each count; eventually it returns to home position and passes a carry to the next more significant position. Cold cathode or thyratron tubes can be used in special configurations. Magnetic elements can be used for counters; special beam deflection tubes have been used—and on and on. Many of these techniques are potentially useful to the computer designer, but not too many of them have proved popular nor have found widespread application.

COLLATERAL READING

1. Siegel, P., *Understanding digital computers;* John Wiley and Sons, New York, 1961; chapter 15.

   Bartee, T. C., *Digital computer fundamentals;* McGraw-Hill Book Co., New York, 1960; chapter 9.

   Flores, I., *Computer logic;* Prentice-Hall, Englewood Cliffs, N.J., 1960; chapter 14.

   Ledley, R. S., *Digital computer and control engineering;* McGraw-Hill Book Co., New York, 1960; chapter 17.

   Smith, C. V. L., *Electronic digital computers;* McGraw-Hill Book Co., New York, 1959; chapter 15.

   McCormick, E. H., *Digital computer primer;* McGraw-Hill Book Co., New York, 1959; chapter 6.

   Murphy, J. S., *Basics of digital computers;* John F. Rider Publisher, New York, 1958; vol. 3, pp. 81–105.

   Richards, R. K., *Arithmetic operations in digital computers;* D. Van Nostrand Co., Princeton, N.J., 1956; chapter 11.

2. Phister, M., *Logical design of digital computers;* John Wiley and Sons, New York, 1958; chapter 11.

   Ledley, R. S., *Digital computer and control engineering;* McGraw-Hill Book Co., New York, 1960; pp. 631–634.

   Smith, C. V. L., *Electronic digital computers;* McGraw-Hill Book Co., New York, 1959; pp. 364–365.

   Murphy, J. S., *Basics of digital computers;* John F. Rider Publisher, New York, 1958; vol. 3, pp. 38–54.

3. Scott, N. R., *Analog and digital computer technology;* McGraw-Hill Book Co., New York, 1960; pp. 402–403.

4. Smith, C. V. L., *Electronic digital computers;* McGraw-Hill Book Co., New York, 1959; pp. 364–384.

   Estrin, G., A description of the electronic computer at the Institute for Advanced Studies; *Proceedings of the Association for Computing Machinery,* Toronto, 12–14 September, 1952; pp. 95–109.

   Chu, J. C., The Oak Ridge automatic computer; *Proceedings of the Association for Computing Machinery,* Toronto, 12–14 September, 1952; pp. 142–148.

   Sims, J. C., Jr. and K. J. Gray, Design criteria for autosynchronous circuits; *Proceedings of the 1958 Eastern Joint Computer Conference,* Philadelphia, 3–5 December, 1958; pp. 95–99.

   Kliman, M. and O. Lowenschuss, Asynchronous electronic switching circuits; *IRE Convention Record,* pt. 4, 1959; pp. 267–274.

   Reports of the Digital Computer Laboratory, University of Illinois, Urbana, Ill., for example, see report 66 (Mueller), 73 (Poppelbaum *et al.*), 75 and 78 (Mueller *et al.*), and 96 (Bartky).

5. Maley, G. A. and J. Earle, *The logic design of transistor digital computers;* Prentice-Hall, Englewood Cliffs, N.J., 1963; chapter 6.

    Reports of the Digital Computer Laboratory, University of Illinois, Urbana, Ill., especially various reports by Mueller.

6. Buchholz, W., *Planning a computer;* McGraw-Hill Book Co., New York, 1962; chapter 11.

    Smith, C. V. L., *Electronic digital computers;* McGraw-Hill Book Co., New York, 1959; pp. 384–386.

7. Buchholz, W., *Planning a computer;* McGraw-Hill Book Co., New York, 1962; chapter 15.

    Blaauw, G. A., Indexing and control word techniques; *IBM Journal of Research and Development,* vol. 3, July, 1959; pp. 288–301.

8. Buchholz, W., *Planning a computer;* McGraw-Hill Book Co., New York, 1962; pp. 31, 196–197.

9. Brooks, F. P., Jr., A program-controlled program interruption system; *Proceedings of the 1957 Eastern Joint Computer Conference,* Washington, 9–13 December, 1947; pp. 128–132.

    Turner, L. R. and J. H. Rawlings, Realization of randomly timed computer input and output by means of an interrupt feature; *IRE Transactions on Electronic Computers,* vol. EC-7, June, 1958; pp. 141–149.

10. Grasseli, A., The design of program modifiable micro-programmed control units; *IRE Transactions on Electronic Computers,* vol. EC-11, February, 1962; pp. 336–339.

    Blankenbaker, J. V., Logically micro-programmed computers; *IRE Transactions on Electronic Computers,* vol. EC-7, June, 1958; pp. 103–109.

    Wilkes, M. V., Microprogramming; *Proceedings of the 1958 Eastern Joint Computer Conference,* Philadelphia, 3–5 December, 1958; pp. 18–20.

    Kampe, T. W., The design of a general purpose microprogrammed control computer with elementary structure; *IRE Transactions on Electronic Computers,* vol. EC-9, June, 1960; pp. 208–213.

11. Siegel, P., *Understanding digital computers;* John Wiley and Sons, New York, 1961; pp. 143–146.

    Bartee, T. C, *Digital computer fundamentals;* McGraw-Hill Book Co., New York, 1960; pp. 95–99.

    Flores, I., *Computer logic;* Prentice-Hall, Englewood Cliffs, N.J., 1960; pp. 196–206.

    Scott, N. R., *Analog and digital computer technology;* McGraw-Hill Book Co., New York, 1960; pp. 345–348.

    Smith, C. V. L., *Electronic digital computers;* McGraw-Hill Book Co., New York, 1959; chapter 9.

    Murphy, J. S., *Basics of digital computers;* John F. Rider Publisher, New York, 1958; vol. 2, pp. 13–18, 114–116.

    Phister, M., *Logical design of digital computers;* John Wiley and Sons, New York, 1958; pp. 117–119, 135–137.

    Richards, R. K., *Arithmetic operations in digital computers;* D. Van Nostrand Co., Princeton, N.J., 1956; chapter 7.

    Grosdoff, I. E., Electronic counters; *RCA Review,* vol. 8, September, 1946; pp. 438–447.

12. Smith, C. V. L., *Electronic digital computers;* McGraw-Hill Book Co., New York, 1959; pp. 197–201.

13. Campeau, J. O., The synthesis and analysis of digital systems by Boolean matrices; *IRE Transactions on Electronic Computers,* vol. EC-6, December, 1957; pp. 231–241.

   Kautz, W. H., State logic relations in autonomous sequential networks; *Proceedings of the 1958 Eastern Joint Computer Conference,* Philadelphia, 3–5 December, 1958; pp. 119–127.

14. Smith, C. V. L., *Electronic digital computers;* McGraw-Hill Book Co., New York, 1959; pp. 202–212.

   Ware, W. H., Logical principles of a new kind of binary counter; *Proceedings of the IRE,* vol. 41, October, 1953; pp. 1429–1437.

   Golay, M. J. E., The logic of bidirectional binary counters; *IRE Transactions on Electronic Computers,* vol. EC-6, March, 1957; pp. 1–4.

   Robertson, J. E., Odd binary asynchronous counters; *IRE Transactions on Electronic Computers,* vol. EC-5, March, 1956; pp. 12–15.

15. Brown, R. M., Some notes on logical binary counters; *IRE Transactions on Electronic Computers,* vol. EC-2, June, 1955; pp. 67–69.

16. Smith, C. V. L., *Electronic digital computers;* McGraw-Hill Book Co., New York, 1959; pp. 201–202.

   Murphy, J. S., *Basics of digital computers;* John F. Rider Publisher, New York, 1958; vol. 2, p. 117.

   Phister, M., *Logical design of digital computers;* John Wiley and Sons, New York, 1958; pp. 251–253.

   Brigham, R. C., Some properties of binary counters with feedback; *IRE Transactions on Electronic Computers,* vol. EC-10, December, 1961; pp. 699–701.

   Grosdoff, I. E., Electronic counters; *RCA Review,* vol. 8, September, 1946; pp. 438–447.

17. Smith, C. V. L., *Electronic digital computers;* McGraw-Hill Book Co., New York, 1959; pp. 215–217.

18. Smith, C. V. L., *Electronic digital computers;* McGraw-Hill Book Co., New York, 1959; pp. 212–215.

19. Ware, W. H., Logical principles of a new kind of binary counter; *Proceedings of the IRE,* vol. 41, October, 1953; pp. 1429–1437.

20. Siegel, P., *Understanding digital computers;* John Wiley and Sons, New York, 1961; pp. 146–149.

   Burks, A. W., Electronic computing circuits of the ENIAC; *Proceedings of the IRE,* vol. 35, August, 1947; pp. 756–767.

EXERCISES

13.1. Draw the circuit diagram of a register suitable for the instruction register of HYPAC-I. What features must it have? Use vacuum-tube or transistor technology, as you wish, and select an appropriate gating scheme.

13.2. List the numeric operation parts of HYPAC-I, and identify the Boolean expression that must be recognized for each of them. Now sketch the logical block diagram of a decoder that will provide a unique output for each of the operation parts in the repertoire. Include all information flow paths and gates.

Draw the detailed circuit diagram. Use first diode logic, then NOR logic. Assume that the complements as well as the direct variables are available.

13.3. Sketch a functional block diagram of the HYPAC-I instruction counter. What features must it have? Include all special inputs, gates, output terminals, etc.

13.4. Sketch the functional block diagram of the HYPAC-I arithmetic counter. Indicate all input and output terminals, gates, etc. Decide how the counter will be handled to indicate the completion of a Shift instruction. Decide how to handle the counting of the steps in a Multiply or Divide instruction.

13.5. Describe the events that must happen in the "control-of-the-control" wired-in procedure that cycles the HYPAC-I control through the fetch-interpret-execute sequence for each instruction. Decide on the sequence in which the events must happen; and indicate any which may co-occur with others, or whose position on the list is somewhat flexible. Keep in mind that the arrangement must work for every kind of HYPAC-I instruction.

13.6. From the sequenced event list of the previous example, construct a timing chart for the "control-of-the-control" sequence. Define literal symbols as required for various time intervals. For example, let

t_A be the read-in time of the instruction register
t_B be the clear time of the instruction register
t_C be the time to insert a 1 into the instruction counter
t_D be the carry time of the instruction counter
t_E be the cycle time of the store
t_F be the read access time of the store
t_G be the reaction time of the decoder
t_H be the time to establish a few-input gate

$\cdot$

$\cdot$

$\cdot$

etc.

Decide when the instruction counter is advanced, when to route the address, how to accommodate the special action required by the Branch and Jump instructions.

13.7. For each operation part in the HYPAC-I instruction, list the detailed events which must occur to complete it. Decide on the sequence in which events must happen; and indicate any which may co-occur with others, or whose position in the list is somewhat flexible.

13.8. From the event lists of the previous exercise, construct a timing chart for each kind of HYPAC-I instruction. Define literal symbols as required for various time intervals. For example, let

t_1 be the carry time of the adder
t_2 be the gate-in time of MQ
t_3 be the clear time of MQ
t_4 be the gate-out time of MQ
t_5 be the time to inspect the sign of the Accumulator
t_6 be the time to establish a simple few-input gate
t_7 be the time to establish a many-input gate or one with a heavy load such as an end-to-end register connection

t_8 be the cycle time of the store
t_9 be the read access time of the store

.

.

.

etc.

Assume that the execution of the instruction begins with all signals from the interpret phase of the control quiescent and established. The address is present and ready to be used during execution.

13.9. From the event lists of exercise 13.7, identify which events (or groups of events) are common to more than one instruction. Then check the timing charts from exercise 13.8 to see if the common events occur at the same relative time during execution. If so, the inputs from the several outputs of the decoder (one for each kind of instruction in which the event occurs) can be ored together and then anded with a suitable timing signal to control the event. Where possible, adjust the time position of events to maximize the number of groups of events which are common to several kinds of instructions. This may require putting an event in a different place in its sequence or rounding some time intervals upward to reduce the number of different time intervals involved. (The progression of design through exercises 13.7, 13.8, and 13.9 continues with problem 13.1.)

13.10. In problem 14.5, we will complete the design of hypac-i's console. For the moment, decide how signals from the console can be inserted into the control

(a) to stop it after the completion of each instruction;
(b) to make it repeat the instruction it has just completed;
(c) to make it stop after the fetch, after the interpret, and after the execute phase.

At this time do not be concerned about any synchronizing problems that may result from console operation.

13.11. Why might it be desirable not to advance the instruction counter until the completion of the current instruction? (*Hint:* consider the information which the programmer needs in case the machine fails to complete an instruction.)

13.12. Assume that the simple zero-address Index instruction described on page 13.38 is added to the hypac-i repertoire. Describe how to implement such an instruction type. Preserve the maximum amount of information for the programmer as protection against machine malfunction. Describe what extra equipment is needed in the control section, what extra events must occur, and what changes must be made in existing equipment in the control.

13.13. Suppose that hypac-i is given seven index registers as described on pages 13.37 *ff.* The word length is increased by three bits to permit an indexing option on every instruction.

Decide on a set of operation parts to be added to the hypac-i repertoire to handle these registers properly. There must be a capability for loading and storing each index register. There must be a Branch instruction which tests the contents of a given register for equality to 0. If not zero, the Branch is unsatisfied and the given index register is counted up by 1. If equal to 0, the Branch is satisfied.

13.14. For the indexing option described in the previous exercise, describe what new events must be prefixed to the execution of each instruction. Give the timing and the sequence of these new events. What additions and changes to the control must be made?

13.15. For each of the instruction types added to the machine repertoire in exercise 13.13, determine the event list and the timing chart. Indicate the necessary additions and changes to the control.

13.16. In the next chapter, HYPAC-I will be given a variety of input-output devices. From time to time one of them will need attention (e.g., new information for printing or punching). Would it be sensible to include such attention requests within the framework of an interrupt-trapping scheme such as described on pages 13.44 *ff.*?

13.17. Describe how to make a one-stage binary counter from
      (a) the asymmetrical toggle,
      (b) the dynamic toggle.
Describe any extra components that are added to the basic circuits. Identify any temporary storage that may be present. Try to achieve the design: first, by adding extra components within the toggle proper, and second, by adding components external to the toggle.

13.18. Draw the circuit diagram of a 4-stage counter having as storage elements
      (a) the symmetrical toggle using relays (see problem 8.19),
      (b) the dynamic toggle,
      (c) the asymmetrical toggle,
      (d) the toggle based on logical elements (see problem 8.18).
In each case describe how you have arranged the interstage coupling. Discuss the resolution and settling times of each case.

13.19. In view of the discussion on page 13.51, reconsider the decision that you made in exercise 13.4 concerning the counting of multiplication and division steps. Can you optimize your choice?

13.20. Draw the circuit diagram of a 4-stage counter using external steering gates. How many inputs have you decided to use for each steering gate? Why? What constraints does your design levy on the input signal?

13.21. Draw the detailed circuit diagram of a 4-stage half-adder counter. Select a toggle and appropriate gating techniques for the half-adders. Describe the operating sequence of such a counter, and specify all input signals.

Design the logic of an input mechanism which accepts a single input signal and produces for each one the set of signals necessary to operate the counter through a complete cycle.

13.22. Layout the interstage and intrastage logic of a double-ranked counter that progresses in either direction.

13.23. Select some number in the true rank of a double-ranked counter, and deduce how the corresponding dual number can be constructed in the false rank.

Correlate your discussion with numbers of the normal and reflected binary number systems and ways for converting between them.

13.24. Consider a 4-stage binary counter. Determine what additional logic must be added to the counter so that it counts in base 10. After the count of 9, it must return to 0 and produce a decimal carry. Show circuit details.

PROBLEMS

13.1. Draw a functional block diagram of the complete control of HYPAC-I. Include all information paths, gates with all inputs, registers, decoders, toggles, etc., to handle all instructions in the original repertoire of the machine and the "control of the control." Indicate those gate inputs which require timing inputs, but leave them unspecified for the moment. As required, use the results of exercises 13.5 through 13.9.

13.2. From exercise 13.9, you have developed considerable insight into the timing requirements of HYPAC-I. Assume that timing will be done synchronously. Decide on the details of the clock. Is a multiphase arrangement desirable? Lay out the logic of the scheme you have decided on. Assume that the original source of signals is a stable oscillator producing an output pulse at regular intervals.

13.3. Suppose that the HYPAC-I control is to be asynchronous. Lay out the logical diagram of that part of the control which governs the fetch-interpret-execute sequence. Do not include the sequencing required to handle the individual steps of an instruction. Assume that an invitation signal is sent to another part of the control to sequence each instruction, and that this other part reports completion of the instruction. Your design is to include all details of the fetch, advancing the instruction counter, routing information to the decoder, etc.

How can the carry delay time be accommodated in an asynchronously organized control?

13.4. Sketch the logical block diagram of the special part of a control required to sequence the events of floating-point arithmetic.

13.5. Construct a block diagram of an electronic commutator. A single input signal is to be connected periodically to a sequence of output terminals. Sketch the gating networks required to implement the commutator.

13.6. Draw a logical block diagram of the equipment necessary to implement the results of exercises 13.14 and 13.15. Indicate all gates and their inputs; include the instruction register and instruction counter in the diagram; indicate all timing signal inputs.

13.7. Suppose that HYPAC-I has the drum store proposed in exercise 12.11. Each drum contains its own timing tracks. When the drum communicates via the arithmetic section to the primary store, either all timing must be determined by the drum clock, or somehow the clock of HYPAC-I's synchronous control must be synchronized with the drum.

How would you handle this problem? What options are available? Will the tolerances on the time position of the drum clock interact with the circuit design and detailed timing of other parts of the machine? Reconsider the situation for an asynchronously organized HYPAC-I control. How can initiation and sequencing of events be turned over to the drum clock? Sketch the block diagram of any equipment that is necessary to bridge the interface between the internal control and the drum timing signals.

13.8. Rewrite the routine of problem 6.9 assuming that HYPAC-I has the indexing scheme of exercise 13.12. Rewrite the routine again, but assume the indexing scheme described in exercise 13.13. Is one indexing scheme significantly more powerful than the other?

13.9. An index register can be used to increment or decrement the base address to form the effective address. Is one of the two possibilities more advantageous to the programmer?

13.10. Consider an extension of the indexing scheme described in exercise 13.13. A second 3-bit field is added to the instruction format, so that the contents of two index registers can be used to modify the instruction. Furthermore, assume that there are only six index registers. The contents of the instruction counter is considered as the seventh indexing quantity, and the eighth circumstance is that of no indexing.

Is the ability to index by the contents of the instruction counter a valuable one for the programmer? Will it help the problem of relocating routines in the store (see exercise 6.21)? Will it help the problem of calling subroutines in from a library for insertion into a new problem routine? Does it make sense to index all kinds of instructions by the contents of the instruction counter?

13.11. In indexing, the programmer may wish to either increment or decrement the base address. This suggests that the indexing quantity may have to be a signed quantity, and that subtraction may be required in the control.

Discuss this issue. What are the various solutions to the problem? If the indexing quantity is signed, must all addresses then become signed quantities? Can the whole problem somehow be side-stepped? What is your recommended way for a hardware arrangement that will give the programmer the desired flexibility? Justify your stand.

13.12. Consider a machine which automatically indexes every appropriate instruction by the contents of the instruction counter. There might also be the more usual index registers under control of an address field. What are the implications of this for the programmer? Is it convenient or not? Is it useful? Desirable? Troublesome? Awkward? A nuisance?

13.13. Describe some schemes (other than the one on page 13.41) for verifying that the control responded properly to a given instruction. How much equipment is involved? Does such a scheme impose any time penalty on a machine? If so, is there a way around the problem?

13.14. Describe what modifications must be made in HYPAC-I's control to give a look-ahead of one instruction. The next instruction will be obtained during the execution of the current one. Keep in mind that the fetch of the next instruction requires a consultation of the store, but the execution of the current instruction also may require this. Describe how to resolve this conflict and priority problem. Consider what can happen if the current instruction is completed before the next fetch is finished. Indicate the new equipment that must be added to the control, and determine a new event list and timing chart.

What happens if the next instruction is a Halt? Should the look-ahead be disabled? What happens if the current instruction turns out to be a satisfied Branch, and the already fetched instruction is not needed? How is the look-ahead refilled? (This same problem also occurs when starting on a new routine.)

13.15. We have described relative addressing as one way to direct the control to obtain information from the store. In a multiaddress format, one address field could be the relative address of the next instruction.

Under what circumstances might relative addressing be useful or desirable?

13.16. Describe how interlock registers can be added to HYPAC-I. What equipment is needed? What new kinds of instructions are needed? How does each kind of instruction operate? Describe the new events that the control must prefix to each instruction. Determine the event list and the timing chart.

Suppose that a programmer were not interested in using the interlock registers. How must the system be arranged to accommodate this? Can the control be arranged so that it spends no time checking the interlock registers when the programmer is not using them?

13.17. Describe how to organize the logic of a control to deal with variable length instructions. What extra equipment is required? How does it operate? How is it interconnected?

13.18. Suppose that HYPAC-I were to acquire the indexing, look-ahead, and interlock registers suggested in various problems and exercises. Revise your reply to problem 13.1 to cover the augmented HYPAC-I organization. Reconsider your answer to problem 13.2. Are changes necessary in the details of the clock?

13.19. Draw the detailed circuit diagram of a counter which is suitable for the instruction counter of HYPAC-I. Repeat, but for the arithmetic counter.

Repeat each of the above, but specifically use double-ranked counters. Keep in mind that for an arbitrary starting point, the false rank must contain the proper dual number.

13.20. Determine the logical requirements for a 3-stage decimal counter to operate in

        (a) the 5, 4, 2, 1 code,

        (b) the 2*, 4, 2, 1 code,

        (c) the 5, 3, 1, 1 code.

For each case, draw a logical block diagram and estimate the amount of equipment.

Now lay out the logical diagram of a 3-stage counter operating in the 8, 4, 2, 1 code (see exercise 13.24), and add to it a diode matrix to convert the 8, 4, 2, 1 code to each of the others. Give the truth table which defines the converter in each case, and determine the amount of equipment in it. Decide whether, in each case, it is preferable to build the 8, 4, 2, 1 counter plus converter or to build a counter directly in the code of interest.

13.21. Draw the circuit diagram of a 3-stage double-ranked counter using relays for all elements.

13.22. Lay out the logic of an externally-steered 4-stage counter which counts frontward and backward.

13.23. We have seen that a counter can be designed which has two disjoint modes of operation (pages 13.55 *ff.*). If the operation part of the current instruction were used as the initial state of such a counter, the successive states belonging to the mode determined by the initial value might be used to cycle the machine through the sequence of configurations required to execute the instruction. Discuss this possibility. Will the length of the operation part have to be much longer than the size of the operation catalog might otherwise imply? Could a catalog of 2^n entries be accommodated by an n-place counter?

fourteen

Input—Output

REVIEW

The *input-output* section of a machine provides the principal contact with the environment in which the machine is imbedded (1). Through the input devices flow the data and routines needed to solve a problem. The machine may also require cues or assistance from operating personnel; such information, generally manually inserted through one or more *consoles* is also a kind of input information. The input devices are the machine's listening link with its world.

If the machine's world is that of people, the input devices are likely to be keyboards, punched-card equipment, paper or magnetic tapes, etc. If the machine's world is that of other machines, input devices may include, in addition, analog-digital converters or digital-digital converters. The latter may be required to convert one machine coding of information (*machine language*) into a different coding.

The output devices are the machine's speaking link with its world. Through this channel flows finished or intermediate results of a problem, or isolated pieces of information which relate to status of the machine, progress in the problem, etc. Frequently, status information or indications which require operator attention are presented on one or more consoles; visual display of intermediate or final problem results may also occur at a console.

If the machine's world is that of people, the output devices might include page printers, line printers, card equipment, visual displays, paper or magnetic tapes, plotters, etc. For a world consisting of other machines, digital-analog or digital-digital converters may be needed.

How Fast

Since the bulk of the information which a machine requires or produces must flow through the input-output, there is an obvious requirement to have such devices operate at as high an information flow rate as possible, consistent with the general operating speed of the machine. Unfortunately, presently available input-output devices tend to be slower than the internal electronic speeds of a machine.

Suppose that a machine could not modify nor create instructions, and that the concept of looping did not exist. Each instruction which entered through the input device could be executed only once. In such a situation, the maximum rate at which the system can execute instructions is exactly equal to the maximum rate at which instructions can be trafficked through the input device. It is clear, therefore, that the concept of looping, plus the ability of a machine to make a choice and to modify or create instructions, all help to ease any mismatch between fast internal machine speeds and slower input speeds.

Tricks can be employed to raise the effective speed of input or output devices. A multiplicity of devices might be operated in an interleaved fashion; so to speak, the group of slow devices time share the faster parts of the system. The system may be arranged so that other events can occur simultaneously, or nearly so, with input or output operations. The precise details of such tricks will appear as our discussion develops.

CARD EQUIPMENT

A common input device for a digital machine is a reader for punched paper cards; a common output device, a punch for producing punched paper cards. In either case, the *unit record* of information is a paper card, which is a handy unit record and has some advantages. It is easily handled and additional information can be inserted into a deck of cards—or spurious information deleted—by adding or removing cards. The card art is a carry over from older techniques of punched-card accounting equipment (2).

A card is considered to contain so many columns and so many rows into which information can be put. The presence of information is generally associated with the presence of holes in the card.

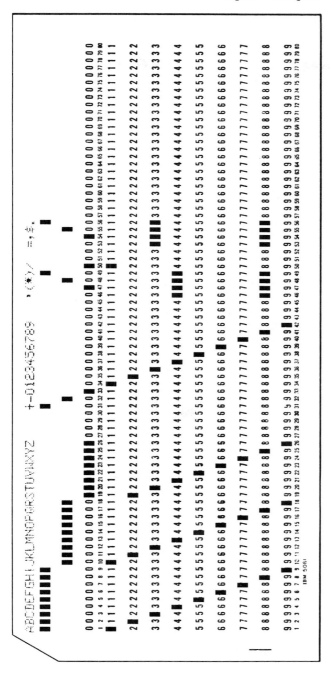

Figure 14.1. A typical IBM card format.

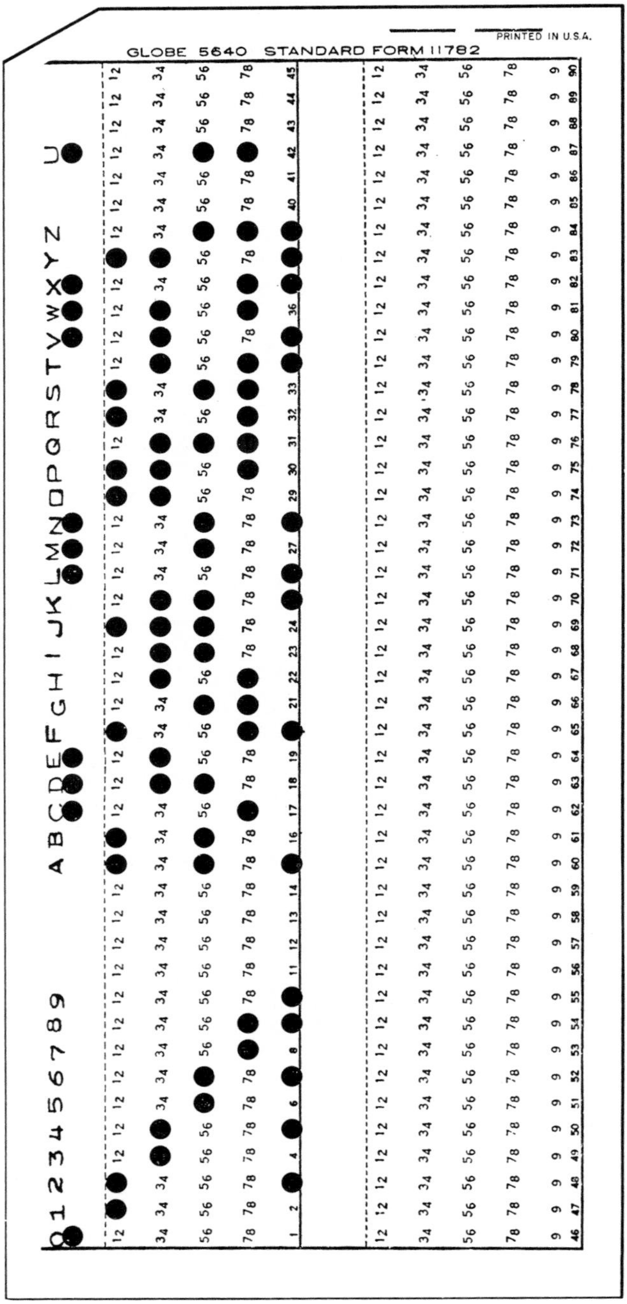

Figure 14.2. A typical Remington Rand card format.

In the IBM format, the card contains twelve rows and eighty columns, and it can, therefore, contain a maximum of 960 punches, each of which is a rectangular hole. If each column is considered to be a 12-place binary number, there can be 2^{12} or 4096 different entries in any column. However, except for a card punch which happens to be an output device for a computer system, normally only single, double, and a few triple punches are permitted in any column. Typically, a *machine alphabet* of forty-seven characters is available—numeric, plus the letter alphabet, plus punctuation and special symbols. Figure 14.1 shows a typical alphabet; the punctuation marks and special symbols may be changed to suit particular cases.

We see that numeric information is represented by a punch in one of ten row positions. Alphabetic information is represented by a punch in one of nine *numeric positions* plus a *zone punch* which can be either in the 0-*row*, or in one of two additional *over-punch* or *high-punch* rows, X and Y. The few characters which require triple punches are easily seen. Sometimes a zone punch is used to indicate special information, such as algebraic sign.* The interpretation of the punches depends on the way the information is subsequently handled by the routine. The particular kind of card code shown in Figure 14.1 is often called a *Hollerith code*.

In the Remington Rand card format, physically the card is forty-five columns by twelve rows; punches are round. However, logically the card is usually regarded as ninety columns by six rows. A more sophisticated coding is used to represent alphanumeric information in each of the two six-row positions of each column. Figure 14.2 shows a typical Remington Rand card code.

For either kind of card, devices exist for originating a card from a keyboard, for comparing cards, for sorting cards, for reproducing cards, for printing the contents of a card, and for doing moderately simple logical and arithmetic operations with the data on a card. Card devices often contain relay selectors and plug boards which together permit simple data manipulations.

The Card Reader

A *card reader* consists of a mechanism for feeding a card from an input hopper, a mechanism for sensing the holes in the card, and a

---

* A zone punch can be used for the special mark which HYPAC-I requires to terminate loading. See page 6.9 of Volume I.

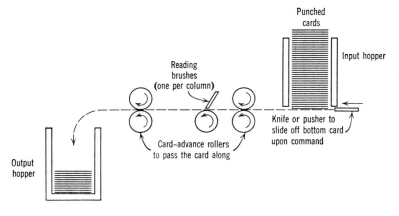

Figure 14.3. The mechanism of a typical card reader.

mechanism for stacking the card in an output hopper (Figure 14.3). The feed mechanism can be either a mechanical device to pick the card from the input hopper, or vacuum operated. Generally the feed can stop between cards. This gives the programmer freedom to feed one or several cards as he requires. A series of rollers or drums is used to move the card and to position it for reading.

The hole sensing mechanism can be mechanical pins, brushes, a light-photocell arrangement, etc. In each case, the card is usually read one row at a time; there will generally be as many reading brushes (or photocells) as physical columns in the card. Reading is, therefore, parallel by column but serial by row. Sometimes more than one reading station is provided so that a card can be read more than once, e.g., for checking. In some readers, the card is fed end-on rather than broadside so that reading is parallel by row and serial by column. The columns are read in time sequence to produce parallel character codes.

The stacking mechanism drops the cards into an output hopper, and hence the stack of cards after reading is in the same sequence as before reading.

Unusual forms of card handlers can be conceived. For example, one form uses vacuum to stick the card to the surface of a rapidly rotating drum. Air jets can be used to flip cards onto or off of drums, or from one drum to another.

Card-reading rates vary from a few tens per minute to a few thousand per minute. As the speed increases, the difficulty of moving the card without skewing increases, as does the uncertainty in actual card position. For slower rates, it is sufficient to use electrically marked angular positions of a shaft (e.g., with a commutator) to in-dicate which position of the card is currently under the reading station. At high card speeds, uncertainty in the starting time plus slippage in the drive rollers makes it necessary to use other techniques. One pos-sibility is to start a timing device as the leading edge of the card passes some point; if the velocity from card to card is sufficiently constant, the time at which each row will be read can be deduced.

A card reader—or punch, or other electromechanical device for that matter—may be a severe source of electrical noise. Such spurious signals can interfere with other electronics, especially high-speed cir-cuits which are responsive to a wide band of noise energy.

The Card Punch

The *card punch* is basically a slower device than the reader because it is necessary to physically move material in order to create the hole (Figure 14.4). Punching is generally done by a mechanically driven die, which implies that generally the card must stop at each row position. The actual selection of the dies to be driven can be done either mechanically or electrically, but the information governing the selection mechanism, of course, is contained in electrical signals from other parts of the machine system.

The card-feeding device and stacker are generally similar to those of a reader. Typically, card punches operate at one to a few hundred cards per minute.

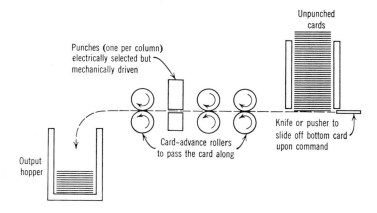

Figure 14.4. The mechanism of a typical card punch.

Card Codes

So far as the central portion of the computing system is concerned, each hole position read in any card simply conveys one bit of information. To the system, there may well be no intrinsic meaning to the pattern of holes in the card. The meaning will be developed by the routine as it manipulates the card information as prescribed by the programmer. Often, each row of a card is read and placed in the store as one or more words; a punch might correspond to a binary 1 and no punch to a 0, or vice versa. After all twelve rows have been read, the store will contain a *card image* expressed as a pattern of 1's and 0's. The routine must then manipulate such data in an appropriate fashion (3).

EXAMPLES

1. In a machine whose word length is forty bits, each row of an eighty-column card can be stored in two words. Therefore, a complete card image of twelve rows will take twenty-four words in storage.

2. If the word length of a machine were thirty-six bits, the effective card width will probably be seventy-two columns; the eight extra columns can be used for information which the system will not read, or perhaps will deal with in a different way.

3. The information from one column of a card will be distributed in consecutive words in the store but in the same column of each word. To interpret the card image, the routine must extract the jth bit from the appropriate words of the image and reassemble the twelve bits into a new machine word which can then be recognized as an appropriate character. Each vertical column of the card must "turn the corner" and become a horizontal machine word before further processing can be done. The recognition of such character codes can be done conveniently by storing a table of symbol equivalences. For example, in a machine which is internally binary but uses Hollerith code for input, the first few lines of the table are as follows:

CARD CHARACTER	IMAGE CHARACTER	TABLE ENTRY
1	000000000001	00 · · · · 0001
2	000000000010	00 · · · · 0010
3	000000000100	00 · · · · 0011
4	000000001000	00 · · · · 0100
·	·	·
·	·	·
·	·	·

Each line of the table carries the binary equivalent of the corresponding decimal digit; the image character is, effectively, address information which is used to enter the proper line of the table. Among other things, the routine must construct the proper address from the image character (see exercise 14.1).

4. If the card code is fixed for a given machine, the table of symbol equivalences can equally well be wired into the machine. It will probably appear as a gating matrix which has as input the image character, and has as output the machine representation of the corresponding card characters (exercise 14.6). Alternatively, the table of equivalences can be placed in a read-only store.

In the light of these examples, notice the influence that the number of card columns has in deciding the word length of a system.

Because the card image contains a complete record of all information on the card, and because the image can be processed in a flexible manner by the routine, the programmer in principle is free to use any card code which he wishes. However, the keypunch for originating cards is normally restricted to one standard code. If the cards produced by a computer are to be processed by other punched-card devices, it may not be possible to use an arbitrary code for output punching because other punched-card equipment may be incapable of interpreting a non-standard code. If the output cards are to be reused as input for a digital machine, the programmer can do as he sees fit. In particular he may attempt to maximize the amount of information contained on each card; this minimizes both punching and reading time.

EXAMPLES

1. An eighty-column card can be used to contain twenty-four 40-bit words; each word is contained in the right or left forty columns of a row.

2. A forty-five column card can contain ninety 6-bit alphanumeric characters; each character is contained in the upper or lower group of six-row positions of a column.

3. In seventy-two columns of each row of a card, there can be placed twelve 6-bit alphanumeric characters.

4. An eighty-column card can convey 960 bits of information; a forty-five column card, 540 bits.

It is clear that when outputting cards, the routine must first construct the image of the card to be produced and then feed this image to the punch one word at a time as each row comes into punching position.

It is, of course, true that the card image method need not be used. Converters—either electronic or electromechanical—might be provided in the punch and reader to convert from the card code to the machine code. This results in a loss of flexibility to the user, but will relieve the machine of a certain time burden, and the users of a certain programming burden.

Timing

Since the card is in motion during reading, the signals read from each row are transient. When the information is available, the machine must accept it. So to speak, the card reader has a certain amount of priority once a card has been set in motion; when it is ready to speak, it must be listened to. On the other hand, compared to electronic speeds, a fair amount of time elapses between successive rows of a card—especially for the slower readers. Commonly, therefore, routines for processing cards are arranged to compute between the rows of a card. Often enough time is available to permit the card image to be completely processed by the end of the card; this might include conversion of information to binary form.

EXAMPLE

Assume that the card-reading rate is a hundred cards per minute; furthermore, assume that the spacing between successive cards is one-half the height of the card (equivalent to six card rows). The row rate is $(12 + 6) \cdot (100)$ or 1800 rows per minute or 30 rows per second. Between successive rows, $\frac{1}{30}$ sec (33 msec) is available for computing; between cards roughly 200 msec is available. From these figures must be subtracted whatever time is required to actually read the row, plus whatever time is allowed to guard against tolerance problems. Even for a machine whose addition time is, say, 300 μsec, considerable computation can be done between rows. Obviously, the only restriction is that the routine must be ready to accept a row's worth of information when it comes.

For punching, a similar situation exists. Computing can be done between rows, but the routine must be ready to provide a row's worth of information when the punch needs it. Typically, the computation between rows includes preparation of the card image, and perhaps also conversion of binary data to a decimal or alphanumeric representation.

PAPER-TAPE DEVICES

Punched paper tape can be thought of as a variant of a card; the number of rows is indefinite, but the number of *channels* (rather than columns) is now from five to eight. In each position (*line*) across the tape, a character of five to eight bits is contained; its meaning can depend on the designer or on the user. Devices exist for preparing punched tape from a keyboard, for comparing two tapes, for reproducing a tape, and for operating a character-at-a-time printer (typewriter) (4).

The paper-tape transport generally can stop between adjacent characters so that the programmer can read one or more characters at a time. Reading speeds vary from a few hundred characters per minute for mechanical sensing of the holes, to several hundred or a thousand characters per second for photoelectric sensing of the holes. Punching speed is 10–60 characters per second. The punching dies may be electrically or mechanically driven.

Many of the remarks about cards also apply to paper tape. Computing can be done between characters; there is considerable flexibility in what code the programmer (or designer) uses; the tape motion is synchronous in nature so that timing between the central part of the machine and paper-tape units must be watched.

PRINTERS

Printing devices may be characterized by a variety of features:

1. page printing versus line printing,
2. character at a time versus line at a time,
3. number of carbon copies,
4. number of columns,
5. number of characters (size of alphabet or font),
6. paper format control, perhaps including a high-speed slewing motion,

7. printing mechanism,
8. character selection.

EXAMPLES

1. A typewriter is a character-at-a-time page printer which can make several carbon copies, provides many tens of characters per line, offers a font usually of 80–90 characters, and has a certain amount of format control in each line (tab stops). Some typewriters have a format control which allows slewing of the paper to predetermined positions. Character selection is by choice of key plus choice of upper or lower character on the key; printing is by impact of the hammer which prints the type face through an inked ribbon onto the paper.

2. A particular tabulator from a line of punched-card equipment prints an entire line at a time, and is a page printer; it makes several carbon copies, offers 120 characters (columns) per line, and has available an alphabet of forty-seven characters. Through an auxiliary punched-paper, carriage-control tape, paper can be slewed to a variety of designated positions. Character selection—as will be seen later—is by choosing the proper angular position of a type wheel, and printing is again by impact of the wheel through an inked ribbon to the paper.

3. The printer of the stock market ticker tape is a character-at-a-time line printer.

Roughly speaking, the features of a mechanical printer divide into two kinds: those that have to do with character selection and the printing mechanism—getting a character onto paper; and those that have to do with motion of the paper—getting the paper to the right place to receive the character (5).

Stopped-Character Printing

One kind of mechanical printing selects the character and moves it so that the only motion is perpendicular to the inked ribbon and paper at the time of impact. In the typewriter, the characters are contained on distinct hammers; selection consists of moving the proper one. In a *type-bar* printer, each character is on the end of an individual slug (6); the slugs are mounted vertically in a carrier (Figure 14.5). Selection consists of raising the carrier to the appropriate vertical position, at which time a hammer drives the slug to impact. There is a complete set of slugs for each column of a line-at-a-time printer.

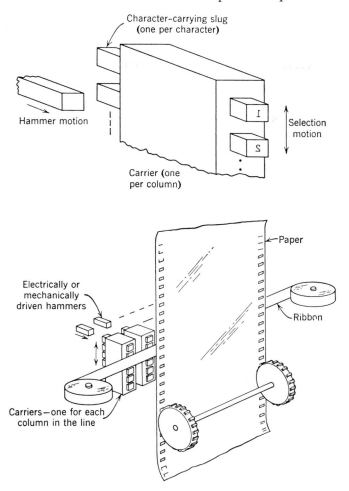

Figure 14.5. The type-bar printing mechanism.

In a *type-wheel* printer, the characters are engraved around the circumference of a wheel; there is a separate wheel for each column of a line-at-a-time printer (6). Selection consists of rotating the wheel to the proper angular position and then moving it to impact the paper. For high-quality printing, it is preferable that there be no lateral motion between wheel and paper at time of impact. Either the wheel can be stopped in the desired angular position, or it can continue to rotate. In the latter case, the carriage which carries the

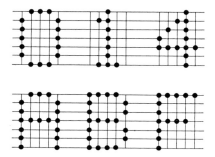

Figure 14.6. Matrix character formation.

rack of wheels can be moved in such a way that during impact, the lateral motion of the wheel relative to the paper is zero.

In a *matrix-impact* printer a rectangular array of small wires is provided; typically, thirty-five wires are arranged in a 5-by-7 cluster (7). Character selection consists of choosing that set of wires which will form the desired character from a dot pattern (Figure 14.6). Usually some form of mechanical selector is used to determine the set of wires for each character; the selected set is then moved forward to impact the paper and ribbon.

Stopped-character line-at-a-time printers are often just numeric or alphanumeric plus some punctuation and special characters. The size of the alphabet is generally about fifty characters. Character-at-a-time mechanical printers offer both upper- and lower-case alphabetic, plus numeric, plus special symbols and punctuation. Character-at-a-time printers generally operate at about ten characters per second, and the line printers being discussed, at 150 or so lines per minute.

EXAMPLE

Suppose that a ten-character per second typewriter requires 12 secs to print a 120-character line. Its line speed is, therefore, five lines per minute versus 150 lines per minute for a typical line-at-a-time printer of 120 columns. It is the same old tradeoff: speed versus amount of equipment (and, therefore, money).

Moving-Character Printing

If the duration of the impact between the print face, the inked ribbon, and the paper can be made short enough, there is no need to stop the print wheels during printing (8). Printers of this kind use high-speed hammers to drive the paper toward a continuously rotating drum (or group of wheels) on whose surface is engraved the characters (Figure 14.7). Along an axial element of such a drum, a character will be found as many times as there are columns to be printed; around a circumferential element is found the successive characters of the font.

Character selection consists of energizing the hammer in each column as the desired character comes opposite. If, say, A is to be printed in all columns, all hammers will be energized when the angular position of the drum is such that the row of A type faces is opposite the hammers. If successive characters of the font are to be printed in successive columns, then the hammers will be triggered successively as the drum rotates. It can take as much as one full revolution of the drum to complete printing of a line.

A variable reluctance magnetic device or a photoelectric optical arrangement can be used to provide the information about the angular position of the drum.

Drum printers of this type usually provide up to 64 characters in the font, operate from 300 to 1800 lines per minute, have up to 120 columns, and also have multiple copy and format features.

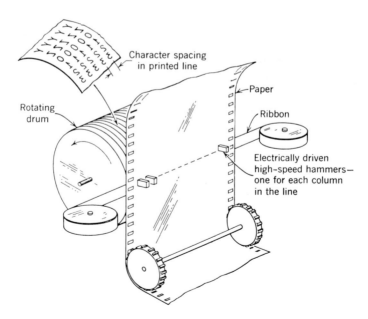

Figure 14.7. A rotating-drum printer.

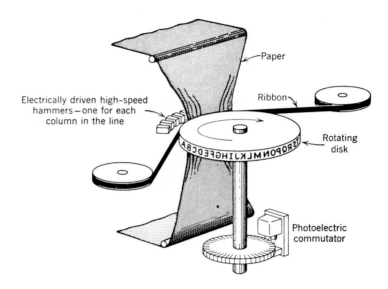

Figure 14.8. A horizontal wheel printer.

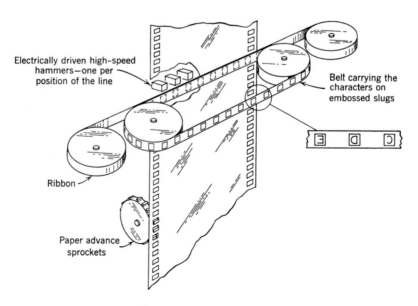

Figure 14.9. A belt printer.

It is also possible to use a horizontal wheel for high-speed impact printing (Figure 14.8) (9). There may be more than one font around the periphery of the wheel. To avoid having to curve the paper, the wheel can be replaced by a chain or belt of racetrack form (Figure 14.9). The "home stretch" and "back stretch" are at least equal to the width of the paper. Timing is a little different than the drum printer. If, say, an A is to be printed in all columns, a ripple of activity will sweep down the hammers as the A type face passes successive columns. If the English alphabet is to be printed in adjacent columns, a consecutive group of twenty-six hammers operates simultaneously.

Non-mechanical Printing

There are other ways than impact printing to produce the image of a character at a desired position on a piece of paper (10). One such way utilizes a character-forming cathode-ray tube (Figure 14.10), which uses a character mask to shape the electron beam to the desired cross section (11). One deflection system directs the beam through the desired aperture in the mask (character selection), and the other deflection system positions the selected character on the face of the tube. The desired message is built up a character at a time within each line; characters can be displayed at a rate of many thousands per second.

Generally, an optical system is used to image the displayed characters onto a photographic film or onto other means of reproduction, e.g., the selenium surface of a xerographic device (12). Multiple copies can be made from the intermediate image. Obviously such a character-forming tube can also be used as a visual display. The font of such a visual display need not be limited to alphanumeric characters. It can include characters in the shape of such things

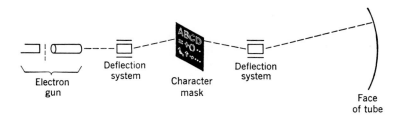

Figure 14.10. The principle of a cathode-ray-tube printer.

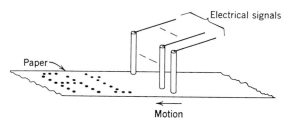

Figure 14.11. The principle of electrostatic printing.

as airfields, straight lines, arcs of circles, points, crosses, square brackets, or even whole words. If the tube has a storage feature, each character continues to be displayed as it is written, and the entire message can be visible all at one time (13). Otherwise the image will be transient and must be continually renewed if a long-term display is required. It may be necessary to continuously execute a loop in the routine to maintain the display. On the other hand, supplementary storage can be provided to accept information from the machine proper; repeated reading of the extra store then maintains the display.

A related technique uses specially shaped deflection voltages on a conventional cathode-ray tube rather than a beam-masking technique (14). Generally a set of signals is generated—various line segments, arcs of circles—and each character is built up from such elementary pieces.

A second non-mechanical printing technique uses small rods placed close to the paper surface to deposit electrostatic charge on the paper. One arrangement (Figure 14.11) provides a line of rods which is impulsed several times per character as the paper moves by (15). This effectively constructs each character from a matrix of dots. The latent image is developed by passing the paper through a dry bath of ink particles which adhere to the charged spots. Fixing usually consists of flash heating the surface of plastic-coated paper so that the ink particles become imbedded in the surface.

Shaped magnetic fields might also be used to deposit magnetic ink particles into desired shapes (16).

Paper Handling

To some extent, the details of the paper motion depend on the printing technique; e.g., the electrostatic technique deposits charge so rapidly that the paper can be in continuous motion. Some impact methods require that the paper be standing still during the deposition of ink. Thus the paper handling mechanism may be required to stop the paper at each line and to move it rapidly between lines; such a mechanism is frequently an arrangement of clutches and brakes, but it may also include some positive-acting latch arrangement to insure precise positioning of the paper. The paper often carries at each edge a row of perforations by which cogged wheels impart motion to it. To prevent tearing of the perforations under high acceleration of the paper, the cogged wheels are often replaced by a pin-carrying tractor tread; thus several pins engage the paper at the same time.

In printing formatted material, blank lines or groups of blank lines commonly occur. Paper-advancing mechanisms are frequently provided with a *slewing mode* which enables the paper to advance two or more lines without stopping at each line; the paper advances in a smooth motion for the required distance rather than in a start-stop mode. Slewing can move the paper at the same linear speed as between lines, or it can move the paper at a much higher linear speed.

Sometimes control of the line format on a page is accomplished by a carriage-control endless paper tape; the length of the tape corresponds to the height of the page to be printed. Holes in this tape control the positioning of any page of paper to a predetermined line. Choice of the hole to be used often can be made from the routine. For example, the address field of a Slew instruction might be used to designate a specific hole in the format tape.

Another scheme of format control directs the paper to advance by a specified number of lines from its present position; the address part of an instruction can convey this information.

If the printing mechanism has a great deal of flexibility in the positioning of a character—the cathode-ray tube schemes, for example—paper (or film) motion can be very simple. The skipping of lines can be done by the character-originating device, and the handler need only bring successive pages into position.

Communication and Timing

The printer either must be told what character (including none) is to be printed in each column, or it must be told which characters go into what columns. The character-at-a-time printer is the easiest to handle; since it is constrained to print columns sequentially, the information to it need only be in the same order as it is to appear in the line. Information must also be supplied to indicate spacing, carriage return, paper advance, and similar format structure.

Usually the information from a machine is encoded in an appropriate binary n-tuple, e.g., a 6-tuple of bits for alphanumeric information. Decoding these groups to 1-of-2^n choices is necessary to make the character selection; it may be done electronically (gating networks), but it is often done by an electromechanical arrangement of magnets and code bars.

Type-wheel, type-bar, or pin-matrix printers are often adaptations of punched-card tabulators. As such, they were at one time accustomed to receiving information from a card and, therefore, generally contain some sort of mechanical decoder to set up the character selection mechanism according to electrical inputs. By delivering card images to such a printer, it effectively acts as if it is receiving information from cards. If the input is in binary code groups, electronic decoding is necessary to provide the proper electrical inputs to the mechanical selection mechanism. Printers sometimes contain an electrical plug board that governs which input information is routed to which column. A blank column is easily obtained by not routing information to it. If no plug board is present, a printer must be specifically told not to print in the proper columns; the input to the printer must include suitable blank symbols for the empty columns. All other columns will receive information which specifies the character to be printed.

EXAMPLE

Only fifty columns of a 120-column format are to be used; there are to be ten blank columns, then twenty information columns, then five blank, then fifteen information columns, and then all else blank. For each line to be printed, a 120-character message will be supplied to the printer. The first ten symbols of the message will each be the one that represents the blank or "no print"; the next twenty will be information symbols, then five blank symbols, then fifteen information symbols and then seventy blank symbols.

The rotating-drum printer needs more detailed information. As each row of characters is before the hammers, each hammer must receive one bit which tells it whether or not to operate. Generally, such printers are handled on an image basis. Each line of the image contains as many bits as columns in the printer; there are as many lines to the image as characters in the font. The central machine may have to generate the image. Alternatively, supplementary equipment may be provided to accept code groups from the central machine and provide appropriate image information to the printer. In a sense, a small wired-routine, special purpose digital processor has been provided to handle the printer. It could be regarded in a large sense as a kind of printer local control.

EXAMPLES

1. An eighty-column drum printer whose font is fifty characters needs a fifty-line image of eighty bits per line. The successive lines of the image must be supplied to the printer at the proper time. If the image is constructed by the central machine, there may not be enough time between successive line positions of the printer drum to do much computing.

2. A printer operates at twenty lines per second; in any given line, the first and last character of the font might appear. Thus the character drum must make a complete revolution per printed line which implies that the drum must rotate at least at 1200 rpm. However, in the fifty milliseconds devoted to each printed line, the fifty lines of the image for each printed line must be supplied to the hammers. There is something less than one millisecond of free time between lines of the image, which implies very little computing between lines of the image. Generally, there is just enough time for the routine to execute the few instructions needed to get the next image line from the store.

The character-forming tube printers can be handled very simply, if it can be assumed that printing is systematically from one side to the other and from top to bottom of each page. Control is essentially like that for a typewriter. Within each line, the horizontal positioning mechanism steps uniformly from one side to the other. The vertical position steps from top toward bottom at the completion of each line. The horizontal positioning rate is set by the time required to display a character. If there are n characters per line, the vertical positioning rate is n times slower than the horizontal.

Other arrangements are possible. Two modes might be provided, one a uniform progression over the page, and the other a relative position scheme. In it, each character is positioned relative to the preceding one. In effect, there is a slewing action from one character to the next. The choice of positioning modes can be under control of the routine, or of a supplementary printer control mechanism. Possibly, the two modes can be arbitrarily mixed within one page. It is clear what factors are involved. For additional complexity in the printer control mechanism (i.e., money), a faster printing rate is obtained. No time is wasted on blank positions.

Another possibility is that such a printer might be required to place a character at an arbitrary position on the page; then position information (an X and Y coordinate) must accompany each character group.

EXAMPLE

A cathode-ray-tube printer must place 1-of-64 characters in an arbitrary square of a 128-by-128 matrix. For each character to be printed, six bits must be supplied to select the character, and seven bits must be supplied for each of the X and Y coordinates of the desired position; a total of twenty bits per character must be supplied.

Electrostatic matrix printers might be controlled in a variety of ways. One way would be to create an image for each character; the image will be, say, five lines by seven bits and will control impulsing of the row of seven pins. Another method would be to generate the 35-bit images of all characters in the font and to store them in a small supplementary store, say, in the printer. Each code group to be printed then, in effect, selects which 35-bit image is to be used for the occasion.

ANALOG-DIGITAL AND DIGITAL-ANALOG CONVERTERS

Such converters typically appear as input-output devices on a machine which communicates with other machines or with other physical processes (17). If conversion in one direction can be accomplished, then conversion in the other direction can be done with the same device plus supplementary equipment. Suppose that a converter is available to transform an analog representation (A) of information into a digital representation (D). To convert in the other direction, make a guess at the A that corresponds to a given D; using the available analog-digital converter, convert A to digital form, D'. Compare D with D', and on the basis of the difference between them, refine the A to produce A'. Convert A' to D''; compare D'' with D, and refine the estimate to A''. And so it goes, until the overall precision of the system stops the process; i.e., the precision with which A can be represented as D is one unit in the least significant digit of D.

For digit encoding of shaft position, a code wheel with brush **pick-off** might be used, or a system of slots might be counted (optically, elec-

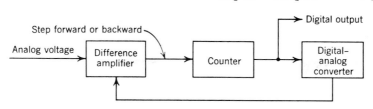

Figure 14.12. One method of analog-digital conversion.

trically, or mechanically) starting from some reference position. Positioning of a shaft to a digitally specified position follows the generalized example previously given. A motor is used to drive the shaft and is controlled by the difference between the present position of the shaft and the desired position.

For voltage, conversion from digital to analog is the easier job. One way is to have currents (or voltages) available which are proportional to the binary weights—. . . 8, 4, 2, 1. A 1 in the jth column of the binary expression switches on, say, a current of weight 2^j. Adding all such currents produces the desired analog representation. The inverse conversion frequently uses a counter connected to a digital-analog converter (Figure 14.12). A high-gain differential amplifier compares the output of the converter with the given analog voltage, and determines whether the count should be increased or decreased. The sequence of values in the counter is the repeatedly refined estimate of the digital equivalent of the given voltage.

There are many variants as well as other basic ways of changing an analog representation of information to a digital representation, or vice versa. The principles are generally similar to those described.

Plotters

A plotter is a form of digital-analog converter in which the analog representation is distance from a reference origin. Generally, a linear resistance element which is physically as long as the dimension of the plotter bed, is used to establish a voltage which is linearly proportional to distance. The incoming digital information on each coordinate is first converted to a voltage, and then the plotter head is motor driven until it finds a place on the linear resistance at which the voltage matches the input voltage. Plotters sometimes have such additional features as:

1. a choice of character to be plotted (point, cross, circle, etc.),
2. a numerical head which prints indicative information beside a point,
3. the ability to draw a line through two points,
4. the ability to construct a circle given a center and a radius.

Obviously, a simple cathode-ray tube, given appropriate converters and voltage sources for the deflection system can also be used as a plotting device. A printer can also be used as a plotter. A printer which prints ten lines per inch and has 120 columns in 12 inches will have a resolution of 1-in-10 in each direction.

DISPLAYS

Displays are usually quite specific to the particular application (18). A plotter might be part of a display; so also might be either a character-forming or a common cathode-ray tube. Transilluminated message windows or various indicator lights might also constitute part of a display. Some sort of device for showing characters might also be present (19). For a simple display, say, of the contents of storage cells, the address part of a display instruction can be used to identify the item to be shown.

MAGNETIC TAPE

In a general sense, the input-output function amounts to a mechanism for interchanging information between some collection of equipment called a machine system, and the environment in which the system is embedded. Sometimes input-output devices communicate directly with a human user (e.g., a printer), but not necessarily (e.g., a card punch). Sometimes the device is under program control (e.g., the output device of HYPAC-I) and sometimes it is not (e.g., the initial load function of HYPAC-I). A reel of magnetic tape, removed from its tape transport, is a form of long-term storage. In this sense, it can be regarded as part of the store hierarchy. However, since tape reels in storage are physically unattached to the machine system, magnetic-tape devices are often regarded as part of the input-output function.

This is especially the case if there are supplementary devices which transcribe information to or from other forms from or onto the tape, e.g., keyboard to tape, tape to plotter, card to tape, tape to printer (20).

In magnetic tape technology, the reading operation and the writing operation is combined in one device, the tape transport. Hence a given reel of tape which may contain original problem information can be read into a machine, but the same reel can promptly be rewritten with other information to become literally part of the storage hierarchy. Under program control a magnetic tape system can rapidly switch from the input (or output) function to storage and back. The same characteristic does not appear in card technology. Often the card reader and the card punch are separate pieces of equipment, and the output hopper of one does not lead directly to the input hopper of the other. The reading operation is not combined with the writing operation in one piece of equipment, and rewriting of a once-written card is impossible.

As a magnetic tape is being written under program control, there is nothing about the information which labels it as output information or as information in storage. It depends on what happens to the reel of tape subsequently. However, there is sometimes a distinct difference between tape as an input function and tape as a storage function. The latter we already understand from Chapter 12. We can illustrate the former by assuming that HYPAC-I acquires a tape-storage system, and has a *tape-load operation* similar to the already assumed card-load feature. Upon initiation of the tape-load operation from the console, information is read from a magnetic tape into the store beginning from cell 0000 and proceeding sequentially through consecutive storage cells until the record on the tape is exhausted. The important difference is that the tape during such an operation is not under program control, but is behaving according to a prewired response.

MAGNETIC CARDS

Just as paper tape can be regarded as a continuous punched card, so magnetic cards can be regarded as magnetic tape which has been cut into pieces (21). The ability to reuse a magnetic card or to alter selectively part of the information on the card gives the magnetic-card technique considerably more flexibility than the punched-card technique. Since the data density and the flow rate from magnetic surfaces can be much higher than from a punched card, different forms of mechanical devices are used to physically move and manipulate magnetic cards. A rotating drum on whose surface individual cards are placed or removed by air jets is one possibility.

It is obvious, of course, that a magnetic-card arrangement can be made to double in brass as input-output or as part of the working store.

ON- AND OFF-LINE

The discussion so far has quietly assumed that the input-output equipment—especially card equipment and printers—was directly connected to the electronic parts of the machine; in particular, it had direct access to the information in the store. It was *on-line*.

For the most part, the input-output equipment is relatively slow and while operating, may tie up the central part of the machine. In spite of the tricks—computing between lines of a card, for instance—it is still true that the high-speed electronic (and, therefore, expensive) parts of the machine system are burdened by the demands of the slower input-output gear. This has lead to the operational concept of *off-line* or *peripheral operation*. All of the slow input-output equipment is organizationally if not physically separated from the machine by magnetic tape intermediate storage. This allows the communication to and from the central part of the machine to occur at high information flow rates and thus maximizes the usage of the central processor. Supplementary equipment at any convenient later time transcribes the tape to other representations. If desired, the supplementary equipment could also be designed to relieve the central machine of other burdens, such as formatting of information or the construction of card or printer images. Thus the central machine can communicate with the tape not only at a high rate but in an efficient representation of the information.

EXAMPLE

An on-line 64-character 120-column rotating drum printer requires for each line an image which is 64×120 or 7680 bits. If the off-line printer control can construct the image, the machine proper need supply only 120 6-bit characters or 720 bits. Thus the tape record is roughly one tenth as long, the tape writing or reading time is one tenth as long, and machine time is not needed to maneuver the data into image form.

In a computing installation which operates with the off-line philosophy, there can be a variety of supplementary support equipment. There might be such things as:

1. keyboard to tape,
2. card to tape,
3. tape to printer,
4. tape to plotter,
5. paper tape to magnetic tape.

Frequently, the tape units of the peripheral equipment are not connectable to the computer proper. A manual movement of a tape reel from one transport to another is necessary.

In peripheral operation, the semantic distinction between storage and input-output for the magnetic tape can become muddy. Suppose that all of the peripheral equipment has been combined into a small second machine which is a computer in its own right. Its role in the gross system is to handle what we would normally call the input-output traffic. It is a world-to-tape and a tape-to-world converter. The larger and principal central machine exchanges information with its helper machine by means of manually-moved reels of tape. In a precise sense, the magnetic tape is an intermediate form of storage for transferring information between machines. In effect, there is a storage mechanism which is accessible to both machines. However, so far as the central machine is concerned, all of its contact with the outside is through the tape system. From its point of view, the tape unit is an input-output terminal; although from a larger point of view, the input-output terminal to the world is the input-output equipment of the smaller machine.

Logical Organization

There are several ways in which traffic flow between the input-output devices and the central machine can be arranged. One way is the off-line arrangement already described. The amount of magnetic tape intermediate storage can be as large as necessary, and the off-line transcription to or from the tape, and the subsequent reading or writing of the tape by the central processor, can be separated by an arbitrary time interval or an arbitrary physical distance.

Another scheme is the on-line arrangement in which communication is directly to the central parts of the machine; in this case the arithmetic unit often is tied up by input-output operations.

Another possibility is to *buffer* the input-output function; a fixed amount of supplementary storage is provided for each input and each output device (22). For a card reader, the buffer storage is very likely the size of the card image; for a printer, the size of its image. The buffer storage is such that it communicates to the main machine at high speed but at slower speed to the input-output device. Buffering provides some of the gains of the off-line arrangement, but not all. The flow rate of the information is still that of the input-output device, but the time actually required to transfer the information is set by the characteristics of the buffer store, rather than by the input-output device.

Sometimes a buffer store in a different sense is physically a part of the primary store, although it could also be part of some other storage level. In particular, it is arranged so that, say, an input device transfers information directly to, say, the primary store without bothering the arithmetic unit. Concurrently, the arithmetic unit proceeds with its work. The only conflict will come when both demand access to the primary store, and some priority scheme must control which gets first call. If the programmer has the option of using any part of the store as the part into—or from—which to transfer directly to the input-output, there may be an arrangement in the form of lockout registers to prevent the routine from consulting stale data or from destroying completed results waiting to be outputted (see page 13.43). Into such special registers in the control, the routine will insert, say, the two addresses which define the ends of the block of storage which is acting as the buffer. On the other hand, there may just be a toggle which is in, say, the 1-state so long as the buffered operation is in process, but it resumes the 0-state when the operation finishes. With a Branch instruction which tests the state of such a toggle, the programmer can build his routine to take care of the interlock requirements.

Input-Output Instructions

In Chapter 5 (page 5.43), we suggested a number of input-output instruction types. We can now be more precise about the subject. Some of the common kinds are described in the following examples.

EXAMPLES

1. All of the typical kinds of instructions cited in Chapter 12 for tape storage might be regarded also as input-output types.

2. If all the input-output devices are to be handled on an image basis, commonly there is a *Select* and a *Copy* operation part. The address part of the Select instruction designates which of the many input-output devices is required for action. The Select may only establish a transmission channel to the device, but it may also start the device into action, e.g., start a card into motion, start the magnetic tape into motion. It may be the first Copy instruction after the Select rather than the Select itself which starts the device in motion. In any event, once the device gets into action, information is produced (or required) on some fixed timing schedule which is characteristic of the device itself. Such a timing schedule might be the times at which information becomes available from successive rows of a card, or the successive times at which lines of the image are required by a drum printer. The address of the Copy instruction is the cell in the store to (or from) which a line of the image is transferred.

   If the Copy instruction is fetched, and ready for execution before the instant at which it is needed, it waits until needed and then completes its execution. If the Copy instruction appears too late, the information with which it was to interact has gone by, and some visual or electronic indication must be given to the user. Perhaps a visual signal is given, and the machine halts. Perhaps a toggle is set into, say, the 1-state when a *copy-check* occurs, and a Branch instruction permits the programmer to detect the situation and take such action as he wishes.

   Thus it is clear that for devices which are handled by the routine on an image basis, there is a small loop of instructions often called a *copy loop* to traffic the information to and from the input-output devices. The copy loop must do several things. It must present at the proper time the right number of Copy instructions for the device currently selected, and each Copy instruction must have the address of the appropriate line of the image. Hence a copy loop involves both repeated address modification and counting of the copy instructions. It may also include such other features as testing for a copy-check occurrence or repeating the Select instruction each time to keep the device in motion. The details of the copy loop may be different for each input or output device. To the maximum extent possible, the programmer will try to sandwich other computing such as base conversion between successive Copy instructions. It is clear that the speed of the input-output device and the speed of the machine combine to determine how much computation can be done between, say, the rows of a card.

3. Instead of a Select instruction, there may be a *Feed Card* instruction. This starts a card in motion in the device which is specified by the address part. Thus a multiplicity of card readers and punches can be handled by one kind of instruction.

4. If each input-output unit contains a buffer one image in size, there may be such instructions as *Print, Read Card,* or *Punch Card;* the address of each one designates the cell or the first one of a group of cells in storage to or from which information is transferred. Such an arrangement, of course, ties up the main computer a much shorter time.

The information exchange between input-output and the main machine is typically handled in one of two ways. The central machine may still be required to prepare the image or to decode it. If so, transmission from buffer storage to the central machine is at the high rate of the central machine, but transmission from buffer storage to the input or output device is at device rate. For example, with 80-column cards, the machine must still traffic 960 bits for each card, but the machine is not concerned with executing the copy loop.

Alternatively, the information from the machine may be in the form of code characters, typically 6-tuples. For an 80-column card, the information packet per card is 480 bits—one-half what it was just previously. The buffer store has associated with it whatever equipment is necessary to decode 6-tuples and generate the image. Conversely on an input operation, the buffer equipment transmits code characters into the machine proper. In this case, the input-output equipment even though on-line has the efficiency of communication offered by peripheral operation (page 14.26). It is clear that extra equipment (and cost) in the input-output devices is exchanged for computing time in the central machine.

In either situation above, more than one machine word will be required to store the information packet. In the second case, one way to store a card's worth of information in a 40-bit-word-length machine is in a group of twelve words. The six bits of the jth character occur in the jth column of the first (or perhaps the second) group of six words. The routine must have maneuvered the information into this form. Another way to store the card's information in a 36-bit-word-length machine is six 6-bit characters per word, side by side. For 72 columns of card information, twelve words are required, but each word contains six complete characters.

Hence, in the Print, Read Card, and Punch Card instructions, even though they be single address, typically twelve words of the store must be consulted. The single address, therefore, locates the first one of the twelve, and the execution of the instruction by the control automatically consults the following eleven. With this kind of an arrangement, the programmer must remember that blocks of information for successive input-output records must be spaced by twelve words in the store.

The efficiency of communicating character groups rather than images is particularly clear in the printer example cited on page 14.26.

5. If there is a feature for operating the input-output devices concurrently with other machine functions, the appropriate instructions may resemble the Block Transfer instructions of the magnetic drum when used as a secondary store (see page 12.19). The instruction, which may be a multiaddress one, must specify the amount of information to be transferred to or from the world, and the origin (or destination) of this information in the store. Another possibility is to use lockout or limit registers to specify the block of information to be transferred, and use the address part of a single-address instruction to specify the input or output device concerned. For efficiency, such block exchange of information between the central machine and its on-line input-output devices generally predicates that groups of machine words are exchanged. The words, however, contain character groups directly meaningful to the input-output devices.

6. A typewriter can be handled by a simple Print instruction. The address specifies the cell in storage which contains one or more characters to be printed. The routine will have prepared the appropriate character codes, and probably packed them as many as possible to a machine word. Specific characters must be included for space-bar operation and carriage-return or line-feed operations.

7. In some kinds of output devices, for example, a card punch or a printer, there is a problem of format control. Into which columns of a card is information to be punched? Into which columns and lines of a page is information to be printed? Obviously, an image basis gives the programmer complete control of the situation. For a machine which must prepare large volumes of information all in the same format, for example, public utility bills, it might be appropriate to wire in the format information so that the amount of information required from the machine will be minimum. Alternatively, a somewhat more flexible arrangement might provide special registers or switch circuits which under program control establish the format.

In peripheral operation, if the off-line equipment is itself a programmable device, the format control can be foisted off onto it. For example, the routine of the off-line device might expect the first few words of each information record to contain such format information as the length of each line of information to be printed, the position of the empty columns, or the spacing between successive rows of printing.

From such information, the off-line machine can adjust its own routine to produce the desired format. This arrangement does not require that both the central machine and the off-line have the same instruction repertoire. The only requirement is that the information exchanged be interpretable by either.

8. Displays and plotters will have instruction types which are appropriate to the detailed nature of the device. Generally, the programmer through his routine will have complete control of each device, both electrically and me-

chanically. The same general principles of information flow apply. Such devices may be buffered, off-line, or on-line.

9. Paper-tape devices can be handled by a simple Read or Punch instruction. In each case, the amount of information referred to is a line on the tape. Hence, there may be an implied ground rule in a machine using such devices that so-many lines of tape information will be coalesced into one machine word, and that a machine word will be segmented into so many lines on the tape. Since information on a paper tape appears strictly time (and space) sequentially, there is a minimum of format control. Conversion between paper-tape code and internal machine code may be the province of the central machine or of the tape equipment. Information flow may be buffered, and it may occur in block transfers.

CONSOLES

Manual intervention into a machine's affairs is always necessary. Some of the console control from the operator takes the form of establishing conditions which govern a machine's behavior; other manual operations cause certain events to occur within the machine, while yet others communicate information (data or instructions) to the machine (23).

EXAMPLES

1. The *load button* causes a transfer of information from some input device into the machine. The feature which distinguishes a load operation from an input operation under program control is that it occurs according to some prescribed wired-in pattern of response. The load operation may transfer a whole block of information into the machine (as HYPAC-I did) or it may transfer only a few instructions into the machine. These few instructions when executed transfer the balance of the input information under program control.

2. A *go button* causes the machine to begin the execution of instructions, commencing with the one located by the present contents of the instruction counter.

3. A keyboard or lever switches permit entry of information into specific places in the machine, e.g., Accumulator, Instruction Counter, Instruction Register, MQ.

4. A *printer check* light indicates some trouble with the printer, e.g., paper supply exhausted.

5. An *overflow ignore* switch disables the overflow detection circuit.

6. Register display lights indicate the contents of various machine registers, or of a selected storage cell.

7. Tape assignment switches permit permuting the physical tape units among the addresses which the Tape-Select instructions use to identify various units. This enables a given program to operate, but identify a second tape unit with the same address as it previously used for a tape unit now removed for maintenance.

8. Special switches guide the execution of the routine because their position can be tested by Branch or Sense instructions. Special lights can be turned on or off by, say, Sense instructions to indicate that particular points in the routine have been reached.

9. Special buttons cause the execution of one instruction at a time, or the repeated execution of the same instruction, or the execution of an instruction one step at a time.

The collection of lights, switches, displays, levers, etc., which make up the console is preferably designed for rapid and convenient exchange of information with the human operator. Sometimes it is convenient to provide more than one console, especially if the activities at the several places represent relatively independent functions.

EXAMPLE

Various register displays, entry switches, etc., will be at the main *operating console* while the tape assignment controls might be grouped together on supplementary consoles near the tape transports.

A distinctly different kind of console function is related to maintenance of the machine. Sometimes a *maintenance console* which is separate from the operating console is provided. On it, deeper details of the internal machine configuration will be displayed, and insertion of information into individual toggles may be possible. Some parts of the machine's environment—such as clock rate or supply voltages—can generally be varied from the maintenance position for diagnostic purposes (*marginal checking*). At the maintenance position, the supervisory system will probably report such findings as air temperature too high, some voltage beyond a stated tolerance, or a fuse blown.

The console function is important. It is here that the machine touches the world of people for its minute-by-minute information;

unless exchange of information between machine and man is easy and efficient, the overall system performance can suffer.

Console Instructions

Sometimes a console operation is felt within the machine without the necessity of executing instructions; e.g., load, go, enter information, execute the current instruction. For such features, there will be no operation parts in the machine repertoire. For other console operations, no effect is evidenced within the machine until one or more instructions are executed; e.g., satisfy a Branch instruction according to the position of some switch, Display at the console some information in the store. For such operations, there must be appropriate operation parts in the machine repertoire. The nature of such instructions depends on the particular features of a console; a representative few have been mentioned in Chapter 5 (page 5.45).

Console Design

There are really three aspects of console design. First, there is the matter of what logic must be performed both within the console and within the machine to provide the desired features. In the large, we have the design techniques established and the technology available. Describe the function, demonstrate it as a truth table, translate to an algebraic expression, and build the circuit. Since most console functions tend to be relatively slow, frequently relay circuits are satisfactory. A second aspect of the design is the collection of components which are useful to receive information from a person or deliver information to him. For transfer of information from person to electrical form, the common device is the switch, perhaps a simple two position switch, perhaps a multiposition switch. For visual display, there are such things as: incandescent or glow discharge lamps to indicate the state of a binary digit or of a Boolean variable; special multiposition glow discharge lamps which exhibit a variety of glow patterns, each in the shape of a decimal digit (19); transilluminated displays for alphanumeric or special symbols; or cathode-ray tube patterns for a wide variety of information. Sometimes it is quite uncertain whether a given device is part of a console or really an output device. In the sense that an output device can be argued to be anything which gives information pertinent to a problem and its solution, many console features can be claimed as output features.

The third aspect of console design relates to efficient exchange of information between the man and the console. It is a problem related to the characteristics of a man as he perceives information, and involves certain psychological aspects of human behavior. It became clear to us many pages ago that an otherwise correct routine can give wrong answers because of operator error. Hence it is important to couple machine information to the man efficiently and with minimum chance of misunderstanding. This problem can become especially acute for certain devices which are frequently called consoles, but which are perhaps more correctly described as personal input-output stations, or personal display stations (24). Some large machine systems, especially those which are operating on-line as well as in real-time with a physical process, must exchange large amounts of information with several operators. The action of such operators and their judgment in interpreting information is essential to the proper functioning of the machine system and to the system under control. Hence the success of the complete system hinges, in part, on the efficiency with which machine-generated information can be presented to them, and on the consequences of their decisions communicated back to the machine.

OTHER INPUT-OUTPUT DEVICES

There is a large number of special devices which are sometimes used as couplings between a machine and its world (25). In ever-increasing measure, equipment designers are attempting to improve the interface which exists between a machine and man.

Like many decisions connected with the design of a digital system, the selection of input-output devices generally reflects the world in which the machine is embedded, the class of problems for which it is intended, the required information flow rate into and from the machine, etc. Extant machine designs give some insight into the many factors at play (26).

COLLATERAL READING

1. Siegel, P., *Understanding digital computers;* John Wiley and Sons, New York, 1961; chapter 13.

Bartee, T. C., *Digital computer fundamentals;* McGraw-Hill Book Co., New York, 1960; chapter 8.

Flores, I., *Computer logic;* Prentice-Hall, Englewood Cliffs, N.J., 1960; chapter 15.

Ledley, R. S., *Digital computer and control engineering;* McGraw-Hill Book Co., New York, 1960; pp. 747–756.

Grabbe, E. M. *et al., Handbook of automation, computation, and control;* John Wiley and Sons, New York, 1959; vol. 2, chapter 20.

Smith, C. V. L., *Electronic digital computers;* McGraw-Hill Book Co., New York, 1959; chapter 16.

McCormick, E. H., *Digital computer primer;* McGraw-Hill Book Co., New York, 1959; chapter 9.

Murphy, J. S., *Basic digital computers;* John F. Rider Publisher, New York, 1958; vol. 3, pp. 107–114.

Grabbe, E. M., *Automation in business and industry;* John Wiley and Sons, New York, 1957; chapter 10.

2. Murphy, J. S., *Basic digital computers;* John F. Rider Publisher, New York, 1958; pp. 123–124.

Flores, I., *Computer logic;* Prentice-Hall, Englewood Cliffs, N.J., 1960; pp. 329–331.

3. Smith, H. J. and F. A. Williams, Survey of punched card codes; *Communications of the Association for Computing Machinery,* vol. 3, December, 1960; pp. 638–642.

4. Flores, I., *Computer logic;* Prentice-Hall, Englewood Cliffs, N.J., 1960; pp. 317–329.

Byrnes, W. P., Teletype high speed tape equipment and systems; *Proceedings of the 1954 Eastern Joint Computer Conference,* Philadelphia, 8–10 December, 1954; pp. 35–39.

5. Murphy, J. S., *Basic digital computers;* John F. Rider Publisher, New York, 1958; vol. 3, pp. 115–121.

Rosen, L., High speed printing equipment; *Review of Input-Output Equipment Used in Digital Computers, Joint IRE-AIEE-ACM Conference,* New York, 10–12 December, 1952; pp. 95–98.

Flores, I., *Computer logic;* Prentice-Hall, Englewood Cliffs, N.J., 1960; pp. 344–358.

6. Hosken, J. C., A survey of mechanical printers; *Review of Input-Output Equipment Used in Digital Computers, Joint IRE-AIEE-ACM Conference,* New York, 10–12 December, 1952; pp. 106–112.

7. Diguilio, E. M., Burroughs G-101 high speed printer; *IRE Convention Record,* vol. 4, pt. 4, 1956; pp. 94–100.

8. Masterson, E. and A. Pressman, A self-checking high speed printer; *Proceedings of the 1954 Eastern Joint Computer Conference,* Philadelphia, 8–10 December, 1954; pp. 22–30.

Eckel, C. and D. Flechtner, The RCA 501 high speed printer; *Proceedings of the 1959 Western Joint Computer Conference,* San Francisco, 3–5 March, 1959; pp. 204–207.

Bauer, F. W., and P. D. King, The Burroughs 220 high speed printer system; *Proceedings of the 1959 Western Joint Computer Conference,* San Francisco, 3–5 March, 1959; pp. 212–217.

9. Wild, J. J., High speed printer for computers and communications; *Electronics,* vol. 25, May, 1952; pp. 116–120.

10. Rossheim, R. J., Nonmechanical high speed printers; *Review of Input-Output Equipment Used in Digital Computers, Joint IRE-AIEE-ACM Conference,* New York, 10–12 December, 1952; pp. 113–117.

11. McNaney, J. T., The type C19K charactron tube and its application to an air surveillance system; *IRE Convention Record,* vol. 3, pt. 5, 1955; pp. 31–36.

12. Anon., Xerography; Aircraft Production, vol. 20, May, 1958; pp. 198–202.

13. Smith, H. M., The typotron, a novel character display storage tube; *IRE Convention Record,* vol. 3, pt. 4, 1955; pp. 129–134.

14. Loewe, R. T. *et al.,* Computer generated displays; *Proceedings of the IRE,* vol. 49, January, 1961; pp. 185–195.

15. Epstein, H. and P. Kintner, The Burroughs electrographic printer-plotter for ordnance computing; *Proceedings of the 1956 Eastern Joint Computer Conference,* New York, 10–12 December, 1956; pp. 73–80.

   Epstein, H., The electrographic recording technique; *Proceedings of the 1955 Western Joint Computer Conference,* Los Angeles, 1–3 March, 1955; pp. 116–118.

   Epstein, H. and F. Innes, The electrographic recording technique; *IRE Convention Record,* vol. 3, pt. 4, 1955; pp. 135–138.

16. Seehof, J. *et al.,* The National Cash Register high speed magnetic printer; *Proceedings of the 1957 Eastern Joint Computer Conference,* Washington, 9–13 December, 1957; pp. 243–250.

   Sims, J. C., Jr., Magnetic reproducer and printer; *Proceedings of the 1953 Western Joint Computer Conference,* Los Angeles, 4–6 February, 1953; pp. 160–166.

17. Susskind, A. K., *Notes on analog-digital conversion techniques;* John Wiley and Sons, New York, 1957.

   Burke, H. E., Survey of analog-digital converters; *Proceedings of the IRE,* vol. 41, October, 1953; pp. 1455–1462.

   Burke, H. E., Jr., A survey of analog-digital converters; *Review of Input-Output Equipment Used in Digital Computers, Joint IRE-AIEE-ACM Conference,* New York, 10–12 December, 1952; pp. 98–105.

   Ledley, R. S., *Digital computer and control engineering;* McGraw-Hill Book Co., New York, 1960; pp. 739–747.

18. Loewe, R. T. *et al.,* Computer generated displays; *Proceedings of the IRE,* vol. 49, January, 1961; pp. 185–195.

   Ogle, J., Optical display for data handling system output; *Proceedings of the 1959 Eastern Joint Computer Conference,* Washington, 9–13 December, 1959; pp. 231–232.

   McNaney, J. T., The type C19K charactron tube and its application to an air surveillance system; *IRE Convention Record,* vol. 3, pt. 5, 1955; pp. 31–36.

   Smith, H. M., The typotron, a novel character display storage tube; *IRE Convention Record,* vol. 3, pt. 4, 1955; pp. 129–134.

19. Kuchinsky, S., Special purpose tubes for computer applications; *Proceedings of the 1958 Western Joint Computer Conference,* Los Angeles, 6–8 May, 1958; pp. 96–102.

20. Blumenthal, E. and F. Lopez, Punched card to magnetic tape converter; *Re-*

view of *Input-Output Equipment Used in Digital Computers, Joint IRE-AIEE-ACM Conference,* New York, 10–12 December, 1952; pp. 8–11.

Welsh, H. F. and H. Lukoff, The Uniservo tape reader and recorder; *Review of Input-Output Equipment Used in Digital Computers, Joint IRE-AIEE-ACM Conference,* New York, 10–12 December, 1952; pp. 47–53.

Wilson, L. D. and S. Meyer, The model II Unityper; *IRE Transactions on Electronic Computers,* vol. EC-2, December, 1953; pp. 19–27.

Beaulieu, D. E. *et al.,* The BIZMAC transcoder; *IRE WESCON Convention Record,* pt. 4, 1957; pp. 293–298.

Eckert, W. J. and R. Jones, *Faster, faster;* McGraw-Hill Book Co., New York, 1955; chapter 7.

21. Hayes, R. M. and J. Wiener, Magnacard—a new concept in data handling; *IRE WESCON Convention Record,* pt. 4, 1957; pp. 205–209.

Nelson, A. M. *et al.,* Magnacard—mechanical handling techniques; *IRE WESCON Convention Record,* pt. 4, 1957; pp. 210–213.

Burkig, J. and L. E. Justice, Magnacard—magnetic recording studies; *IRE WESCON Convention Record,* pt. 4, 1957; pp. 214–217.

22. Tasin, B. B. and S. Winograd, Multiple input-output links in a computing system; *IBM Journal of Research and Development,* vol. 6, July, 1962; pp. 306–328.

23. Flores, I., *Computer logic;* Prentice-Hall, Englewood Cliffs, N.J., 1960; pp. 308–314 and 362–372.

24. Corbato, F. J. *et al.,* An experimental time sharing system; *Proceedings of the 1962 Spring Joint Computer Conference,* San Francisco, 1–3 May, 1962; pp. 335–344.

25. David, E. E., Ears for computers; *Scientific American,* February, 1955; pp. 92 *ff. passim.*

David, E. E. and O. G. Selfridge, Eyes and ears for computers; *Proceedings of the IRE,* vol. 50, May, 1962; pp. 1093–1101.

Anon., FOSDIC—a film optical device for input to computers; *Technical Bulletin of the National Bureau of Standards,* vol. 38, February, 1954; pp. 24–27.

Harmon, L. D., A line drawing pattern recognizer; *Proceedings of the 1960 Western Joint Computer Conference,* San Francisco, 3–5 May, 1960; pp. 351–364.

Doyle, W., Recognition of sloppy hand printed characters; *Proceedings of the 1960 Western Joint Computer Conference,* San Francisco, 3–5 May, 1960; pp. 133–142.

Petrick, S. R. and H. M. Willett, A method of voice communication with a digital computer; *Proceedings of the 1960 Eastern Joint Computer Conference,* New York, 13–15 December, 1960; pp. 11–23.

Galli, E. J., The stenowriter—a system for the lexical processing of stenotype; *IRE Transactions on Electronic Computers;* vol. EC-11, April, 1962; pp. 187–199.

26. Byrd, D. J. P. and B. G. Welby, The input-output system of the Ferranti universal digital computer; *Review of Input-Output Equipment Used in Digital Computers, Joint IRE-AIEE-ACM Conference,* New York, 10–12 December, 1952; pp. 126–132.

Stevens, L. D., Engineering organization of the input and output for the IBM 701 electronic data processing machine; *Review of Input-Output Equip-*

ment Used in Digital Computers, Joint IRE-AIEE-ACM Conference, New York, 10–12 December, 1952; pp. 81–85.

Greenwald, S., SEAC input-output system; *Review of Input-Output Equipment Used in Digital Computers, Joint IRE-AIEE-ACM Conference,* New York, 10–12 December, 1952; pp. 31–35.

Gray, W. H., The RAYDAC input-output system; *Review of Input-Output Equipment Used in Digital Computers, Joint IRE-AIEE-ACM Conference,* New York, 10–12 December, 1952; pp. 70–76.

Brustman, J. A., Input and output devices of the RCA BIZMAC system; *IRE Convention Record,* pt. 4, 1956; pp. 88–93.

Forgie, J. W., The Lincoln TX-2 input-output system; *Proceedings of the 1957 Western Joint Computer Conference,* Los Angeles, 26–28 February, 1957; pp. 156–160.

Buchholz, W., *Planning a computer;* McGraw-Hill Book Co., New York, 1962; chapter 12.

EXERCISES

14.1. Suppose that HYPAC-I can accept cards punched in Hollerith code. As an expedient, assume that only nineteen columns of the card are used. The left-most column expresses the algebraic sign. A 0 is plus, a 1 is minus. All other rows of this sign column are unpunched. As a card is read, assume that a 19-bit image of each row is read into the store starting from cell 0. At the completion of the card cycle, twelve 19-bit words are in position in the store. Until the machine signals that it has processed this much information, the following card is not read.

Write a routine for HYPAC-I (starting it in cell 14_8), which will convert the card image into machine language. Assume first that only decimal information is punched in a card, and also that the conversion is to an 8, 4, 2, 1 code representation. The routine is to place the eighteen coded decimal digits in the right-most positions of individual words. Each such word is to have a positive sign, except the word containing the most significant digit. It is to contain the sign read from the card. The eighteen words are to be placed in the store at the end of the routine which you are writing.

Extend the routine to accept the full Hollerith alphabet. Convert the information contained in the image into the code given in Figure 3.5. Place the 6-bit characters in storage as previously indicated.

14.2. Repeat the previous exercise, except assume that the card reader reads cards column-by-column rather than row-by-row. Thus the image will be nineteen 12-bit words instead of twelve 19-bit words. Indicate how the image will be laid in storage, and follow other details as before.

14.3. Write a routine for HYPAC-I which will take eighteen 6-bit characters occupying consecutive cells in the store and produce an image of twelve 18-bit words that can be used to control a card punch. The sign convention is to be the same as in exercise 14.1. Specify any assumptions that you make concerning locations of information in storage and concerning the word formats of the image and character-containing words.

14.4. The brush mechanism of a card reader and the heavy current contactors in a card punch are a source of considerable electrical noise. Indicate how you would protect the noise-sensitive electronic circuits from such noise. Keep in mind that high speed toggles and gates will have to communicate with card equipment.

14.5. Describe several ways in which the special mark required by HYPAC-I's loading scheme might be placed in an input card. Is one scheme better than another in some way? What equipment is required to handle this special mark properly?

14.6. The conversion of Hollerith card code to a binary-coded representation is to be done by an electronic circuit instead of by programming (exercise 14.1). Assume that the output code is the 6-bit code of Figure 3.5, and that all twelve bits of a card column are simultaneously available.

Give the truth table which defines such a one-column character converter. Keep in mind that it must work properly for the sign column as well as for all others. Develop the algebraic expressions which describe it, and simplify them. Draw a logical diagram showing all gating elements of the device. In other words, develop some insight into the amount of equipment and the cost of code converting devices.

Extend the design to work in either direction—Hollerith to binary-coded or vice versa. Try to economize on equipment by making gates serve for both directions where possible.

14.7. Decide what information, especially timing and status, needs to be exchanged between HYPAC-I's control and the card reader in order for the machine to be able to read cards punched in Hollerith code (exercise 14.1). Sketch the block diagram of the equipment (i.e., toggles and gates) needed to give the machine control over the reader and to make it accept information from the reader.

Repeat the above, but for the card punch. Determine what kind of timing or status signal sources must be incorporated into the card handling devices.

14.8. Suppose that HYPAC-I has a 6-channel paper-tape punch; hence three tape characters can be fitted into one word. Write a loop of instructions which will take words (starting from cell 0), fragment each in turn into three characters, and feed one character at a time to the output line. Assume that the programmer will use a character to convey the sign; therefore, the sign position of a word is not punched directly.

Assume that the normal Output instruction feeds information onto the output line. Assume that the repertoire includes a Select (see page 14.29) instruction which for an address part of 0007 couples the tape punch to the output bus. Also assume that the punch sets a toggle when it needs another character. The repertoire includes a Sense-and-Skip instruction (see page 5.45) which for an address of 0017 inspects the state of this toggle and skips if the toggle is set to the 1-state. If the toggle is in 0-state, the machine does not wait but proceeds. Hence this output loop must contain some programmed scheme to keep the machine in a waiting mode until the punch is ready to accept information.

The output loop is to continue the punching of characters until a prescribed number have been handled. The tally-and-test must be included within the loop.

14.9. In a rotating-drum printer, if only numeric information were being printed, might the line printing rate change? Why? What arrangement must there be for handling paper movement?

14.10. Suppose that HYPAC-I were to acquire both an output typewriter and a nineteen column 64-character rotating-drum printer. An address of 0012 in the Select instruction connects the typewriter to the output bus; and an address of 0014, the printer (see exercise 14.8).

What new operation parts must be added to the repertoire to mechanically control these two devices? What role does the address part play in each case?

Assume that the typewriter requires a 6-bit character for each keystroke, including the space. The printer requires an image of sixty-four 19-bit words. In the case of the typewriter, the three characters ready to be printed are to be in cell 0. For the printer, the image is to be in the first sixty-four cells of the store.

Write one routine to handle both output devices. For the typewriter, each word of three characters must be relocated into cell 0 in turn, and put on the output bus by Output instructions in successive thirds. For the printer, the routine must pick up eighteen characters (the most significant of which carries the sign information to be printed), form the image, and place it in the proper part of the store. It must then successively output the lines of the image. There is no time to compute between lines of the image. For expedience, assume that the Output instruction, though invited to proceed by the control, will await the receipt of a timing signal from the printer before proceeding to deliver information onto the output bus.

Would this last assumption be useful for handling other output devices?

14.11. By now you have developed considerable feel for HYPAC-I as a machine and also for the needs of the user. Decide what items should be on the operating console. What switches are needed to control what internal behavior? What features are needed for inserting information into the machine? Into what parts? What features are needed to manually influence the control? What displays of internal conditions are required?

14.12. Assume that HYPAC-I is a synchronous machine. When it is switched on, the various toggles are probably in disordered states. The machine must be brought to its "waiting-to-go" reference state before anything can be done with it. How can this be done from the console? Every time the progress of the control is manually interrupted, it is necessary to get the machine properly reconnected to its timing signals. How can this be done? (This problem may be unusually tricky if instructions can be executed step-by-step from console control.) How can the timing signals be started properly when the "go" button is operated? How can we be sure that the machine will stop at the end of an instruction when the "halt" button is operated?

14.13. The connections to the console of HYPAC-I are likely to be relatively long. Yet the console will have to communicate with the high speed electronic parts of the machine. How would you deal with this problem? How would you avoid having to transmit high-speed signals over relatively long connections? Suppose it were unavoidable? What precautions might then have to be taken?

14.14. Assume that HYPAC-I handles its card reader and card punch on a copy-loop basis (pages 14.29 ff.). Its repertoire includes a Select and a Copy instruction.

Assuming that the image has been prepared and is located in a specific place in the store, write a copy loop which will input (or output) n cards of information. Assume that the Select instruction starts a card in motion through the device but that the card handling is arranged to stop after each card.

14.15. Suppose that HYPAC-I were to be kept as simple as possible. It is to have just a typewriter as an input-output device. Information will be accepted by the machine from the keyboard, and the machine can deliver information to actuate a selected key.

Decide on an appropriate logical scheme for the communication in both directions between typewriter and machine. Image basis? Character basis? Other basis? How are the space bar, the line feed, and the carriage return handled? What timing or status signals are required? Sketch a block diagram of the equipment involved including all information flow paths, gates, timing signals, etc. Show how the typewriter connects into the machine.

PROBLEMS

14.1. Suppose that HYPAC-I is to have a card reader, a card punch, a rotating-drum printer, a cathode-ray-tube display, and a typewriter to be used for both input and output. All devices are to be fully buffered so that communication with the central machine is with maximum efficiency.

Describe a consistent overall arrangement for integrating the several devices into the HYPAC-I system. Indicate what kinds of instructions must be provided, what the role of the address is in each, what information will flow between devices, etc. Also describe all control, timing, and status information that must be provided by the central machine and each input-output device. How many buffers will be required? What will be the characteristics of each? Size? Speed? Organization?

Sketch an overall block diagram of your final arrangement. Show major items of equipment, all input and output terminals, interdevice control, and timing signals, etc.

14.2. Describe a system for using a character-forming-tube printer as an output device for HYPAC-I. It is to place 1-of-6 characters at any position of a 128×128 array of points. Describe any special kinds of instructions which are needed, how information will flow to the printer, what kind of information must be furnished, etc. Make your scheme consistent with other input-output arrangements on the machine.

Assume, first, that the device is on-line, and second, that it is buffered. Repeat the above for each case.

14.3. With reference to exercise 14.10, suppose that the printer were provided with a buffer which can accept eighteen 6-bit characters from the machine, then cast loose from the machine, form the required image, and feed it to the printer. The first character received contains the sign information to be printed.

Lay out the complete logic of such a buffer. Draw a functional block diagram including all information flow paths, special storage, registers, code converters, gates, timing signals, etc.

14.4. Suppose that there existed a typewriter which formed its characters by driving the appropriate wires of a 5×7 matrix array. Lay out the logic of a single-character buffer which accepts a 6-bit input and produces the outputs to drive the wires appropriate to each character.

Estimate the amount of equipment involved for controlling such a typewriter.

14.5. In view of exercise 13.10 and exercise 14.11, describe in detail the connections between the console and all other parts of the HYPAC-I system. In particular, describe how the console connects into the control section.

14.6. Draw a functional block diagram of the console whose design was specified in problem 14.5. Include all information flow paths, gates with their inputs, switches, indicator lights, special toggles, etc.

14.7. Suppose that the HYPAC-I were to have a so-called "stop at address A" feature. From the console, a number equal in length to an address is entered into a special register. When the instruction counter contains the same number, the machine is to halt. This is a way for the programmer to let the machine proceed to a specified cell for an instruction, but have it stop there.

Describe the extra equipment that must be added to the console, indicate any new connections into the control, and sketch a block diagram of the arrangement.

Assume first that the machine is to halt following the execution of the instruction in cell A, and second that it is to halt following the fetch from cell A but before execution. Work out the details of each case.

Describe for each case how the machine will resume from the stopped condition.

14.8. Extend the subroutine of exercise 14.14. Assume that binary-decimal conversion is also to be included in the copy loop. There are n signed words in storage to be punched. The copy loop must convert each in turn to binary-coded-decimal, form the nineteen column image, and send the image a line at a time to the punch. The copy loop must keep the 150 cards-per-minute punch operating at full speed. Hence the computation must be sandwiched between rows of a card and between cards. Decide when each part of the loop is to be completed; specify all storage locations.

From a knowledge of the length of the loop and the card rate, estimate the speed at which HYPAC-I must complete various kinds of instructions. Keep in mind that some instructions are significantly longer than others. Hence infer the general speed range of the machine and the cycle time of its store.

14.9. Write a copy loop to handle a nineteen column 64-character rotating-drum line printer. Assume that there is not sufficient time between lines of characters on the drum to form a line of the image; hence do as little computation between lines as possible. There are n lines to be printed per page, and p pages to be printed. The repertoire contains a Feed Paper instruction. For an address of 0000, it advances the paper in the printer to the position of the first line on the next page.

14.10. For the typewriter arrangement that you designed in exercise 14.15, write whatever subroutines are required for the machine to interact properly with its input-output device. Describe how information is received by the machine, what conversion if any is done, what packing into words if any is done, how the information is placed in the store.

It will probably be convenient to write separate routines for the input and for the output.

14.11. Design the digital-analog converter for the output-printer of problem 14.2. The converter is to accept a digital address and convert it to the deflection voltage required by the cathode-ray tube. Assume that the peak deflection voltage is 100, that it must be precise within ¼ volt independently of the address, that it must settle to within 0.1% of its final position within 3 μsec. Suppose that the capacitance load to be driven by the converter is 35 mmf. Sketch the block diagram and the detailed circuit diagram. Justify that your design can meet the precision and settling time specifications. What stability is required of various components in your design?

fifteen

Generalities

We have looked in detail at the many facets of the computer. We have discussed some background mathematical topics; we have insight into the programming problem; we have studied circuits; and we have demonstrated many of the organizational and hardware details of the functional parts of a machine. We have discussed primarily the general purpose, single-address machine, although we have from time to time pointed out other types of organization. We need now to add a little closure to our ideas and to tie some loose ends together.

HYPAC-I BLOCK DIAGRAM

We have not yet described in detail how HYPAC-I is organized internally. We need not say, for our purposes, what are its detailed circuits, but we should exhibit its internal structure as an information-flow block diagram. Figure 15.1 shows the functional relationship of its various parts, and indicates the flow of information from place to place. In view of our discussion to date, there is little that needs to be added. Not shown, of course, are the details of time sequencing, or any sharing in time, of a common path. For example, the Accumulator and the MQ each connect to a common bus to the store. Only one of them at a time can have access to this bus; the control takes care of such problems.

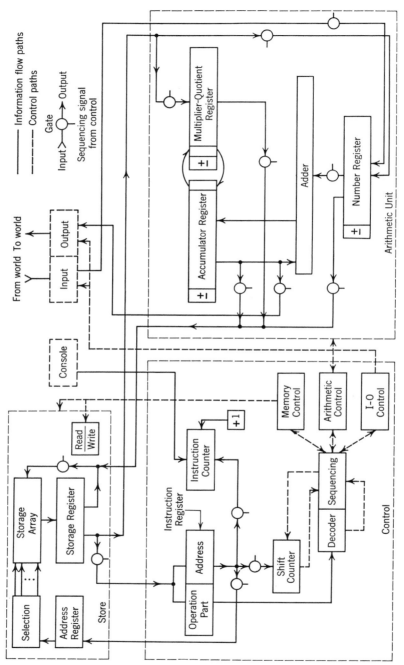

Figure 15.1. The detailed information-flow paths of HYPAC-I.

SYSTEMS DESIGN

From time to time, we have made observations on the systems design problem. As we now appreciate, the overall structure of a computer reflects the requirements imposed by the class of problems (or application), reliability, economic constraints, and capability of the art. In large part, the systems design problem is that of finding techniques which are available or can be developed that meet the application requirement at acceptable cost and with sufficient reliability. The systems design, therefore, starts by defining what is required of a machine in a given application. This is judged against what is available from the technology either already or in the reasonable future. Many possibilities at all levels of detail exist; e.g., what kind of store should be used; should toggles be dynamic, symmetrical, or other; should the circuit technology be transistor, vacuum tube, or magnetic; should the gating be diode or other; should arithmetic be parallel or serial. The resolution of such many-way choices depends partly on the intended application, partly on a judgment of reliability, partly on relative costs, and partly on past experience and tradition.

The importance of experience and tradition must not be discounted. The cycle of development in the computing field tends to be lengthy. Often a new circuit technique or a new organizational idea can be evaluated only after long hours of use in an operational situation. The interplay between the various aspects of a computer is very complex, and a complete assessment of a new idea generally cannot be made a priori. The idea must be incorporated into a completed equipment, and then a substantial amount of problem traffic or equivalent experience must be accumulated.

The normal equipment development time, plus the construction time, plus the time to exploit a new idea or equipment together make a feedback loop with a very long time delay. It can literally be several years before the worth of a new idea can be judged. Hence many decisions related to the systems design may well be preempted by tradition and successful prior experience. A given technique or organization has worked well before, so let us use it again.

It may well be that a long cycle of progress is an inherent characteristic of information processing devices. As we have seen, the machines are tremendously complex and possess an enormous number of internal states and degrees of freedom. Thus, it is hard to accumulate insight. Furthermore, we know so very little about the basic science of information manipulation. We know how to transport information from place to place—we call it communication or transmission of information (1). We know how to do certain kinds of operations on information—such as arithmetic, or columnwise logical ones, or mappings by means of arbitrary tables. We have experience but no general theories to guide us in specifying the complex sequence of primitive steps of manipulation which are necessary to achieve some given end purpose. To use engineering terms, we do not have a theoretical basis for designing a transfer function that will produce specified kinds of output information from given input information.

To bring our discussions to a close, let us consider a few design problems of the whole, problems which do not arise until an entire computer is assembled. We should also have a brief look at typical kinds of applications because from successful applications, we will derive some of our insight for the system design problem. We can also develop insight by studying the designs of existing computers (2).

Overall Circuit Design Problems

Some kinds of circuit problems may arise only after a complete machine—or large parts of it—has been assembled. Such problems can arise because of interactions between parts of a machine system, or simply because a large amount of equipment has been assembled together into one ensemble. The following examples illustrate typical situations.

EXAMPLES

1. The time delays of various path lengths may be poorly known until much of a machine has been assembled. Such delays will influence the timing details in the control.

2. There may be stray couplings between circuits or between functionally separate parts just because they happen to be in physical proximity. Capacitance coupling between nearby wires introduces spurious signals and hence degrades the signal-to-noise ratio.

3. There may be interaction between functionally separate parts (or circuits) because of a mutual power supply. The current requirements of a register can depend on the digital content of the register; a register of dynamic

toggles is a very clear example. Hence digital information can be spuriously coupled into a power source. If the internal impedance of the power supply is not sufficiently low, such spurious signals can be transferred into other parts of a machine. The severity of the stray-coupling problem may be difficult to assess early in the design cycle of a machine.

4. Race conditions may appear because of unforeseen or misestimated time delays. The intended logical conditions may not occur because signals arrive too late or too early at a gate. Alternatively, the logical situation which does occur at some gate may change as the arrival time of signals varies over time. Such a problem can be particularly troublesome in an asynchronous control or between parts of a system which are mutually asynchronous.

5. Because of the proximity of equipment or just the accumulated quantity of it, or because of wiring paths, spurious parasitic oscillations which were not present in prototype designs may appear. The cure of such a problem may require modification of packaging details, insertion of suppression devices such as resistors, or rerouting of long connections in order to decrease stray capacitance couplings.

6. In follower-type gates there is a small voltage shift between input and output. The accumulated shift of a long cascade of such gates may reach a troublesome magnitude for the first time when a substantial part of the machine is assembled.

Overall Systems Characteristics

Some gross characteristics of a machine are related to only one part of a machine and depend on relatively few factors. For example, the size of the store has relatively little to do with the nature of the arithmetic unit, or whether the control is synchronous or not. The size, for the most part, reflects the kind and size of problems which will be done, and will be chosen to optimize programming convenience. On the other hand, some machine characteristics will be determined by the requirements of several machine parts and will depend on a complex mix of factors. As a good example of such a situation, consider the many factors which enter into the determination of word length.

1. The precision of the arithmetic processes reflects the kind and size of the problems to be done; the word length must provide the required precision. The decision of fixed versus floating point will also influence word length.

2. The size of the primary store determines the length of the address part, which in turn partially determines the instruction (and, therefore, word) length.

3. The size of the instruction repertoire determines the length of the operation part of an instruction and, therefore, partially determines instruction and word length.

4. The instruction format helps determine the length of an instruction. Quite aside from the length of the operation part or of the address part, the number of address parts, the presence of extra flag digits or partial address fields, or other special parts of an instruction combine to influence the length of the instruction.

5. Input-output characteristics often interact with the word length. For example, a word length of forty bits fits nicely with the eighty columns of a punched card as an input medium. In one sense, a thirty-six-bit word fits much better; two such binary words fill one row of a card but leave eight extra columns which can be used for identification information for the card. The machine will probably not read the indicative information, but other special devices will.

6. The nature of the information to be represented influences word length. The word length of a decimal machine will be a multiple of four; of an alphanumeric machine, a multiple of six. In some applications a character font of 2^6 is not enough. For example, to represent algebraic expressions, parentheses, square brackets, exponents, superscripts, subscripts, and many other special marks, perhaps a hundred or more characters are necessary. Hence there is reason to have an *enlarged character set* of perhaps 2^8. Thus an 8-bit character (*byte*) will be required, and the word length will be a multiple of eight.

If the programmer may want to structure the word as either 4-bit, 6-bit, or 8-bit characters, the word length will be a multiple of 4, 6, and 8. The routine will have to know what the situation is in each case. There need not but might be specific kinds of instructions for each type of information.

There may be a few extra positions in the word for one or more algebraic signs, and for special marks or identifiers. For example, in a machine which does both floating- and fixed-point operations, it might be convenient to include within each word a single bit which flags the word as fixed- or floating-point representation. In such a case, it will not be necessary to have specific fixed and floating arithmetic instructions in the repertoire even though the machine will be able to execute each kind of arithmetic.

7. The word length can reflect the requirement for the arithmetic precision in unusual ways. Normally the arithmetic word length is chosen so that sufficient precision is available in the final result, in spite of the accumulation of errors due to rounding, truncation, base conversion, or replacement of continuous mathematical processes by discrete difference approximations. For a too short word length, some problems may have to be calculated in double precision; each operand is really two words in length, and the programmer must construct his routine to carry out the arithmetic properly. For a machine which is no faster, but whose word is sufficiently longer, double-precision arithmetic can be avoided, and the problem will run correspondingly faster on the machine.

From a consideration of such factors as these, and perhaps others, the word length of a machine system emerges as (hopefully) an optimized compromise.

APPLICATIONS

The use of the digital computer is often divided into the areas of scientific, business or data processing, and control. To some extent, this is an artificial division in a continuum of problem types. The so-called *scientific* or *engineering problems* tend to be those with modest amounts of input or output data but with a large amount of internal manipulation. As the amount of input or output traffic increases, but the amount of internal manipulation decreases, problems tend to be called *business* or *data-processing types*. There are other dimensions to the continuum. As the information represented departs from the numeric or simple alphanumeric kind and becomes more abstract in nature, problems tend to be called *information-processing types*. As the information represented becomes more symbolic in nature, the relationships represented in the routine become such things as the structure of natural language, the structure of an algebra, the structure of an artificial language, perhaps a programming language, or the structure of a branch of mathematics, for example, plane geometry or logical calculus (3).

As the nature of the problem to be solved becomes more and more fixed and unchanging over time, the application tends to be called special purpose. If the structure of the machine itself is particularized to a given problem, the machine may be called *special purpose*. Different forms of machine organization may be desirable. For example the *digital differential analyzer* may be appropriate (4). In it, the mathematical process of integration is replaced by a finite-difference approximation. Perhaps a general-purpose structure with unusual features such as multiple arithmetic units or the ability to do arithmetic on just part of a word will be required for some situations. If the specialized problem is related to the control of some process or some operation, the situation is often referred to as a *control application.*

Scientific Applications

In the scientific or engineering applications, the amount of input-output traffic is typically modest (5). The emphasis will be on internal speed of operation, and therefore such features as the following are likely to be present: a large primary store; wired-in floating-point operations; indexing; buffered, or off-line input-output; parallel arithmetic; very fast circuits; and a relatively small amount of input-output equipment. These things are not necessary for a machine to handle a scientific problem, but they contribute to its efficiency on such problems.

Data-Processing Applications

The amount of input-output traffic is likely to be large, and there may be a very small amount of internal manipulation for each item handled (6). A utility billing operation is typical. There are a large number of items to be handled, but there is not too much that needs be done for each bill. A large primary store is not particularly necessary, but a large second- or third-level store is required for the voluminous files that will be manipulated. Indexing may be relatively less important, and high internal operation speed may not be essential. A multiplicity of input-output equipment is very likely necessary, and it probably will be operated in a peripheral mode. The machine may be optimized to handle alphabetic information.

The last point has an interesting twist. An obvious way to represent alphanumeric information is in six-bit characters. However, for that part of the time during which only numeric information is being handled, the machine is operating at two-thirds efficiency. It is using six bits where four would do, not only in the store, but also in the arithmetic section and elsewhere. In particular, the information records in magnetic tape storage are half again as long as they really need be (the ratio of six bits to four bits). Hence tape-moving time is half again as long. Therefore, if the proportion of alphabetic information is not very high compared to the numeric, an alphanumeric machine is a poor bet.

It is a poor bet, however, only if we can find another scheme for accommodating alphanumeric information. One such is the following: organize the machine as a decimal machine with four-bit characters. For alphabetic information, consider two four-bit characters to be associated together to form an eight-bit one. Each alphabetic character uses eight bits where six would do, but if this is not done too often, the overall situation may be more favorable than a six-bit character machine. Probably, each machine word will have to be consistent; i.e., it must be all decimal characters or it must be all eight-bit alphanumeric characters. Conceivably, each word can carry a flag digit to identify it as numeric or not. Otherwise the programmer must keep track of the two kinds of words.

We have just flushed a new factor that bears on word length. For a machine that is to represent alphabetic information in terms of paired characters, the word length must be an even (not odd) number of four-bit groups. Moreover, we observe the influence of the application on the situation. The ratio of alphanumeric to plain numeric information in the problem is a very crucial point in guiding the internal machine organization toward or away from a six-bit character structure.

It is clear that so-called scientific machines can handle data-processing problems. Given an adequate set of logical (or extract) instructions, a word can be conveniently fragmented into 4-, 6-, or 8-bit parts and each part handled properly by the routine. However, the large scientific machine is typically a fixed-word-length machine and, therefore, can be parallel, if necessary, to achieve speed. Sometimes, this is a disadvantage for data-processing problems.

If a given item of information exceeds one word length, each such item must spread over more than one word in a fixed-word-length machine. Typically, it will be fitted into an integral number of words; any surplus space in the group of words will be wasted. In principal, an item might be spread over a number of complete words and part of another one, but if the unused part of the last word is used for a different item, a given word will contain information from two or more items. The complication of bookkeeping under such circumstances generally argues against such a technique. For a problem in which the items of information are expected to vary widely in length, a fixed-word-length structure may be very awkward.

If the beginning and end of each word is marked by a special character, a variable-word-length machine can be devised. The store of such a machine will be character oriented, and once started at a given cell, can be arranged to continue to read consecutive cells until a word-end marker is found.

Because of the variability in word length, the arithmetic processes and the transmission of information are almost certainly serial, at least by character. The gains are not without difficulties, however. While the programmer can handle items of variable lengths, he has a more difficult job of storage allocation since this must now be done on a character, rather than a word, basis. In particular, the beginning and end of each word must be known in order not to inadvertently misuse information. It is clear that a character-organized list store (see page 12.85) would be a distinct advantage for variable-item-length problems.

Control Applications

In this situation the machine is probably operating in real time, and therefore the operating speed of the machine on the problem is of utmost importance (7). This is not to say that machines in scientific or data-processing applications do not have deadlines to meet, but in control situations, the necessity of being on time is more binding. Hence we expect that machine organization, and perhaps also circuit speeds, will be selected to optimize performance on the particular problem. There may be an unusual arrangement of the arithmetic unit, or the store, or other parts to improve performance. There may well be much specialized input-output equipment to link the machine with its environment. In a sense, the machine is specialized to its job and might be called special purpose, even though it retains many features of a general purpose organization.

One of the attractive features of a digital control machine is its speed. For many situations, the machine is so much faster than the process which it controls that it is feasible to consider time-sharing the machine among several jobs. In time sequence, it works a little while on each job, but the average attention to each job is high enough to maintain cognizance of the situation. Such *sampled-data systems* can originate new problems of stability in the computation process (8), and require new processing techniques.

The very speed of the digital device raises a new problem. The fast machine is effectively a wide-band device and, therefore, is responsive to noise components which are ignored by slower acting equipment, e.g., relays, motors. It may be necessary for the digital machine actually to time signals which it receives in order to decide that the given signal is real and not spurious noise. Such attention to the fine structure of signals represents an extra chore for the machine and, therefore, also for the programmer; but it represents a consequence of a fast-acting device.

There will probably be many special instruction types to handle interaction with the environment. The address parts of such instructions may specify a particular device that is to be operated or sensed. Just as it may be necessary to monitor incoming signals in order to determine their time duration, so it may also be necessary to monitor devices which have been directed to operate. For example, the control computer may direct a valve to proceed to a given position, or it may direct a valve to operate for a given amount of time. In the latter case the machine must time the duration of operation. As a side observation, we notice the possibility that we may need an absolute scale of time in a control machine; we may need a real-time clock that the machine can read. Alternatively, we might organize the machine on a synchronous basis and use the machine clock for timing of external events.

The digital switching center developed for the telephone central office is a nice example of a control application (9). A fast digital computer specialized to its job time sequentially handles all requests for service from the subscriber. It is clear that the requirement for reliability is extreme. The attractiveness of the electronic center reflects the possibility of a more flexible service to the subscriber, as well as a more economical solution to the central office switching problem. The machine will have to do such things as:

1. Monitor each subscriber line for status—requesting service, dialing, busy, or inactive.

2. Accept dial signals, distinguish them from spurious noise, and record them.

3. Complete the desired connection.

4. Distinguish between classes of calls—long distance, intraoffice, interoffice, party line.

5. Monitor each call in progress in order to free the equipment as soon as the call is completed.

6. Assign storage space in the machine for each call in process in order to keep a record of dial information and status.

7. Monitor ringing operation in order to determine when the called party has responded.

8. Send dial or route information to adjacent offices.

We see that such a machine needs a certain amount of working (i.e., primary level) storage for the calls on which it is working. Such working storage will be used for the dial information, the nature of the call, and information needed to handle the call. For many calls, special routing information is required. Such information is needed promptly in order to complete a call, but it does not change very often. It amounts to a table of information and, therefore, can reasonably be kept in a read-only store (10). The main routine which governs the behavior of the machine also does not change significantly over time, and it too can be kept in a read-only store. This choice has the further advantage that the routine is protected against accidental destruction by machine malfunction. However, we have seen in our programming examples that often an instruction must be modified. If the routine is to be kept in read-only storage, we probably must provide an indexing system for instruction modification.

Since reliability is a prime concern in order to provide uninterrupted service, we can arrange a control machine to perform extensive self-diagnosis. Because of the high machine speed, we might sandwich diagnostic routines in among other tasks, or we might automatically jump to a diagnostic mode during slack periods. Such special trouble-location routines might also be kept in a read-only store.

It will be enlightening to see how the telephone switching machine actually does some of its chores. First of all, the machine activity is high only when a subscriber line changes state. A special scanning part of the machine systematically inspects each line at 0.1-second intervals to determine its status (11). A line which by the presence of current indicates that a subscriber wishes to dial gets special attention. The sampling rate on requesting lines is stepped up to a 0.01-second interval. By detecting the beginning and end of each dial signal, a complete time history of customer dialing can be constructed. Hence if dialing is interrupted part way through, attention to the line can be discontinued.

As soon as all dial information has been received, proper routing information must be obtained from the read-only store and transferred to the working store. On the basis of such information the machine searches under program control for idle trunk lines and establishes the connection. If necessary, dialing information is forwarded to other offices. Having established the connection, ringing commences, and the line is monitored at 0.1-second intervals. If the called party answers, ringing ceases and the talking connection is established. The machine still monitors the connection at 0.1-second intervals in order to determine the duration of the call, and to free the equipment when the call is completed.

This is a much simplified description of the machine performance. We have not touched on many interesting aspects which are relevant to economical use of trunk lines, or on the novel switching devices which are used to establish the connections at electronic speeds (12). The machine is specialized in the sense that it contains particular equipment to link it with the environment—the line scanner and the electronic switching. On the other hand, it is general purpose in the sense that it is under program control and, therefore, flexible in its job. The various scanning rates for example, reflect the execution rates of various subroutines.

There is an interesting point of view to this particular application. The handset of each subscriber can be regarded as a simple console through which the subscriber inputs certain kinds of information to the machine. In a sense, this machine is a central digital computing facility which is time-shared by a large number of users. The machine solves just one kind of problem—but one with many variations —for each user. It is not unreasonable to expect that by dialing special codes, the subscriber can obtain access to particular parts of the routine which can provide him special service. For example, one special feature might be automatic referral of all calls to an alternate number. Prior to leaving his normal number, the subscriber will have to dial into a special part of the routine, and by dialing further, he leaves the substitute number. It is clear that the telephone subscriber cannot input program information to the machine. He can only insert parameter information into a routine which is arranged to accept it. In this sense, his private console is a very primitive one.

As additional customer services are required or conceived, some amount of reprogramming will be necessary, but major changes in the equipment probably will be unnecessary.

It is fitting for us to see what precautions have been taken in an experimental telephone switching center to guarantee reliable around-the-clock operation. First of all, conservative design techniques of the kind that we have discussed have been followed in circuit design (13). Major portions of the equipment are duplicated, and automatic switching to standby equipment occurs when trouble is detected (14). While the equipment is in operation, an extensive test program is periodically executed every 100 msec. All major functions of the central and storage parts of the machine are checked. If trouble is detected, the faulty unit is replaced by its standby. Other test programs are also automatically scheduled and executed during any few milliseconds that the machine is not servicing a call. Approximately half of the 70,000 instructions in the routine are for checking and diagnosis.

The duplexed primary store (a barrier-grid electrostatic store) is checked by matching outputs of the two parts against each other. Incidence of trouble removes the faulty unit and initiates a sequence of trouble-diagnosing problems. The information in the read-only photographic store carries a Hamming error-correcting code which serves to correct transient errors. There are also extensive diagnostic tests that are applied to the standby unit.

Marginal conditions can be imposed on sections of the machine under program control. A record of the conditions found by a test program is outputted to a typewriter for use by maintenance personnel, and special test situations can be created under manual control.

As we observed in Chapter 7, reliability must be considered an integral aspect of machine design and operation. In a situation such as the telephone electronic central where malfunctions must be minimized, reliability must start with the circuit design and go on through systems design, packaging, operation, diagnosis, and maintenance. Reliability must be considered an integral part of programming too. About nine hundred tests are applied to the telephone control machine for diagnostic purposes. Approximately six thousand words of routine are required for this purpose. Such a large piece of routine cannot be tacked on as appendage but must be carefully planned and integrated with the main operational routine.

FINIS

A final comment. Most machines can do most jobs. This is not true, of course, in very special control situations which require unusual couplings to the environment. Aside from that, however, most machines can do whatever comes their way. The rub is, of course, that their performance may not be efficient; they may not be able to make deadlines; the inefficiency may result in excessive costs.

At this stage of computer technology, we know very little about optimization techniques. We do not know how to proceed methodically to the "best" machine for a given case or to the "best" routine for a given problem; we can only guess whether the optimization curve has a sharp peak or a broad plateau or even a maximum. These are things that we look forward to knowing. Meanwhile many of our problems can be done on many machines, and it is to adventuresome workers in programming, machine organization, and circuit technology that we look for new insights and flashes of wisdom.

COLLATERAL READING

1. Grondin, G. F. and F. P. Forbath, Communicating between remotely located digital computers; *Proceedings of the 1957 Eastern Joint Computer Conference*, Washington, 9–13 December, 1957; pp. 194–197.

   Weir, J. M., Digital data communication techniques; *Proceedings of the IRE*, vol. 49, January, 1961; pp. 196–209.

2. Phister, M., *Logical design of digital computers;* John Wiley and Sons, New York, 1958; chapter 1.

   Smith, C. V. L., *Electronic digital computers;* McGraw-Hill Book Co., 1959; chapter 15.

   Serrell, R. *et al.,* The evolution of computing machines and systems; *Proceedings of the IRE,* vol. 50, May, 1962; pp. 1039–1058.

   Bourne, C. P. and D. F. Ford, The historical development and predicted state-of-the-art of the general purpose digital computer; *Proceedings of the 1960 Western Joint Computer Conference,* San Francisco, 3–5 May, 1960; pp. 1–21.

   Adams, C. W., Trends in design of large computer systems; *Proceedings of the 1961 Western Joint Computer Conference,* Los Angeles, 9–11 May, 1961; pp. 361–364.

   Weik, M. H., *A third survey of domestic electronic digital computers;* Ballistic Research Laboratories, March, 1961; report 1115.

   Smith, C. V. L., *Electronic digital computers;* McGraw-Hill Book Co., New York, 1959; chapter 17.

   Andrews, E. G., A review of the Bell Laboratories digital computer developments; *Review of Electronic Digital Computers, Joint IRE-AIEE Conference,* Philadelphia, 10–12 December, 1951; pp. 101–105 (Bell relay machines).

   Everett, R. R., The Whirlwind-I computer; *Review of Electronic Digital Computers, Joint IRE-AIEE Conference,* Philadelphia, 10–12 December, 1951; pp. 105–108.

   Mullaney, F. C., Design features of the ERA 1101; *Review of Electronic Digital Computers, Joint IRE-AIEE Conference,* Philadelphia, 10–12 December, 1951; pp. 43–49.

   Meagher, R. and J. P. Nash, The ORDVAC; *Review of Electronic Digital Computers, Joint IRE-AIEE Conference,* Philadelphia, 10–12 December, 1951; pp. 37–42.

Wilkes, M. V., The EDSAC computer; *Review of Electronic Digital Computers, Joint IRE-AIEE Conference,* Philadelphia, 10–12 December, 1951; pp. 79–83.

Metropolis, N. *et al.,* MANIAC; *Proceedings of the Association for Computing Machinery,* Toronto, 8–10 September, 1952; pp. 13–17.

Mendelson, M. J., Quadratic arc computer; *Proceedings of the Association for Computing Machinery,* Pittsburgh, 2–3 May, 1952; pp. 53–60 (QUAC).

Auerbach, A., ELECOM-100 general purpose computer; *Proceedings of the Association for Computing Machinery,* Pittsburgh, 2–3 May, 1952; pp. 47–52.

Perry, C. L., The logical design of the Oak Ridge digital computer; *Proceedings of the Association for Computing Machinery,* Toronto, 8–10 September, 1952; pp. 23–27 (ORACLE).

Chu, J. C., The Oak Ridge automatic computer; *Proceedings of the Association for Computing Machinery,* Toronto, 8–10 September, 1952; pp. 142–148 (ORACLE).

Sheretz, P. C., Electronic circuits of the NAREC computer; *Proceedings of the IRE,* vol. 41, October, 1953; pp. 1313–1320.

Edwards, D. B. G., The Manchester University high speed digital computer; *Journal of the British Institute of Radio Engineers,* vol. 14, June, 1954; pp. 269–278.

Pinkerton, J. M. M., LEO (Lyons electric office); *Electronic Engineer* (London), vol. 26, 1954; July, pp. 284–291; August, pp. 335–341; September, pp. 386–392.

Felker, J. H., Performance of TRADIC transistor digital computer; *Proceedings of the 1954 Eastern Joint Computer Conference,* Philadelphia, 8–10 December, 1954; pp. 46–49.

Huskey, H. D. and D. C. Evans, The Bendix G-15 general purpose computer; *Proceedings of the IRE WESCON Computer Sessions,* Los Angeles, 25–27 August, 1954; pp. 87–91.

Dunn, W. H. *et al.,* A digital computer for use in an operational flight trainer; *IRE Transactions on Electronic Computers,* vol. EC-4, June, 1955; pp. 55–63.

Alrich, J. C., Engineering description of the ElectroData digital computer; *IRE Transactions on Electronic Computers,* vol. EC-4, March, 1955; pp. 1–10 (ElectroData 205).

Smith, J. E., A new large data handling system—DATAMATIC 1000; *Proceedings of the 1956 Eastern Joint Computer Conference,* New York, 10–12 December, 1956; pp. 22–28.

Astrahan, M. M. *et al.,* Logical design of the digital computer for the SAGE system; *IBM Journal of Research and Development,* vol. 1, January, 1957; pp. 76–83.

Jeeves, T. A. and W. D. Rowe, The NORDIC-II computer; *IRE WESCON Convention Record,* pt. 4, 1957; pp. 85–104.

Frankel, S. P., The logical design of a simple general purpose computer; *IRE Transactions on Electronic Computers,* vol. EC-6, March, 1957; pp. 5–14.

Frankovitch, J. M. and H. P. Peterson, A functional description of the Lincoln TX-2 computer; *Proceedings of the 1957 Western Joint Computer Conference,* Los Angeles, 26–28 February, 1957; pp. 146–155.

Lourie, N. *et al.,* Arithmetic and control techniques in a multiprogram computer; *Proceedings of the 1959 Eastern Joint Computer Conference,* Boston, 1–3 December, 1959; pp. 75–81 (Honeywell 800).

Beck, R. M., A high speed serial general purpose computer using magnetostrictive delay line storage; *Proceedings of the 1960 Eastern Joint Computer Conference,* New York, 13–15 December, 1960; pp. 283–298 (Packard Bell 250).

Anderson, J. P., A computer for direct execution of algorithmic languages; *Proceedings of the 1961 Eastern Joint Computer Conference,* Washington, 12–14 December, 1961; pp. 184–193 (Burroughs B-5000).

Hayes, R. M., Operating characteristics of the National Cash Register decimal computer CRC 102-D; *Proceedings of the 1954 Eastern Joint Computer Conference,* 8–10 December, Philadelphia, 1954; pp. 40–41.

Shiowitz, M. *et al.,* Functional description of the NCR-304 data processing system; *Proceedings of the 1956 Eastern Joint Computer Conference,* New York, 10–12 December, 1956; pp. 34–39.

Maddox, J. L. *et al.,* The TRANSAC S-1000 computer; *Proceedings of the 1956 Eastern Joint Computer Conference,* New York, 10–12 December, 1956; pp. 13–16.

Segal, R. J. *et al.,* Performance advances in a transistorized computer system —the TRANSAC S-2000; *Proceedings of the 1958 Eastern Joint Computer Conference,* Philadelphia, 3–5 December, 1958; pp. 168–174.

Halstead, W. K. *et al.,* Purpose and application of the RCA BIZMAC system; *Proceedings of the 1956 Western Joint Computer Conference,* San Francisco, 7–9 February, 1956; pp. 119–123.

Beard, A. D. *et al.,* Functional organization of data in the RCA BIZMAC system; *Proceedings of the 1956 Western Joint Computer Conference,* San Francisco, 7–9 February, 1956; pp. 124–125.

Owings, J. L., The RCA BIZMAC central system; *Proceedings of the 1956 Western Joint Computer Conference,* San Francisco, 7–9 February, 1956; pp. 126–132.

Beard, A. D. *et al.,* Characteristics of the RCA BIZMAC computer; *Proceedings of the 1956 Western Joint Computer Conference,* San Francisco, 7–9 February, 1956; pp. 133–137.

Bensky, L. S. *et al.,* Programming a variable word length computer; *Proceedings of the 1956 Western Joint Computer Conference,* San Francisco, 7–9 February, 1956; pp. 137–142 (BIZMAC).

Poorte, G. E. and A. D. Kranzley, The RCA 501 electronic data processing system; *Proceedings of the 1958 Western Joint Computer Conference,* Los Angeles, 6–8 May, 1956; pp. 66–70.

Ling, A. T. and K. Kozansky, The RCA 601 system design; *Proceedings of the 1960 Eastern Joint Computer Conference,* 13–15 December, 1960; pp. 173–177.

Eckert, J. P. *et al.,* The UNIVAC system; *Review of Electronic Digital Computers, Joint IRE-AIEE Conference,* Philadelphia, 10–12 December, 1951; pp. 6–14.

Eckert, J. P., UNIVAC®-LARC, the next step in computer design; *Proceedings of the 1956 Eastern Joint Computer Conference,* New York, 10–12 December, 1956; pp. 16–19.

Eckert, J. P. *et al.,* Design of UNIVAC-LARC system—part I; *Proceedings of the*

1959 Eastern Joint Computer Conference, Boston, 1–3 December, 1959; pp. 59–65.

Lukoff, H. *et al.,* Design of UNIVAC-LARC system—part II; *Proceedings of the 1959 Eastern Joint Computer Conference,* Boston, 1–3 December, 1959; pp. 66–74.

Prywes, N. S. *et al.,* UNIVAC-LARC high speed circuitry: case history in circuit optimization; *IRE Transactions on Electronic Computers,* vol. EC-10, September, 1961; pp. 426–438.

Dreyfus, P., System design of the GAMMA-60; *Proceedings of the 1958 Western Joint Computer Conference,* Los Angeles, 6–8 May, 1958; pp. 130–132.

Dreyfus, P., Programming design features of the GAMMA-60 computer; *Proceedings of the 1958 Eastern Joint Computer Conference,* Philadelphia, 3–5 December, 1958; pp. 174–181.

Alexander, S. N., The National Bureau of Standards eastern automatic computer; *Review of Electronic Digital Computers, Joint IRE-AIEE Conference,* Philadelphia, 10–12 December, 1951; pp. 84–89 (SEAC).

Greenwald, S. *et al.,* SEAC; *Proceedings of the IRE,* vol. 41, October, 1953; pp. 1300–1313.

Leiner, A. L. *et al.,* System design of the SEAC and DYSEAC; *IRE Transactions on Electronic Computers,* vol. EC-3, June, 1954; pp. 8–23.

Leiner, A. and S. N. Alexander, System organization of DYSEAC; *IRE Transactions on Electronic Computers,* vol. EC-3, March, 1954; pp. 1–10.

Leiner, A. L., System specification for the DYSEAC; *Journal of the Association for Computing Machinery,* vol. 1, April, 1954; pp. 57–81.

Leiner, A. L. *et al.,* PILOT, the NBS multicomputer system; *Proceedings of the 1958 Eastern Joint Computer Conference,* Philadelphia, 3–5 December, 1958; pp. 71–75.

Leiner, A. L. *et al.,* PILOT, a new multiple computer system; *Journal of the Association for Computing Machinery,* vol. 6, July, 1959; pp. 313–335.

Huskey, H. D. *et al.,* SWAC—design features and operating experience; *Proceedings of the IRE,* vol. 41, October, 1953; pp. 1294–1299.

Sheldon, J. W. and L. Tatum, The IBM card-programmed calculator; *Review of Electronic Digital Computers, Joint IRE-AIEE Conference,* Philadelphia, 10–12 December, 1951; pp. 30–36.

Frizzell, C. E., Engineering description of the IBM 701; *Proceedings of the IRE,* vol. 41, October, 1953; pp. 1275–1287.

Buchholz, W., Systems design of the IBM 701; *Proceedings of the IRE,* vol. 41, October, 1953; pp. 1262–1275.

Hughes, E. S., Jr., The IBM magnetic drum calculator type 650—engineering and design considerations; *Proceedings of the 1954 Western Joint Computer Conference,* Los Angeles, 11–12 February, 1954; pp. 140–154.

Hamilton, F. E. and E. C. Kubie, The IBM magnetic drum calculator type 650; *Journal of the Association for Computing Machinery,* vol. 1, January, 1954; pp. 13–20.

Bashe, C. J. *et al.,* The IBM type 702—an EDPM for business; *Journal of the Association for Computing Machinery,* vol. 1, October, 1954; pp. 149–169.

Eckert, W. J. and R. Jones, *Faster, faster;* McGraw-Hill Book Co., New York, 1959 (NORC).

Lesser, M. L. and J. W. Haanstra, The RAMAC data processing machine—system organization of the IBM 305; *Proceedings of the 1956 Eastern Joint Computer Conference,* New York, 10–12 December, 1956; pp. 139–146.

Avery, R. W. *et al.,* The IBM 7070 data processing system; *Proceedings of the 1958 Eastern Joint Computer Conference,* Philadelphia, 3–5 December, 1958; pp. 165–168.

Svigals, J., The IBM 7070 data processing system; *Proceedings of the 1959 Western Joint Computer Conference,* San Francisco, 3–5 March, 1959; pp. 222–231.

Herwitz, P. S. and J. H. Pomerene, The HARVEST system; *Proceedings of the 1960 Western Joint Computer Conference,* San Francisco, 3–5 May, 1960; pp. 23–32.

Bender, R. R. *et al.,* A description of the IBM 7074 system; *Proceedings of the 1960 Eastern Joint Computer Conference,* New York, 13–15 December, 1960; pp. 161–172.

Buchholz, W. (editor), *Planning a computing system—project* STRETCH; Mc-Graw-Hill Book Co., New York, 1962.

Dunwell, S. W., Design objectives for the IBM STRETCH computer; *Proceedings of the 1956 Eastern Joint Computer Conference,* New York, 10–12 December, 1956; pp. 20–22.

Brooks, F. P. *et al.,* Processing data in bits and pieces; *IRE Transactions on Electronic Computers,* vol. EC-8, June, 1959; pp. 118–124 (STRETCH).

Bloch, E., The engineering design of the STRETCH computer; *Proceedings of the 1959 Eastern Joint Computer Conference,* Boston, 1–3 December, 1959; pp. 48–58.

Blosk, R. T., The instruction unit of the STRETCH computer; *Proceedings of the 1960 Eastern Joint Computer Conference,* New York, 13–15 December, 1960; pp. 299–324.

Beckman, F. S. *et al.,* Developments in the logical organization of computer arithmetic and control units; *Proceedings of the IRE,* vol. 49, January, 1961; pp. 53–66 (STRETCH).

Amdahl, G. M., New concepts in computing system design; *Proceedings of the IRE,* vol. 50, May, 1962; pp. 1073–1077 (post-STRETCH ideas).

Lawless, W. J., Developments in computer logical organization; *Advances in electronics and electron physics;* Academic Press, New York, 1959; vol. 10, pp. 153–184.

Corbato, F. J. *et al.,* An experimental time sharing system; *Proceedings of the 1962 Spring Joint Computer Conference,* San Francisco, 1–3 May, 1962; pp. 335–344.

Bledsoe, W. W., A basic limitation in the speed of digital computers; *IRE Transactions on Electronic Computers,* vol. EC-10, September, 1961; p. 530.

Gelernter, H., A note on the system requirements of a digital computer for manipulation of list structures; *IRE Transactions on Electronic Computers,* vol. EC-10, September, 1961; pp. 484–489.

Hawkins, J. K., Self-organizing systems; *Proceedings of the IRE,* vol. 49, January, 1961; pp. 31–48.

3. Session on learning machines (6 papers); *Proceedings of the 1955 Western Joint Computer Conference,* Los Angeles, 1–3 March, 1955; pp. 85–110.

Locke, W. N., Translation by machine; *Scientific American,* January, 1956; pp. 29 *ff. passim.*

Newell, A. *et al.*, Empirical explorations of the logic theory machine; *Proceedings of the 1957 Western Joint Computer Conference*, Los Angeles, 26–28 February, 1957; pp. 218–229.

Newell, A. and J. C. Shaw, Programming the logic theory machine; *Proceedings of the 1957 Western Joint Computer Conference*, Los Angeles, 26–28 February, 1957; pp. 230–240.

Von Neumann, J., *Computer and the brain;* Yale University Press, New Haven, Conn., 1958.

Bernstein, A. and M. de V. Roberts, Computer versus chess player; *Scientific American*, June, 1958; pp. 96 *ff. passim.*

Newell, A. *et al.*, Report on a general problem solving program; *Proceedings of the International Conference on Information Processing (ICIP)*, Unesco House, Paris, France, 1959; pp. 256–264.

Gelernter, H., Realization of a geometry proving machine; *Proceedings of the International Conference on Information Processing (ICIP)*, Unesco House, Paris, France, 1959; pp. 273–282.

Hiller, L. A., Computer music; *Scientific American*, December, 1959; pp. 104 *ff. passim.*

Neisser, U. and O. G. Selfridge, Pattern recognition by machine; *Scientific American*, August, 1960; pp. 60 *ff. passim.*

Bauer, W. F. *et al.*, Advanced computer applications; *Proceedings of the IRE*, vol. 49, January, 1961; pp. 296–304.

Minsky, M., Steps toward artificial intelligence; *Proceedings of the IRE*, vol. 49, January, 1961; pp. 8–30.

Minsky, M., A selected descriptor-indexed bibliography to the literature on artificial intelligence; *IRE Transactions on Human Factors in Electronics*, vol. HFE-2, March, 1961; pp. 39–55.

Lazovick, P. B. *et al.*, A versatile man-machine communication console; *Proceedings of the 1961 Eastern Joint Computer Conference*, Washington, 12–14 December, 1961; pp. 166–173.

Licklider, J. C. R. and W. E. Clark, On-line man-computer communication; *Proceedings of the 1962 Spring Joint Computer Conference*, San Francisco, 1–3 May, 1962; pp. 113–128.

4. Donan, J. F., Serial memory digital differential analyzer; *Mathematical Tables and Other Aids to Computation*, vol. 6, April, 1952; pp. 102–112.

Sprague, R. E., Fundamental concepts of the digital differential analyzer; *Mathematical Tables and Other Aids to Computation*, vol. 6, January, 1952; pp. 41–49.

Palevsky, M., Design of the Bendix digital differential analyzer; *Proceedings of the IRE*, vol. 41, October, 1953; pp. 1352–1356.

Mendelson, M. J., Decimal digital differential analyzer; *Aeronautical Engineering Review*, vol. 13, February, 1954; pp. 1–13.

Braun, E. L., Design features of current digital differential analyzers; *IRE Convention Record*, pt. 4, 1954; pp. 87–97.

Mitchell, J. M. and S. Ruhman, The TRICE—a high speed incremental computer; *IRE Convention Record*, pt. 4, 1958; pp. 206–216.

Wortzman, D., Use of a digital-analog arithmetic unit within a digital computer; *Proceedings of the 1960 Eastern Joint Computer Conference*, New York, 13–15, December, 1960; pp. 269–282.

Bradley, R. E. and J. F. Gemma, Design of a one megacycle iteration digital differential analyzer; *Proceedings of the 1962 Spring Joint Computer Conference,* San Francisco, 1–3 May, 1962; pp. 353–364.

5. Grabbe, E. M. *et al., Handbook of automation, computation, and control;* John Wiley and Sons, New York, 1959; vol. 2, chapter 10.

Ledley, R. S., *Digital computer and control engineering;* McGraw-Hill Book Co., New York, 1960; chapter 1.

Wong, S. Y., Traffic simulation with a digital computer; *Proceedings of the 1956 Western Joint Computer Conference,* San Francisco, 7–9 February, 1956; pp. 92–94.

Ledley, R. S., Digital electronic computers in biomedical science; *Science,* vol. 130, 6 November, 1959; pp. 1225–1234.

Krautz, F. H. and W. D. Murray, A survey of digital methods for radar data processing; *Proceedings of the 1960 Eastern Joint Computer Conference,* New York, 13–15 December, 1960; pp. 67–82.

Thomas, O. F., Analog-digital hybrid computers in simulation with humans and hardware; *Proceedings of the 1961 Western Joint Computer Conference,* Los Angeles, 8–11 May, 1961; pp. 639–644.

Burns, A. J. and R. E. Kopp, Combined analog-digital simulation; *Proceedings of the 1961 Eastern Joint Computer Conference,* Washington, 12–14 December, 1961; pp. 114–123.

6. Grabbe, E. M. *et al., Handbook of automation, computation, and control;* John Wiley and Sons, New York, 1959; vol. 2, chapters 3–11 except 10.

Lessing, L. P., Computers in business; *Scientific American,* January, 1954; pp. 21 *ff. passim.*

Larson, H. T. and A. Vazsonyi, Data processing requirements for production and inventory control; *Proceedings of the 1955 Western Joint Computer Conference,* Los Angeles, 1–3 March, 1955; pp. 48–61.

Redmond, G. H. and D. E. Mulvihill, The use of binary computers for data processing; *Proceedings of the 1960 Eastern Joint Computer Conference,* New York, 13–15 December, 1960; pp. 159–162.

Rowe, A. J., Computer-based management control; *Proceedings of the 1961 Western Joint Computer Conference,* Los Angeles, 8–11 May, 1961; pp. 587–592.

7. Burbeck, D. W. *et al.,* The DIGITAC airborne control system; *Proceedings of the 1954 Western Joint Computer Conference,* Los Angeles, 11–12 February, 1954; pp. 38–44.

Braun, E. L., Digital computers in continuous control systems; *IRE Convention Record,* pt. 4, 1957; pp. 127–135.

Gunning, W. F., Computers in the process industry; *IRE Convention Record,* pt. 4, 1957; pp. 136–141.

Sampson, D. K. *et al.,* The Univac Airlines reservation system; *Proceedings of the 1958 Eastern Joint Computer Conference,* Philadelphia, 3–5 December, 1958; pp. 152–156.

Truxal, J. G., Computers in automatic control systems; *Proceedings of the IRE,* vol. 49, January, 1961; pp. 305–312.

Perry, M. N. and W. R. Plugge, American Airlines SABRE electronic reservation system; *Proceedings of the 1961 Western Joint Computer Conference,* Los Angeles, 8–11 May, 1961; pp. 593–602.

Bonini, C. P., A simulation of a business firm; *Proceedings of the 1962 Spring Joint Computer Conference,* San Francisco, 1–3 May, 1962; pp. 1–14.

8. Tou, J. T., *Digital and sampled-data control systems;* McGraw-Hill Book Co., New York, 1959.

9. Malthaner, W. A. and H. E. Vaughan, An automatic telephone system employing magnetic drum memory; *Proceedings of the IRE,* vol. 41, October, 1953; pp. 1341–1347.

Lewis, W. D., Electronic computers and telephone switching; *Proceedings of the IRE,* vol. 41, October, 1953; pp. 1242–1244.

Malthaner, W. A. and H. E. Vaughan, Control features of a magnetic drum telephone office; *IRE Transactions on Electronic Computers,* vol. EC-4, March, 1955; pp. 21–26.

Ketchledge, R. W., An introduction to the Bell System's first electronic switching office; *Proceedings of the 1957 Eastern Joint Computer Conference,* Washington, 9–13 December, 1957; pp. 204–208.

Joel, A. E., Jr., An experimental switching system using new electronic techniques; *Bell System Technical Journal,* vol. 37, September, 1958; pp. 1091–1124.

Seckler, H. N. and J. J. Yostpile, Functional design of a stored-program electronic switching system; *Bell System Technical Journal,* vol. 37, November, 1958; pp. 1327–1382.

An experimental electronic telephone switching system; special publication, Bell Telephone Laboratories, New York, September, 1960.

10. Hoover, C. W., Jr. *et al.,* Fundamental concepts in the design of the flying spot store; *Bell System Technical Journal,* vol. 37, September, 1958; pp. 1161–1194.

Hoover, C. W. *et al.,* System design of the flying spot store; *Bell System Technical Journal,* vol. 38, March, 1959; pp. 365–401.

Greenwood, T. S., A 2.2 megabit photographic store for an electronic telephone switching system; *An experimental electronic telephone switching system;* special publication, Bell Telephone Laboratories, New York, September, 1960; paper no. 5.

Greenwood, T. S. and R. E. Staehler, A high speed barrier grid store; *Bell System Technical Journal,* vol. 37, September, 1958; pp. 1195–1220.

Gallaher, L. E., Beam positioning servo system for the flying spot store; *Bell System Technical Journal,* vol. 37, March, 1959; pp. 425–444.

11. Feiner, A. and L. F. Goeller, Jr., A high speed line scanner for use in an electronic switching system; *Bell System Technical Journal,* vol. 37, November, 1958; pp. 1383–1403.

12. Dunlap, K. S. and R. L. Simms, A gas tube space-division network for an electronic telephone switching system; *An experimental electronic telephone switching system;* special publication, Bell Telephone Laboratories, New York, September, 1960; paper no. 3.

13. Yokelson, B. J. *et al.,* Semiconductor circuit design philosophy for the central control of an electronic switching system; *Bell System Technical Journal,* vol. 37, September, 1958; pp. 1125–1160.

14. Ulrich, W., Maintenance and administration methods in an electronic telephone switching system; *An experimental electronic telephone switching system;* special publication, Bell Telephone Laboratories, New York, September, 1960; paper no. 7.

EXERCISES

The exercises and problems for this chapter will, in many cases, depend on discussion and information from all previous chapters. Some questions simply could not have been asked until the discussion of all facets of the machine was completed. Some questions are reasked, because intervening discussion has enlarged the context and introduced new points.

Detailed designs of parts of HYPAC-I can now be completed, although not all aspects of machine design can be treated on paper. The design aspects discussed on pages 15.4 *ff*. must be treated experimentally, for the most part. We must leave those for any adventuresome reader who actually builds a HYPAC-I for himself.

15.1. Figure 15.1 is not as complete as the block diagrams which you have drawn in various problems and exercises for parts of HYPAC-I. Pull together these various block diagrams into an integrated overall functional picture of the machine. Resolve any ambiguities and unsettled questions which may arise. Show all registers, gates, toggles, timing signals, counters, address selection circuits, etc.

Assume that the machine above has only the original repertoire of HYPAC-I, only a magnetic core primary store, and a simple typewriter for input and output.

15.2. Discuss the role of the input-output devices in helping to determine the overall speed range of a machine system.

15.3. Construct a repertoire of three-address instruction types which implement the same set of operations as the HYPAC-I repertoire. Do not include any extra operations in the three-address repertoire.

Now extend the three-address repertoire, and try to find an efficient and effective use for all addresses in each instruction.

15.4. In the light of exercise 15.3 and of the experience in programming, estimate how many single-address instructions correspond to a three-address instruction. If the same routine were coded for a single-address and a three-address machine, what would be the relative lengths of the two routines?

15.5. Lay out a design and production schedule for a small machine such as HYPAC-I. Assume that current state-of-the-art technology is to be used, but that machine specifications, logical design, packaging design, prototype construction, and prototype testing must be included in the design schedule. Include such things in the schedule as

    (a) when each phase of each part of the machine starts and completes,

    (b) what sort of team is active during each phase—engineer, programmer, etc.,

    (c) when production specifications can be released,

    (d) when procurement for production can begin,

    (e) when production testing begins,

    (f) when specification, writing, and checkout of the programming package (utility routines, assemblers, compilers) that accompanies the machine begins and ends.

From this procedure, insight may be gained into the overall design and construction process of a machine. What is your estimate of the total elapsed time and the number of people required to build the first production model?

15.6. A machine is delivered to a customer with only fixed-point arithmetic operations. It is decided to retrofit the machine in the field with floating-point arithmetic operations; therefore, at least the control and the arithmetic unit must be changed.

Discuss this proposal. Estimate how much extra equipment must be added to all parts of the machine, and how large a modification is implied. In your opinion, is it reasonable to suggest that this modification be accomplished in the field? Why?

15.7. Repeat the previous exercise, but assume that indexing is to be added to the machine in the field.

15.8. Repeat exercise 15.6, except assume that a second printer is to be added to a machine which already contains a printer. How can the machine distinguish the two printers?

15.9. In a binary-coded-decimal machine which represents an alphanumeric character by a pair of decimal digits, how large would you expect the character set to be? How many factors influence such a parameter?

15.10. From the point of view of each of the four sections of a machine system and of the programmer, discuss fixed versus variable word-length organization.

Consider such things as programming convenience, machine speed, complexity of machine organization, cost of the equipment, and the efficiency of equipment utilization.

15.11. Any signal carrying wire in a machine will exhibit some impedance to ground. For the moment, assume that it is purely resistive (R). Such a wire is coupled through stray capacitance (C) to other wires in its vicinity. In terms of the parameters R and C, determine the maximum spurious signal that can be coupled onto the wire of interest from a nearby wire carrying a signal which rises linearly at A volts per second.

If the signal rises for T_r seconds at the rate of A volts per second, what is the amplitude of the spurious signal? What is the physical significance of the parameter ARC which appears in the expressions?

15.12. A number of special characteristics were ascribed to HYPAC-I to avoid the possibility that -0 should arise. At the time we did not appreciate the details of implementing arithmetic, nor did we understand the implications on other parts of the machine. We had to include such special provisions. We now know several ways to avoid the -0 difficulty. Discuss this topic and describe some ways to avoid the negative zero. Whatever arrangement you select, HYPAC-I must appear to the user as a sign-magnitude machine.

15.13. In view of the complications of performing multiplication with complement numbers (see exercise 2.14 and problem 2.8), but of the convenience of doing subtraction with them, discuss the relative equipment cost of implementing the four arithmetic operations in a sign-magnitude representation versus the cost in complement representation. What implications has the resolution of this problem for the other parts of the machine?

15.14. All parts of the machine considered, what factors influence the selection of a binary code for representing decimal information?

15.15. Describe what equipment must be provided and in what parts of the machine to implement indirect addressing (see exercise 5.20).

15.16. With your added insight and information, repeat exercises 5.18 and 5.19.

15.17. In view of the extensive intervening discussion concerning kinds of instructions and their use, repeat exercise 5.6.

PROBLEMS

15.1. In various exercises and problems, additions to HYPAC-I have been suggested. Collect all such suggestions and define a HYPAC-III augmented system having all such features. If there are conflicting suggestions, decide on one and justify your choice. Describe in detail what features HYPAC-III has, and give its enlarged repertoire. Describe how each kind of instruction operates. Describe how the input-output devices are organizationally and logically arranged. Describe the store hierarchy and how each level is addressed. Give a complete description of the machine. Estimate the amount of equipment in HYPAC-III compared to HYPAC-I.

15.2. Contrast the various ways of providing an indexing feature. Which method(s) look preferable from the programmer's point of view? From the hardware point of view? From the designer's point of view? For the most expensive indexing scheme, estimate how much more efficient it must make the machine-programmer team to justify its cost. Keep in mind that indexing may pay off by decreasing programming time, and that therefore running time for the problem may be decreased.

15.3. A motor drives an escalator to raise production parts from one floor to another in a factory. The number of parts on the escalator is not constant in number nor is their weight. The load on the motor depends on the number of items being carried and on the speed of the belt. Design a digital control machine that will maximize the speed of the escalator without overloading the motor. Define any parameters or constants needed.

Decide how the machine will sense the number of items on the belt and also the weight of each item. Decide what computation needs to be done to determine the appropriate motor speed. Indicate how the motor speed can be controlled by a suitable output device. Might some approximation methods be in order? For example, if the average weight and the statistical distribution of the weights of the objects were known, might it be possible to avoid sensing weight or number of items on the belt? Might such a statistical approach lead to difficulty?

Describe the numerical process which you intend to use and program it for HYPAC-I. Might HYPAC-I be a suitable machine? Is a special purpose design indicated?

15.4. Do the detailed circuit design of the control section of HYPAC-I. (Use the results of problem 13.1.) Select a toggle circuit, an appropriate gating technique, a counter configuration, and a register. Design to accommodate ±5% fluctuation in resistors, ±3% variation in supply voltages, and ±25% variation in current capability of active elements. Use vacuum-tube or transistor technology, as you wish, and a gate technique of your choice. See pages 8.92 to 8.93 and 9.68 to 9.69 for appropriate characteristic curves.

15.5. Repeat problem 15.4, but for the arithmetic section of the machine. (See problems 11.27 and 11.28.)

15.6. Repeat problem 15.4, but for the magnetic core store suggested in exercises 12.20 to 12.24. Assume that the half-select current is 500 ma and must be controlled to ±2%. Design the address selection circuit and the current drivers. Assume that a core will transition in 2 μsec and that a string of sixty-four of them provide an inductive back voltage of 5 volts in the speed range of interest. Design for a cycle time of 10 μsec.

15.7. Repeat problem 15.5, but for the input-output system described in exercise 14.15.

Repeat the above, but for the more elaborate input-output arrangement of problem 14.1.

15.8. Consider a machine participating in an air-traffic-control system. It is required, among other things, to keep current status information (e.g., wind, precipitation, cloud layer, conditions of runways) for five hundred runways. Messages are received from time to time and the machine must update its file of information.

A message is received concerning an airfield labeled as number 719. The message is accepted and, of course, is in error, but the machine does not know it. There is no entry in the airfield table labeled 719, but the machine will find some cell in the store and proceed to process the information. It might invade a sine routine, be in the middle of a table of constants, etc. Whatever it does, there will be glorious chaos.

What precautions can be taken to guard against such problems? Discuss the general problem of editing for format and checking for errors in the input system of a machine engaged in on-line processing.

15.9. Suppose that a machine is to be time-shared among several users. Each user's problem will be in the machine at the same time and each problem will be worked on in turn. It may be that a problem is not completed all at once but is worked on periodically until finished. It is obviously imperative that no routine be able to damage any of the others currently in the machine. Yet we know that programming errors and machine malfunctions can let a machine have access to wrong parts of the store.

How can this problem be dealt with? How can selected parts of the store be preserved from accidental destruction of information? (This same kind of difficulty can arise with the interpretative mode described in Chapter 6. A user's routine might accidentally destroy part of the interpreter.)

Reconsider this problem in the light of the machine engaged in process control or in real-time processing. In either of these cases the costs of an accident can be excessive. What programming safeguards can be used? What hardware safeguards? What sort of machine organization is favorable?

15.10. Considering all aspects of the machine design, discuss the relative merits of designing a decimal machine using

      (a) one of the 4-bit codes,
      (b) one of the 2-of-5 codes,
      (c) the biquinary code.

15.11. Suppose that the HYPAC-III were to have its word length increased sufficiently to incorporate a single error-detecting and -correcting, double error-detecting Hamming check scheme into the machine. How much longer is the word length? Estimate the amount of equipment in all parts of the machine (in a relative sense) required to incorporate such a check. What will be done with the check digits during an arithmetic process?

15.12. Discuss the changes required in all parts of HYPAC-III to allow it to perform either decimal or binary arithmetic. To allow it to behave completely as a decimal machine or as a binary machine.

15.13. In the light of the interveing discussion, repeat problem 7.2. Compose a list of the situations which ought to be included in the interrupt system of the machine.

15.14. Discuss the case of the serial machine versus the parallel machine. What advantages can be realized from each? For what circumstances might one or the other be a preferred choice? What would you expect the relative cost-effectiveness of the two types to be?

Index